**WITHDRAWN
LENOIR-RHYNE UNIVERSITY**

DATE DUE			
Dec 10 69			
Jan '70			
Oct 21 '75			
Dec 15 '75			
GAYLORD			PRINTED IN U.S.A.

Continental Drift

International Geophysics Series

Edited by

J. VAN MIEGHEM

Royal Belgian Meteorological Institute
Uccle, Belgium

Volume 1 BENO GUTENBERG. Physics of the Earth's Interior. 1959

Volume 2 JOSEPH W. CHAMBERLAIN. Physics of the Aurora and Airglow. 1961

Volume 3 S. K. RUNCORN (ed.). Continental Drift. 1962

IN PREPARATION

JUNGE, C. E. • Atmospheric Chemistry and Radioactivity

FLEAGLE, R. G., AND BUSINGER, J. A. • Atmospheric Physics

DUFOUR, L., AND DEFAY, R. • Thermodynamics of Clouds

Continental Drift

Edited by

S. K. Runcorn

King's College
Newcastle-upon-Tyne
England

Academic Press • New York and London • 1962

CARL A. RUDISILL LIBRARY
LENOIR RHYNE COLLEGE

ALL RIGHTS RESERVED

NO PART OF THIS BOOK MAY BE REPRODUCED IN ANY FORM,
BY PHOTOSTAT, MICROFILM, OR ANY OTHER MEANS,
WITHOUT WRITTEN PERMISSION FROM THE PUBLISHERS

ACADEMIC PRESS INC.
111 FIFTH AVENUE
NEW YORK 3, N.Y.

551.41
R 87 c

United Kingdom Edition
Published by
ACADEMIC PRESS INC. (LONDON) LTD.
BERKELEY SQUARE HOUSE, BERKELEY SQUARE,
LONDON W.1

50011
June 1965

Library of Congress Catalog Card Number 62-13124

PRINTED IN GREAT BRITAIN BY W. S. COWELL LTD
AT THE BUTTER MARKET, IPSWICH

List of Contributors

HUGO BENIOFF, *Seismological Laboratory, California Institute of Technology, Pasadena, California, U.S.A.*

P. CHADWICK, *Mathematics Department, University of Sheffield, England*

T. CHAMALAUN, *Physics Department, King's College, Newcastle-upon-Tyne, England*

ROBERT S. DIETZ, *U.S. Navy Electronics Laboratory, San Diego, California, U.S.A.*

T. F. GASKELL, *British Petroleum Exploration Company Limited, B.P. House, London, England*

JOHANNES GEORGI, *Borsteler Chausee 159, Hamburg, Germany*

BRUCE C. HEEZEN, *Lamont Geological Observatory, Palisades, New York, U.S.A.*

JOHN H. HODGSON, *Dominion Observatory, Ottawa, Canada*

F. A. VENING MEINESZ, *Potgieterlaan 5, Amersfoort, Netherlands*

N. D. OPDYKE, *University College of Rhodesia and Nyasaland, Salisbury, Southern Rhodesia*

P. H. ROBERTS, *Physics Department, King's College, Newcastle-upon-Tyne, England;* now at *Yerkes Observatory, Williams Bay, Wisconsin, U.S.A.*

S. K. RUNCORN, *Physics Department, King's College, Newcastle-upon-Tyne, England*

VICTOR VACQUIER, *Scripps Institution of Oceanography, La Jolla, California, U.S.A.*

Preface

Fifty years ago Alfred Wegener, the German meteorologist, published his theory of continental drift (*Petermanns Mitt.*, 1912, **58**, pages 185–195, 253–256, and 305–309; *Geol. Rdsch.*, 1912, **3**, pages 276–292). The first edition of his book "Die Entstehung der Kontinente und Ozeane" appeared in 1915. His theory that the continents of South America, India, Australia and Africa had formed one continent of Gondwanaland in the comparatively recent history of the earth was, like most ideas in science, not entirely new. Antonio Snider ("La Création et ses Mystères Devoilés", Librarie A. Franck, Paris, 1858) had produced maps that showed the supposed former contiguity of the two sides of the Atlantic, which are remarkable in their resemblance to some of Wegener's reconstruction. Also F. B. Taylor of the U.S.A. had suggested from tectonic consideration that a considerable redistribution of the continents had taken place in geological time. The development of the theory owed much to the discovery in the last half of the last century of the Permo-Carboniferous glaciation of the southern hemisphere.

The publication of Wegener's book gave rise to a vigorous controversy in the 1920s. Lack of a decisive test, however, and strong arguments against the theory on the part of geophysicists caused the idea of continental drift to be abandoned, at least by the majority of geologists in England and America. About ten years ago the development of studies of rock magnetism gave rise to new interest in this theory and has caused geophysicists in other fields to reconsider the ideas in relation to their own studies. It therefore seemed worth while to bring together within one volume a discussion of the geophysical evidence relating to horizontal movements in the earth's crust in its widest sense. This is not the time for a reappraisal of Wegener's work but it is hoped that this volume will stimulate a serious interest in a subject formerly considered by many earth scientists as already closed.

Newcastle-upon-Tyne   S. K. RUNCORN
July 1962

CONTENTS

List of Contributors.. v

Preface.. vii

Chapter 1 by S. K. RUNCORN

**Palaeomagnetic Evidence for Continental Drift and
its Geophysical Cause**   1

References... 39

Chapter 2 by N. D. OPDYKE

Palaeoclimatology and Continental Drift   41

   I. Introduction.. 41

  II. Sedimentary Climatic Indicators........................... 43

 III. Uniformitarianism and the Study of Palaeoclimates......... 44

 IV. Distribution of Cainozoic Climatic Indicators............... 45

  V. Discussion of Cainozoic Climate........................... 48

 VI. Distribution of Climatic Indicators during the Mesozoic....... 52

VII. Distribution of Palaeozoic Climatic Indicators.............. 53

VIII. Palaeomagnetism and Palaeoclimatology..................... 60

 IX. Conclusions.. 63

References... 64

Chapter 3 by JOHN H. HODGSON

**Movements in the Earth's Crust as indicated by
Earthquakes**   67

   I. Introduction.. 67

  II. Studies of Earthquake Mechanism......................... 68

 III. Interpretation on the Collapse Model...................... 78

 IV. Interpretation on the Fault Model......................... 81

  V. Summary and Conclusions................................ 99

References... 102

Chapter 4 by HUGO BENIOFF

Movements on Major Transcurrent Faults   103

  I. General Considerations.................................... 103
 II. Circum-Pacific Shallow Faults............................. 106
III. Other Large Transcurrent Faults.......................... 131
 IV. Deep Faults of the Circum-Pacific Margins................. 132
References... 133

Chapter 5 by VICTOR VACQUIER

**Magnetic Evidence for Horizontal Displacements in
the Floor of the Pacific Ocean**   135

References... 144

Chapter 6 by F. A. VENING MEINESZ

Thermal Convection in the Earth's Mantle   145

   I. Introductory and Summary.............................. 145
  II. The Constitution of the Mantle......................... 146
 III. Arguments in Favour of Convection Currents in the Mantle... 153
  IV. Convection Currents in a Plane Crystalline Layer........... 156
   V. Spherical Harmonics................................... 159
  VI. Convection Currents in the Crystalline Mantle.............. 162
 VII. Spherical Harmonic Development up to the 31st Order of the
        Earth's Topography.................................. 164
VIII. Interpretation of the Spherical Harmonic Development of the
        Topography; Convection Systems in the Mantle; Origin of
        Continents; Relative Displacements of Continents.......... 169
References... 176

Chapter 7 by T. CHAMALAUN and P. H. ROBERTS

**The Theory of Convection in Spherical Shells and
its Application to the Problem of Thermal Convection
in the Earth's Mantle**   177

  I. The Geophysical Problem................................ 177
 II. The Mathematical Stability Problem....................... 181
III. Solution of the Stability Problem......................... 185
References... 193

Chapter 8 by P. CHADWICK

Mountain-Building Hypotheses

Mountain-Building Hypotheses 195

I. Introduction... 195
II. Facts to be Accounted for by Theories of Crustal Evolution... 198
III. Diastrophic Forces..................................... 212
IV. Mountain-Building Hypotheses........................... 224
References... 232

Chapter 9 by BRUCE C. HEEZEN

The Deep-Sea Floor

The Deep-Sea Floor 235

I. Introduction... 235
II. The Ocean Floor....................................... 236
III. Seismological Evidence for a Difference between the Continental
    and Oceanic Mantle.................................... 263
IV. Petrography of the Oceans.............................. 268
V. Age of Ocean Basins................................... 269
VI. Discussion of the Hypotheses of Continental Drift........... 276
References... 286

Chapter 10 by ROBERT S. DIETZ

Ocean-Basin Evolution by Sea-Floor Spreading

Ocean-Basin Evolution by Sea-Floor Spreading 289

I. Introduction... 289
II. Spreading Sea-Floor Concept............................ 292
III. Implications of the Concept............................. 294
References... 297

Chapter 11 by T. F. GASKELL

Comparisons of Pacific and Atlantic Ocean Floors in Relation to Ideas of Continental Displacement

**Comparisons of Pacific and Atlantic Ocean Floors
in Relation to Ideas of Continental Displacement** 299

References... 307

CONTENTS

Chapter 12 by J. GEORGI

Memories of Alfred Wegener   309

References.. 323

Author Index.. 325
Subject Index... 331

Chapter 1

Palaeomagnetic Evidence for Continental Drift and its Geophysical Cause

S. K. RUNCORN

The hypothesis of continental drift supposes that it is possible for the relative positions of the continents, and therefore their relation to the earth's axis of rotation, to have changed during geological time. Any method therefore by which the geographical meridian and the latitude of sites within continents can be determined at any time in the geological past will settle the question whether relative motion of the continents has taken place since that time. If the former longitudes of the sites were also known, the topography of the globe could be worked out for that time.

Palaeoclimatology has hitherto been the method by which geologists have attempted to fix the latitudes of the continents in the past. Nairn [1] has recently edited a book describing the latest position in this subject. Determinations of palaeowind directions provide the only method in this field of determining the orientation of the continents to the geographical pole [2, 3]. The latter method is restricted, of course, to the infrequent examples of aeolian sandstones and, because there is no satisfactory theory of the general circulation of the atmosphere, we cannot be absolutely sure that the latitude ranges of trade wind and westerly wind belts have not changed. The more general palaeoclimatic studies are handicapped by the somewhat subjective considerations by which interpretations of the geological record have to be made. The development of a precise physical method for the measurement of latitude and orientation, that of palaeomagnetism, has therefore, in the last ten years, revolutionized the discussion of continental drift.

The method is based on the supposition, suggested by its present distribution, that the mean geomagnetic field is that of an axial dipole at the geocentre. The field direction is conveniently specified by two angles. The angle of declination (D) is the angle between the field direction and the geographical meridian and is taken as positive eastwards. The angle of magnetic dip or angle of inclination (I) is the angle made by the field direction with the horizontal and is counted positive

1

if the positive or north-seeking direction of the field vector dips below the horizontal and negative if it points above the horizontal. This is related to the angle of latitude (λ) and angle of colatitude (θ) by the expression

$$\tan I = 2 \tan \lambda = 2 \cot \theta \qquad (1)$$

if the field is that of an axial dipole.

This may be proved as is shown in Fig. 1, in which the axial dipole, M,

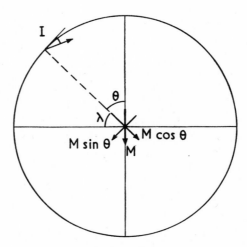

Fig. 1. Field of axial dipole.

being a vector, is resolved into a component $M \cos \theta$ along the radius vector through the surface site and a component perpendicular to the radius vector in the geographical meridian passing through the site. The former component produces a downward vertical field $Z = 2M \cos \theta / a^3$ at the site and the latter a horizontal field in the north direction $X = M \sin \theta / a^3$, where a is the radius of the earth.

$$\therefore \quad \tan I = Z/X = 2 \cot \theta.$$

The directions of the mean magnetic field of the earth obtained for an epoch in the geological past are found to be different from those of the present but are still interpreted in terms of a dipole field by assuming that the relative positions of the continents and the axis of this dipole have changed. The palaeomagnetic data from any continent is therefore commonly displayed in one of the two ways:

(1) by plotting on a projection of the present globe the pole or axis of that dipole which would, at the site where the rocks were obtained, give a field coincident with the mean direction of magnetization

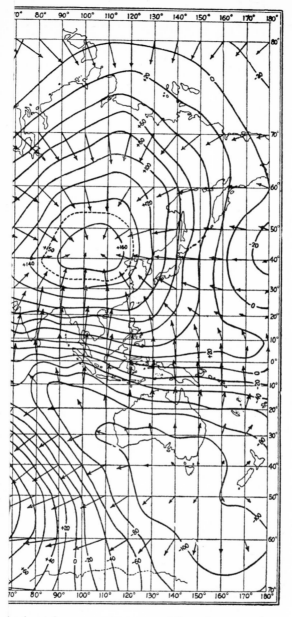

horizontal component, an arrow 9·3 mm long represents

of the rock specimens, after they have been returned, if necessary, to their original position by a geological dip correction. The poles refer, of course, to one continent, assuming that relative movements in the continent due to tectonics are not large enough to be taken into account at present. A map of the successive positions of the poles so calculated is known as a polar wandering path. The value of this method is that it provides a clear method of demonstrating the fact that the magnetic directions in one continent for one geological age are consistent. Also a discrepancy between the polar wandering curves for the different continents shows that relative movements have occurred up to the time when the curves become coincident.

(2) on an imaginary grid of lines of latitude and longitude with the dipole axis as centre, the successive positions of the continent throughout geological time are plotted. This has the advantage that it shows clearly the obvious point that the latitude and orientation of the continent, but not its longitude, can be determined— the latitude from equation (1) and the orientation from the palaeomagnetic declination which is the angle made by the longitude lines with the present meridian in the continents. Clearly the reconstruction of the topography of the globe in the past is accomplished by comparing such projections for the different continents.

The palaeomagnetic method of investigating continental drift therefore depends on two postulates: (1) that the mean geomagnetic field has always been dipolar and (2) that the rocks used in such studies have acquired a magnetization which, to within a degree or so, is coincident with the direction of the geomagnetic field at or soon after the time of their formation and which has been retained unchanged since.

We examine these two basic assumptions in turn. The former is at first sight contrary to our present day knowledge: the geomagnetic field at an epoch has considerable parts which are not representable by a dipole along the axis of the earth's rotation. Today it is better represented if the dipole is inclined by about 11° to the axis of rotation, but even then the difference between this field and that observed is considerable as is shown in Fig. 2. The deviations are greater than 0·1 oersted in many places. Further the field has a secular change. The longest series of measurements of the direction of the geomagnetic field are those for London and Paris, the angles of declination and inclination being shown in Fig. 3. When observations of the geomagnetic field were very sparse it was natural for it to be thought that the secular variation of the field was the result of a precession of the dipole about the earth's axis of rotation, which would of course cause the field at London and Paris to change roughly as shown in Fig. 3. However, it is now clear that this is a much too simplified picture. Vestine, Laporte, Lange and Scott [4] analyse the geomagnetic field for the epochs 1912·5, 1922·5,

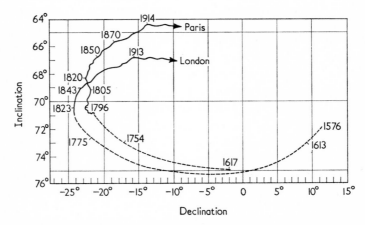

FIG. 3. Values of declination and inclination in London and Paris. After Gaibar-Puertas.

1932·5, and 1942·5 by the method of spherical harmonic analysis. They show, as others also have, that the field may be represented in terms of a scalar potential V, which can be expanded in the series

$$V = a \sum_{n=0}^{\infty} \sum_{m=0}^{n} (a/r)^{n+1} P_n^m(\theta) \left[g_n^m \cos m\lambda + h_n^m \sin m\lambda \right] \qquad (2)$$

where a is the radius of the earth, r, θ, and λ are spherical polar co-ordinates and $P_n^m(\theta)$ is the associated Legendre function. Vestine *et al.* calculate the coefficients g_n^m and h_n^m and, using earlier spherical harmonic analyses, it is possible to plot the variation of the coefficients with time back to the early part of last century, when extensive surveys of the earth's magnetic field were commenced consequent on Gauss's discovery of the method of making absolute determinations of the field intensity by the deflection and vibration magnetometer. These results are shown in Fig. 4, the vertical scales being in 10^{-4} oersted and λ measured eastwards.

The periods decrease with the order: thus much of the secular change of the main geomagnetic field results from the westward drift of its non-axial components. Elsasser [5, 6] and Bullard and Gellman [7] have convincingly shown that the geomagnetic field is maintained by a process in the earth's fluid, electrically conducting core, which is similar to that of a self-excited dynamo, in which the electric current generated by induction in the rotor provides the necessary magnetic field. While the general problem of self-excited dynamos is still riddled

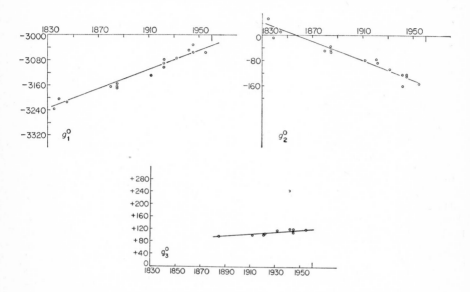

FIG. 4a. Values of spherical harmonic coefficients g_1^0, g_2^0, and g_3^0 since 1830.

with mathematical uncertainties, the physical picture of the earth's core is clear. Radioactive heating and possibly potential energy released by the settling of iron towards the earth's centre provides the kinetic energy of the convection currents. Electromagnetic induction causes the transfer of some of this energy into magnetic energy. The problem of the earth's magnetism is therefore part of the subject of magneto-hydrodynamics. To gain a physical insight into this subject it has been found useful to return to the Faraday-Maxwell concept of visualizing a magnetic field by supposing the lines of force to be elastic strings having a tension but also repelling one another. By Lenz's law there is a tendency for the lines of force to remain attached to the fluid particles— they would have no relative motion at all if the fluid had infinite electrical conductivity. Most modes of motion will stretch the lines of force and therefore increase the magnetic energy per unit volume. In a fluid with finite electrical conductivity and with no motions the magnetic field decays, lines of force diffusing through the fluid. The

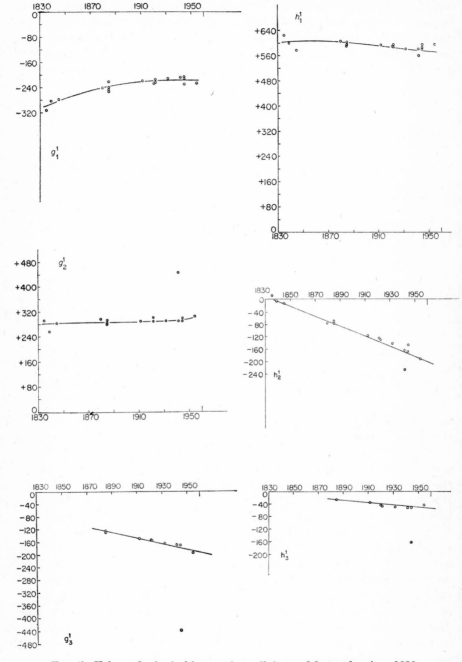

Fɪɢ. 4b. Values of spherical harmonic coefficients of first order since 1830.

maintenance of the geomagnetic field is therefore a balance between the
magnetic amplifying process of the fluid motions and the process of free
decay. Paradoxically, if the core were infinitely conducting there would
be no observable magnetic field: it would be entirely enclosed within

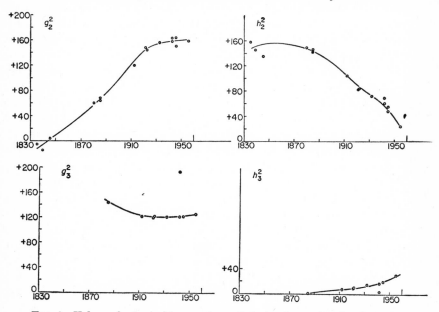

FIG. 4c. Values of spherical harmonic coefficients of second order since 1830.

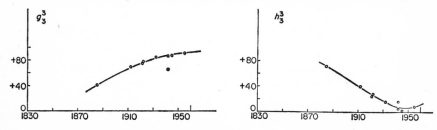

FIG. 4d. Values of spherical harmonic coefficients of third order since 1830.

the core, the lines of force lying parallel to the velocity vector at every
point. The existence of a field outside the earth and its change relative
to the core are therefore consequences of the finite conductivity of the
latter. It therefore appears entirely fundamental to interpret the westward drift of the geomagnetic field as a motion of the core as a whole
relative to the mantle at the rate of about 1/5° per year.

The electrical conductivity of the lower mantle is known to be much
smaller than that of the core, but it is estimated to be about 1 ohm⁻¹

B

cm^{-1} and is the result of intrinsic semiconduction. Were the mantle a perfect insulator, one might well wonder why the angular velocity of the core and mantle should be so nearly the same (about 1 part in 10^8) for it is easy to show that the viscous friction between the core and mantle is exceedingly small. The eddy currents induced in the mantle through the relative rotation of the non-axial parts of the magnetic field generated in the core are sufficient to keep the core and mantle rotating at nearly the same speed. However, the changes of the field relative to the core induce currents in the mantle which will give torques of either sign and consequently speed up or slow down the rate of westward drift of the core relative to the mantle. Conservation of angular momentum implies that the mantle's angular velocity will change with a time scale similar to that of the secular variation of the geomagnetic field—an effect long known by astronomers as the irregular fluctuations in the length of the day. An exceedingly important result follows from this: the exact equality of the rate of rotation of the core and mantle is seen to be an unusual state of affairs and one not likely to persist over many periods of the secular variation, i.e. more than about a thousand years.

Thus although at any epoch the geomagnetic field may have, as it has today, a considerable part not symmetrical about its axis, it is certain that, on the average, over times greater than a few thousand years, the mean geomagnetic field is axial [8]. An observer on the surface will follow the field around a line of latitude on the core and, when a mean is taken, the axial field will be left. Returning to equation (2) the potential is given by

$$V = a \sum_{n=0}^{\infty} \sum_{m=0}^{n} (a/r)^{n+1} P_n^m(\theta) \left[g_n^m \cos m(\varphi + \Omega t) + h_n^m \sin m(\varphi + \Omega t) \right]$$

where Ω is the westward drift and t the time. The mean potential vanishes for $m \neq 0$ for whole numbers of complete relative rotations of core and mantle.

In rock magnetism, directions of magnetization are determined from a number of rock samples collected over a sufficient stratigraphical thickness in order to ensure that many times the secular variation period is being examined. Order of magnitude calculations on the rates of deposition of deltaic deposits indicate that some hundreds of feet of sandstone will in general suffice [9]. Even intensive sampling of rocks which have essentially been formed at a point in time such as a single lava flow will clearly not satisfy this vital criterion. The directions of magnetization from one geological formation are each given unit weight and their vector mean calculated. This is not quite the same as averaging the scalar potential and if there were only one spherical harmonic term present in the variations of the geomagnetic field a small systematic error between the vector mean and the axial field would be present [8]. This, however, disappears where, as in the case of the secular variation shown in Fig. 4, there are a number of spherical harmonic terms present.

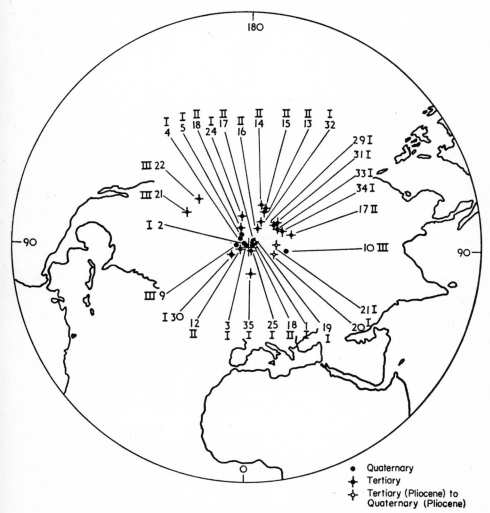

FIG. 5. Pole positions determined from European rocks of Cainozoic age.

It is natural to assume that the mean geomagnetic field is dipolar as well as axial, as this is the simplest type of field. The theory of the geomagnetic field does not provide a simple argument for this assumption which would be acceptable to the sceptic. There is strong evidence that since middle Tertiary times the mean geomagnetic field has been a dipole along the present geographical axis and the geological evidence that the continents and pole have not moved substantially since then is overwhelming.

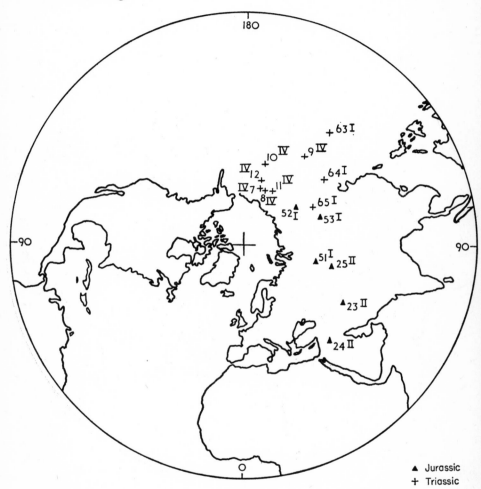

FIG. 6. Pole positions determined from European rocks of Mesozoic age.

In Figs. 6 to 18 the roman numerals refer to Irving's [10] four lists of palaeomagnetic observations, the arabic numerals to the order in each list.

The simplest way to show this is to plot the pole positions on the present globe derived from all the Tertiary and Quaternary rocks so far examined. Figure 5 shows those for Europe, Fig. 9 for North America, Figs. 13, 14, 15, 16, 17 for Asia, Australia, India, Africa and Antarctica. In Fig. 5 poles 21 and 22, which are far from the present pole, are based on 2 and 3 lava flows respectively and cannot therefore be regarded as

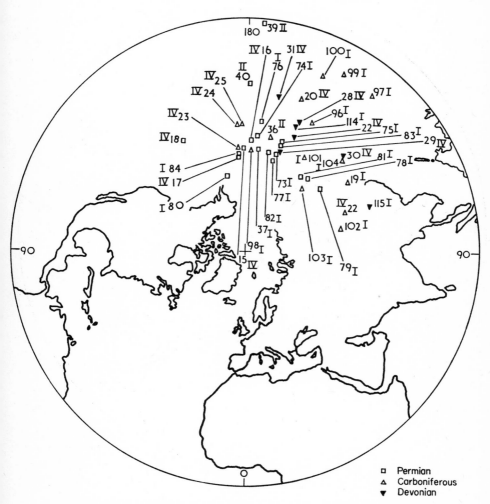

FIG. 7. Pole positions determined from European rocks of Late Palaeozoic age.

having adequately smoothed out the secular variation. In Fig. 9, pole I36 is puzzling—Cox and Doell determined it from six Siletz flows in Oregon. Possible explanations are tectonic displacements or that the flows cover a small interval of time during which the secular variation was particularly large. The overall picture from all the continents, however, shows that the mean geomagnetic field has been dipolar since the early Tertiary.

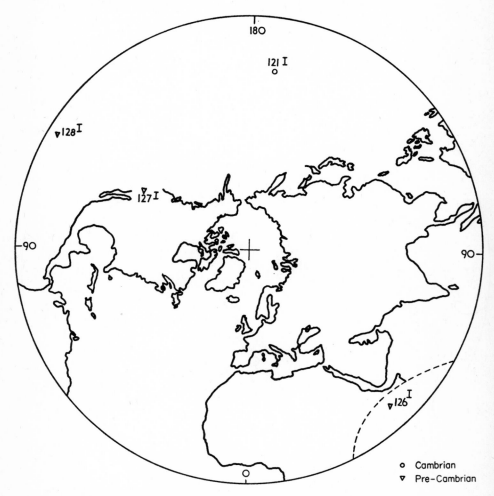

FIG. 8. Pole positions determined from European rocks of Pre-Cambrian and Early Palaeozoic age.

From Irving's [10] compilation of palaeomagnetic observations we have plotted for different geological eras and periods, the pole positions determined from rocks of different continents. Different palaeomagnetic workers have used different methods of sampling and measurement and combined their results by different statistical methods. Consequently, it does not seem possible, for the purpose of examining the whole of the palaeomagnetic results, to do more than plot the pole positions determined by, or from the results of, various workers. This procedure at

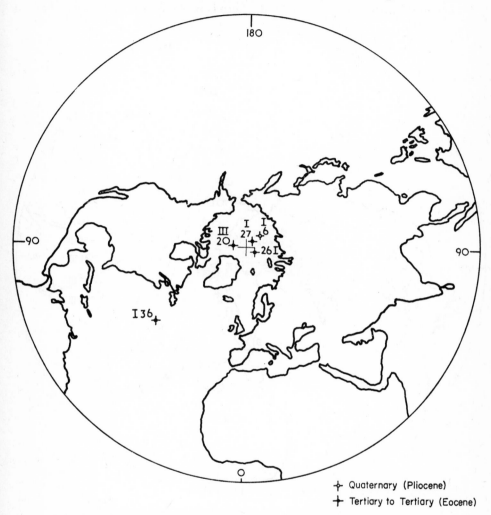

Fig. 9. Pole positions determined from North American rocks of Cainozoic age.

least avoids the obvious criticism that in relying only on the results of one group of workers, using the same procedures, serious bias might go undetected. However, not all the pole positions are to be considered equally well based and the scatter of the poles must not be regarded as giving in any sense the limiting accuracy of the palaeomagnetic method.

We now return to a discussion of the second assumption on which palaeomagnetic research has been based, that if well-bedded, fine-grained, unmetamorphosed red sandstones or undeformed and unmeta-morphosed lava flows are sampled, there is every reason to believe that

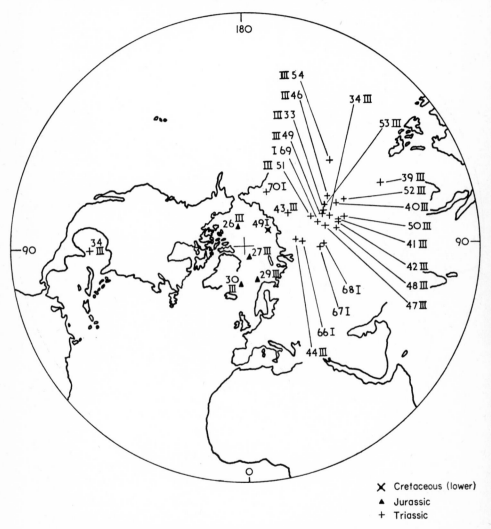

Fig. 10. Pole positions determined from North American rocks of Mesozoic age.

the natural remanent magnetization was acquired at the time of the formation of the rock or soon afterwards and has remained substantially unchanged since. It has been urged that this conclusion is unwarranted in the absence of exact knowledge of the way in which the rocks became magnetized. It has been suggested by Graham [11] that magneto-striction is a factor which, because of the constancy of directions of fault patterns in many geological formations over considerable areas, could

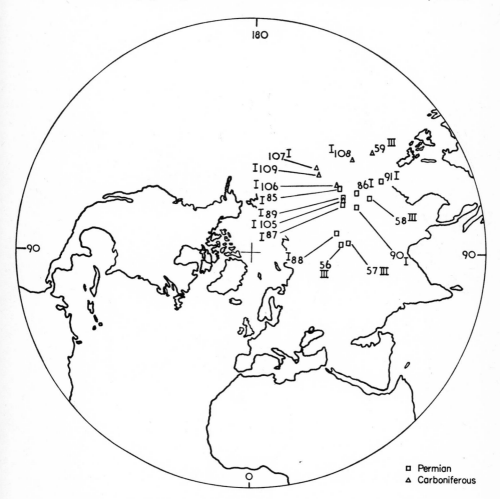

FIG. 11. Pole positions determined from North American rocks of Late Palaeozoic age.

result in a consistent magnetization not in agreement with the geo-magnetic field at the time of the formation of the rock. No field evidence was presented for this idea, though laboratory experiments showed that axial pressure had a reversible effect on the remanent moment of certain

B*

rocks. I have maintained that there is an inherent contradiction about this kind of argument [12]. The critic first alleges that the palaeo-magnetic worker has no complete knowledge of the process whereby the rock has become magnetized originally, but he then goes on to argue that

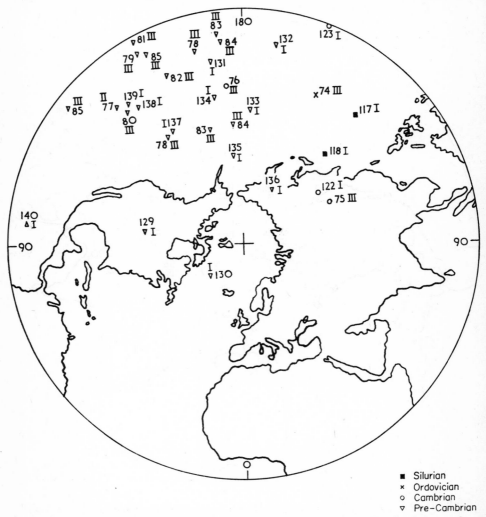

FIG. 12. Pole positions determined from North American rocks of Pre-Cambrian and Lower Palaeozoic age.

other physical and chemical processes during or after the formation of the rocks have influenced the magnetization more than the geomagnetic field at the time. Even the methods of investigating the properties of the remanent magnetization in the laboratory which are now extensively used, demagnetization by alternating magnetic fields or thermal demagnetization by heating the specimens in zero magnetic field, cannot give definite information on the method by which the rock became

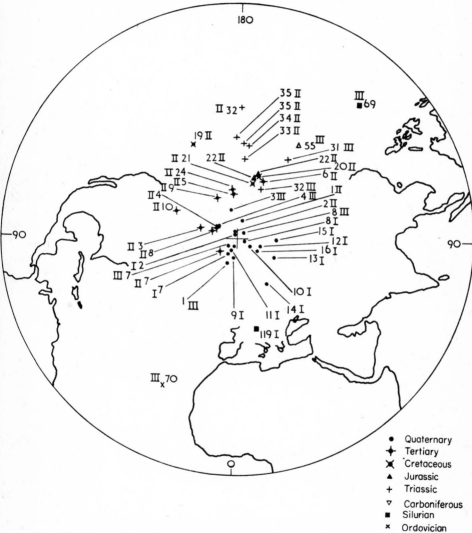

FIG. 13. Pole positions determined from Asian Rocks of Cainozoic, Mesozoic and Palaeozoic age.

magnetized. However unpalatable it may be, it is not at present possible to decide this question, and the development of this subject, and other scientific disciplines, would not have made progress if this kind of philosophy had guided the early work. It has been much more fruitful—and I believe much more in the tradition of scientific enquiry—to

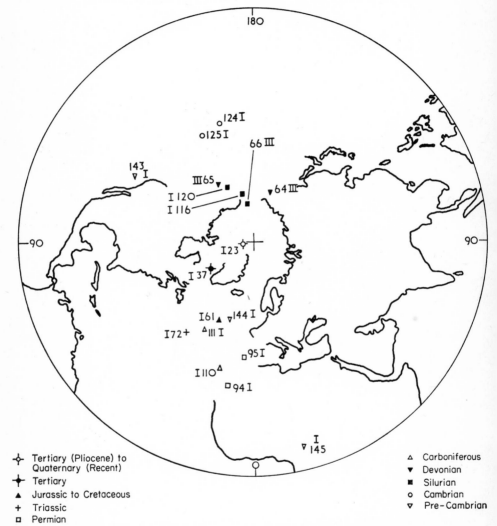

FIG. 14. Pole positions determined from Australian rocks of Cainozoic, Mesozoic, Palaeozoic and Pre-Cambrian age.

obtain accurate observations and ask what sense can be made of them, i.e. to compare the observations with a simple theory.

The simplest theory is that for reasonably short periods of geological time the pole is almost stationary and so the pole positions for one continent plotted on the present globe should be coincident. If they are, especially if the samples, as is often the case, come from different for-

Fig. 15. Pole positions determined from Indian rocks of Mesozoic and Tertiary age.

mations and widely different sites, the various hypotheses that the magnetization is locally distorted by physical and chemical mechanisms other than the geomagnetic field are excluded. In practice, errors prevent one excluding these entirely but show them at most to have had a minor role. The pole positions for Mesozoic, Palaeozoic and Pre-Cambrian times for the various continents are given in Figs. 6–8 and 10–17. The Triassic poles for North America, Europe and Asia and the

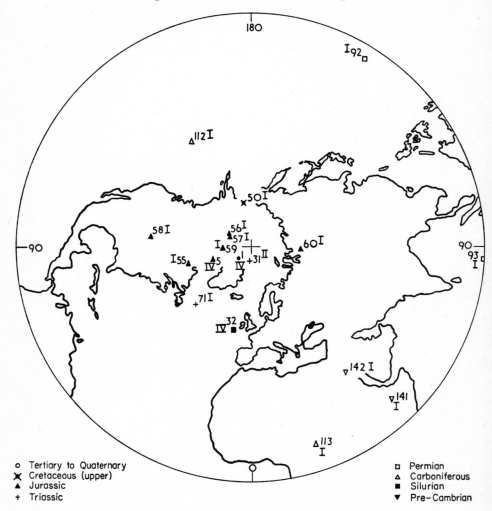

o Tertiary to Quaternary	□ Permian
✖ Cretaceous (upper)	▲ Carboniferous
▲ Jurassic	■ Silurian
+ Triassic	▼ Pre-Cambrian

FIG. 16. Pole positions determined from African rocks of Cainozoic, Mesozoic, Palaeozoic and Pre-Cambrian age.

Permian for Europe are numerous and well grouped. Results of the palaeomagnetic surveys of Great Britain and North America [13, 14, 15, 16] in the form of polar wandering curves (Fig. 19) show the movement of the pole around the present North Pacific Ocean at a rate of about

1/3° per million years. The earliest polar wandering paths for Europe [13] and that for North America [15], which were based on comparatively few specimens though widely spread through the geological column, are not

FIG. 17. Pole positions determined from Antarctica rocks of Cainozoic, Mesozoic and Palaeozoic age.

different in broad outline from the much more detailed ones shown in Fig. 19 and demonstrate the essential observation that the pole positions form a serial progression with age. Just as the grouping of poles for a particular geological age from one continent provides strong support for the basic assumptions of the palaeomagnetic method, so the fact that the poles form this progression in time is proof that here we are not dealing with a phenomenon mainly dependent on local causes.

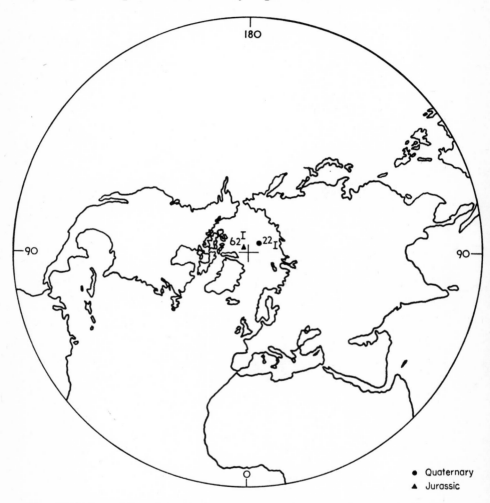

FIG. 18. Pole positions determined from South American rocks of Quaternary and Mesozoic age.

We conclude therefore that the palaeomagnetic observations relate to the ancient geomagnetic field. The vector mean pole has been computed for each continent and geological period from Irving's compilation and is plotted as an open circle or triangle on Fig. 19 to compare with the results of Collinson, Creer, Irving and Runcorn [14] and

Collinson and Runcorn [16] which are plotted as full circles and triangles. These comparisons show that no bias exists in these workers' surveys in Europe and North America.

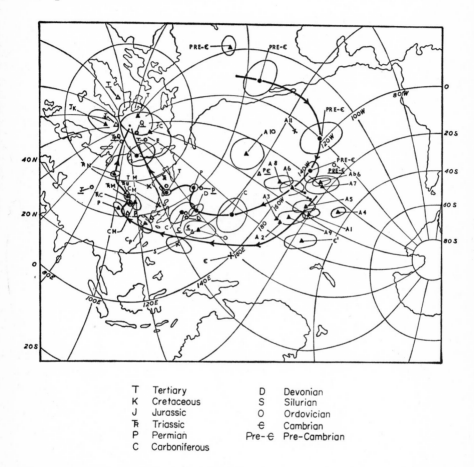

T	Tertiary	D	Devonian
K	Cretaceous	S	Silurian
J	Jurassic	O	Ordovician
Ŧ	Triassic	Є	Cambrian
P	Permian	Pre-Є	Pre-Cambrian
C	Carboniferous		

FIG. 19. Polar wandering curves based on European and North American rocks. (Mean poles based on all determinations are underlined. European poles are denoted by dots, and American poles by triangles and crosses.)

We next note that a polar wandering hypothesis alone does not explain the palaeomagnetic results, for there is a wide divergence between the polar wandering paths for the various continents, as shown schematically in Fig. 20. To reconcile the results relative movements of the continents are clearly necessary. Because of the detailed palaeomagnetic results in Europe and North America the comparison between the polar wandering paths based on rocks from these two continents is of especial interest. Figure 19 shows that the smooth curve passing through the American poles lies about 30° west of the British curve.

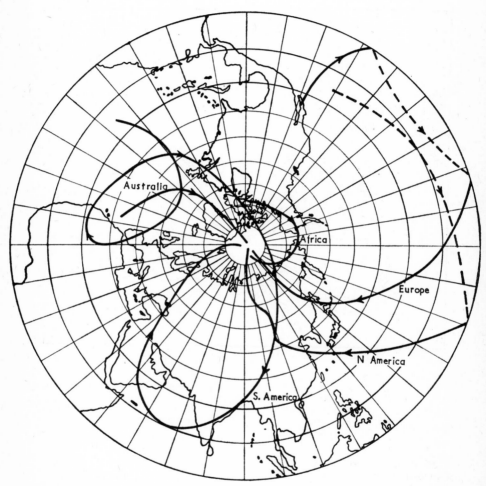

Fig. 20. Schematic polar wandering curves from all the continents. (Reproduced by permission from *Research*.) The curve for S. America is after K. M. Creer, *J. Geomagn. Geoelect.*, *Kyoto*, **13**, Nos. 3 and 4, 154–165 (1962).

Figure 21, where the longitudes of the poles are plotted against geological time, shows this more clearly. It is possible to separate the European and American points almost completely by a straight line, and the separation is seen to exist until after the Triassic. It is clear that if, following Wegener's suggestions, America and Europe were closer together for most of geological time until the Triassic and moved apart by about 30° afterwards the palaeomagnetic data would be satisfied.

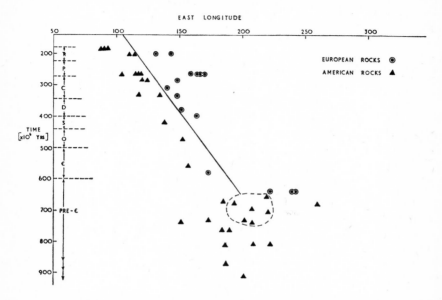

FIG. 21. Longitudes of pole positions derived from American and European rocks. (European poles are indicated by dots, and American poles by triangles.)

The next step in the subject is to reconstruct for each geological period the topography of the globe. Unfortunately the indeterminacy of the ancient longitudes presents a difficulty. In Fig. 22 the positions of Australia through geological time, inferred from Irving and Green's results [17] are plotted on a stereographic projection about the pole and clearly show the convincing correlation between the Permo-Carboniferous glaciations and the palaeomagnetic results; but the longitudes must be determined otherwise.

The final question to be discussed is whether there are explanations of these discrepancies between the polar wandering curves which do not require the hypothesis of continental drift.

Firstly, the difference in longitudes of the European and American pole positions has been discussed in a previous publication [18]. One of the most commonly observed ways in which the original magnetization of red sandstones is altered is by the acquisition of a secondary magnetization along the present dipole field [15]. This is often present to varying degrees in samples from one formation and leads to a planar distribution of directions of magnetization instead of a circular one. It is always, however, found to contain the present dipole field. Even if this secondary component cannot be removed or allowed for, it causes

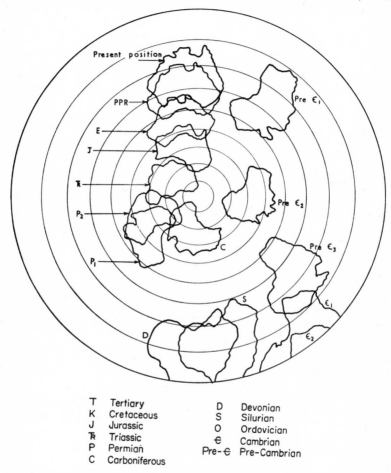

T	Tertiary	D	Devonian
K	Cretaceous	S	Silurian
J	Jurassic	O	Ordovician
Ŧ	Triassic	Є	Cambrian
P	Permian	Pre-Є	Pre-Cambrian
C	Carboniferous		

FIG. 22. Positions of Australia relative to the South Pole throughout geological time.

an error in the latitude but not in the longitude of the pole position calculated from the mean direction [18]. The divergence between the polar wandering paths for Europe and America is not therefore to be explained in this way.

Secondly, the possibility must be recognized that even though the field in pre-Tertiary times must on theoretical grounds be axially symmetrical, there seems no absolute reason why it should not have a non-dipole form. This possibility has been considered [19], and it has been shown that, postulating polar wandering but not continental drift, the divergence between the best determined polar wandering curves for Europe, North America and Australia can only be reconciled by putting Australia in low latitude in the Triassic, which on palaeoclimatic grounds does not seem reasonable.

The palaeomagnetic observations have thus revived interest in the theory of continental drift, which had become widely disregarded. Apart from the serious doubt which existed of the necessity of postu-lating continental drift to explain the geological and palaeontological records in the various continents, two very general criticisms of the hypothesis were made. The first arose from the widely held view that an event of such magnitude in the evolution of the crust might well have occurred but not so late in geological time [20]. The second was that no tenable dynamical theory of continental drift had been proposed [21] and especially that there was no suggestion at which level in the earth's interior the motion occurred. These were not arguments against study-ing seriously the evidence for continental drift: no one in the last few centuries has disbelieved in the existence of the earth's magnetic field in spite of there being no theory of it! It is, however, now possible to ask the question how present geophysical models of the earth's interior need to be modified to admit of such large continental displacements in the latter part of geological time.

Wegener [22] saw that the key to the understanding of the mechanism of continental drift is the fact that the isostatic equilibrium of the continents is almost complete. The readjustment of the heights of continental areas consequent on changes of loading, such as the removal of the Fennoscandian ice sheet about 10,000 years ago, involves be-haviour of a fluid nature in the upper mantle below the Moho. The continuity equation implies that horizontal flow as well as vertical flow must occur. Further it appears that lunar tidal friction is causing the earth's angular velocity to decrease at a rate, which extrapolating to its early history requires that the earth's ellipticity was once about twice its present one. The consequent slow change in this has involved flow in the upper mantle. In the years since Wegener published his theory, the most active branch of the geophysics of the solid earth has been seismology. Geophysicists therefore became conditioned to the earth's response to the short period stresses of earthquakes, with periods of seconds and minutes. Thus seismology and the study of the earth's nutation of 12 and 14 months periods has been based on the assumption that the mantle is a classical elastic solid (e.g. [21]). Recently Jeffreys [23] has departed from this position by examining whether a modified elastic equation could account for the damping of the nutation and the rotation of the satellites of planets. He was led to do this as a result of some torsional experiments on rocks at ordinary temperatures and pressures done by Lomnitz [24], who found that, as in many metals and other materials, an instantaneous strain p/E (as in classical theory) occurs on applying a stress p, followed by an additional strain increasing with time, as shown in Fig. 23, by line A, to a constant value. On removing the stress the strain decreases with time, as shown by line B, leaving no permanent set.

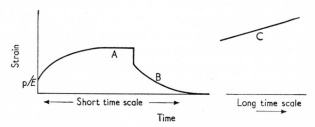

FIG. 23. Long-term mechanical behaviour of rocks under constant stress (C) compared with short-term behaviour (A B). (Reproduced by permission from *Nature*.)

Jeffreys shows that, under an adverse temperature gradient, convection does not persist in a material with such a delayed elastic behaviour following a small perturbation to the equilibrium, and he excludes the movements in the mantle which we shall presently see to be required to cause continental drift. However, in addition to the elastic behaviour of solids, we must expect that if the stress is maintained, creep is likely, occurring at a rate dependent on the stress, as shown in the figure by line C. This deformation does not have the property of decaying slowly once the stress is removed. Thus the response of the earth to the stresses of seismicity and nutation is not a guide to its behaviour under stresses applied constantly for millions of years. The folds and contortions in geological strata provide field evidence of the reality of creep in rocks and laboratory experiments at high pressure are beginning to provide direct evidence.

From the viewpoint of modern physics classical elasticity is a less simple and fundamental process than creep—but we do not see the mechanical behaviour of solids in this light simply because of the laboratory scale. On the geophysical time scale, the resulting distortional strain in a solid under a shearing stress deranges the order within the crystals, but in the long run various physical processes occur to re-establish it, for example thermal agitation will re-arrange the atoms into states of lower free energy. The constantly applied stress will, therefore, cause the re-establishment of fresh strain and creep or flow will occur. Thus it seems incontestable that in the long run any material will flow accordingly to curve C. That most of the mantle is likely to be at temperatures not much below the melting point is further cause for suspecting that such behaviour will occur.

We shall therefore assume that, when subjected to shearing stresses with periods of millions of years, the mantle behaves as a Newtonian fluid. Hitherto, the thermal history of the earth has been discussed (e.g. by Jacobs [25]) by assuming that transport of heat has been by conduction and, to some extent, by radiation. Convection in the mantle is a more effective agent for removing heat than conduction. Thermal convection in a horizontal layer under gravity (as in the atmosphere) or in a spherical shell under a radial gravitational field (as in the mantle) occurs when the temperature gradient exceeds the adiabatic gradient by an amount such that the temperature differences necessary to drive the convection currents are able to maintain themselves against the thermal equalizing tendency of the conduction process. This excess critical temperature gradient (Rayleigh's criterion) is almost negligible in geophysical problems.

To establish the quantitative possibility of convection the viscous and buoyancy forces in the mantle are equated [27]. The acceleration of gravity g is nearly constant through the mantle. Let α be the coefficient of volume expansion and ΔT the temperature difference between the up-going and down-going currents on a spherical surface in the mantle.

$$g\rho\alpha\Delta T = \frac{\mu v}{(R-r)^2}$$

where μ is the viscosity of the mantle, $(R-r)$ its depth, and v the velocity of the convection currents. Taking $\mu = 10^{21}$, $g = 10^3$, $\rho = 5$, $\alpha = 2 \times 10^{-5}$ we have

$$\Delta T = 10^5 v$$

We shall see that the primary effect of convection is to settle the main topography of the globe, the continents moving towards the places where the currents are descending. The secondary effect to be expected from convection currents is crumpling of the surface layers of continents and the ocean floor. Vening Meinesz [34] suggested this as an explanation of the ocean deeps and gravity anomalies off the East Indies.

It is now necessary to estimate v. If convection is to be the main energy source in tectonic processes, it seems reasonable to expect a few overturns per geological period, i.e. 50,000 km in 50 m.y. or 100 cm/year.

Further, it is natural to infer from the observed movements along transcurrent faults at the present day that their cause lies in movements of a similar rate in the mantle. The most famous of these is the San Andreas fault in California [26]. Geodetic measurements since 1880 show that south-western California is moving north at 5 cm/year. Considerable offsetting of streams on either side of the fault indicate that the movement has proceeded in the same sense for a much longer time. Since the Jurassic the fault seems to have moved at a mean rate of 0·6 cm/year, judging by the present offsetting of certain matching deposits. Palaeomagnetic measurements provide estimates of the velocities of polar wandering and continental drift as follows:

30° of westward displacement of North America from Europe since the Triassic [16]: 2×10^8 cm in 200 m.y.

60° of northward displacement of India since the Jurassic [28]: 6×10^8 cm in 150 m.y.

60° of displacement of Australia away from the South Pole since the Permian [29]: 6×10^8 cm in 250 m.y.

Since surface motions will be much slower than those at depth we take v as 100 cm/year or 3×10^{-6} cm/sec. Thus $\Delta T = 0\cdot3°$.

The heat carried by such a convection system will require a heat flow out of the core into the mantle and out of the crust of the order of $\rho\sigma\Delta Tv$ where σ is the specific heat. As $\rho\sigma = 1$ for most substances, the convective heat flow is 9×10^{-7} cal/sq. cm/sec., which is less than the observed heat flow at the earth's surface. This is satisfactory since some of the heat escaping from the earth must arise from the granitic rocks of the crust, which are found to have a higher concentration of radio-activity than the more basic rocks below.

A more rapid convection, of the order of 1 cm/sec, is expected in the earth's fluid core. This is a necessary condition for the generation of the geomagnetic field, but Bullard [30] showed that the heat conducted out of the core under the adiabatic gradient, which must be exceeded if convection is to occur, is more than can be transported through the mantle by conduction. It seems, therefore, that convection in the mantle is required for convection in the core to take place.

The first proposals that convection currents existed in the earth's mantle were made to suggest an adequate mechanism for tectonic activity. Griggs [31] put forward a theory of mountain building in which he postulated convection cells consisting of cylinders rotating about horizontal axes, their radius being of the order of 100 km and of considerably greater length. Similarly, Vening Meinesz [32] sought an explanation of the line of negative gravity anomaly along the ocean deep off the East Indies by postulating descending currents below the anomaly. The displacements of thousands of kilometres postulated in continental drift theories appear to require convection currents of the dimensions of the depth of the mantle, whereas the smaller scale of tectonically active zones, at least in their breadth, perhaps suggest smaller cells nearer the surface. It seems reasonable to suppose that continental drift is the primary consequence of convection in the mantle and tectonic activity the secondary result.

A further requirement of a convection theory of the earth's mantle, in addition to supposing that the mantle acts as a liquid over times of the order of hundreds of millions of years, is that the mantle should, on a large scale, be chemically homogeneous. Birch [33] in his analysis of the seismic data, has shown the mantle to be chemically uniform below the depths of 700 km associated with the 20° discontinuity in the seismic velocity–depth curves. There remains doubt as to the nature of the discontinuity, for above it he finds the evidence inadequate to draw the same conclusion, though does not rule it out. The 20° discontinuity has been thought to be either an actual change of chemical composition or a phase change, or to represent a rapid change of the elastic constant as the atoms are pressed closer together by the pressure. If it represented chemical segregation convection currents could not cross the boundary, and convection occurring above it would consist of cells of the order of the depth to the discontinuity, which seem too small to be effective in continental drift, though they might satisfy the requirements of a theory of tectonic activity. If the phase change hypothesis is correct, changes of phase will occur as the mantle material rises and falls through the critical depth; if this happens slowly, it will not affect the convection.

The further assumption that the theory of convection in the mantle can be developed as a perturbation from a condition of spherical symmetry seems reasonable though the continental areas may have a blanketing effect which will upset the temperature gradient in the mantle to some degree.

Vening Meinesz [34] and Chandrasekhar [35, 36] have discussed the Rayleigh problem of convection in a fluid contained in a spherical shell under a radial gravitational field. They showed, as is intuitively reasonable, that as the ratio of the radius of the inner spherical boundary to that of the outer increases, the convection which is excited at marginal stability is characterized by harmonics of higher degree. Chandrasekhar concluded that for a core of the present radius, 0·55 of the earth's radius, harmonics $n = 3$, 4 and 5 are almost equally likely to be excited at marginal stability.

Such large scale convection cells extending through the whole of the mantle may be expected to impose some regularity on the distribution of the oceans and continents. G. F. S. Hills [37] invoked convection to explain the present concentration of sial in one hemisphere. He supposed that a single convection cell swept the less dense acidic continental material together while the earth was still fluid, as shown in Fig. 25. He was following Jeffreys' theory of the evolution of the earth, in which it was supposed to have condensed as a liquid from a gas cloud, and would then cool by convection after gravitational separation had rapidly formed the core and crust. Jeffreys showed, however, that the single cell convection assumed by Hills would not form in the presence of a dense core of the present radius and that the more complicated convection pattern would not concentrate the continental material in a single hemisphere.

Vening Meinesz [34] also showed that there is a certain regularity in the positioning of the continents which suggests convection in the mantle. Prey [38], in order to study isostasy, had taken values of the height of the land above and the depths of the ocean below sea level, counting the latter negative, and he expressed these values as a series of spherical harmonics. The predominant term is, of course, of degree $n = 1$, expressing the fact that the continents are concentrated in a single hemisphere. The terms $n = 2$ and those above $n = 5$ are relatively weak, the terms $n = 3$, 4 and 5 being strong. Terms of odd degree have opposite signs at antipodal points, therefore Prey's analysis simply gives mathematical expression to the fact that the continents are antipodal to oceans. This had seemed of significance to an older generation of geologists who based on it a theory that the earth in cooling took on a tetrahedral shape, the faces forming the oceans and the vertices the continents—a theory, of course, which was destroyed by the discovery of isostasy. However, this fact that only 4% of the area of the continent is antipodal to continent demands explanation and Vening Meinesz reasoned that this regular positioning of the continents today might be the result of a large scale regular pattern of convection motions in the mantle similar to that predicted by the Rayleigh theory. The continental material would tend to be moved to the places where the currents were descending. Vening Meinesz further attached considerable weight to the fact that, except for the $n = 1$ harmonic, the reciprocals of the amplitudes in Prey's expression of the various harmonics was proportional to the Rayleigh numbers. But because the presence of the $n = 3$, 4 and 5 harmonics depended simply on the geometry of the problem, it was not easy to see why the convection would cause a change in the position of the continents, especially in the recent life of the earth.

In contrast to the older theories, Urey [39] advanced reasons why the earth must have had a cold origin: for example, the volatile elements would not otherwise be present in the earth's crust in their observed abundances. He recognized that a theory of the earth's evolution which envisages it starting from a mixture of planetesimals, presumably similar to the iron and stony meteorites, has difficulty in explaining the separation of the core, and Urey supposed that this occurred slowly:

Fig. 24. Attempted reconstruction of the southern hemisphere for mid-Mesozoic time. - - - present position; ⸺ reconstructed position. (Reproduced by permission from *Nature*.)

perhaps by the iron creeping downwards along the boundaries of the silicate crystals. Urey speculated that the growth of the core might still not be complete. Comparison between the secular accelerations of the sun and moon over the last two thousand years shows that, allowing for the deceleration of the earth by lunar tidal friction, there is an acceleration, which Urey attributed to a gradual decrease in the earth's moment of inertia, but a more likely explanation [3, 40] lies in the interchange of angular momentum between the core and the mantle resulting from the varying electro-magnetic coupling of the core and mantle. However,

both mechanisms could be present. The gradual growth of the core
through the earth's history seems to provide a simple explanation of
why the convection pattern could change and re-position the continents.

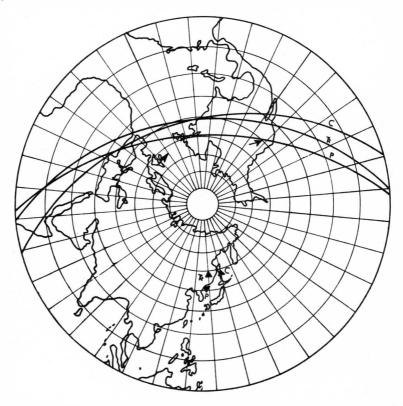

FIG. 25. Positions of Europe and North America relative to the equator for late Palaeozoic and early Mesozoic. (Reproduced by permission from *Nature*.)

It is likely that the process of convection by creep will assist in
the chemical separation of the accreted earth, the iron being carried
down to the core and the sialic material left at the surface. We have
found that there is evidence that the growth of the core is not complete
and consequently it may not be unrealistic to postulate that the concentration of the sialic material at the earth's surface has gradually
occurred through the earth's life and still may be proceeding. The fact
of the ocean ridges suggests that there are lines in the ocean floor where
there are concentrations of lighter material, which may represent sialic
material collecting near the upwelling convection currents. Oceanographers have recently found evidence that the Mid-Atlantic ridge has

a central valley over which there is a strong magnetic anomaly. This suggests that the ocean floor is parting and new basaltic material is rising into the rift and on cooling acquires a strong thermo-remanent magnetization giving rise to the observed magnetic anomaly. The pattern of these ridges is shown in Fig. 28 and suggests convection of degree $n = 5$.

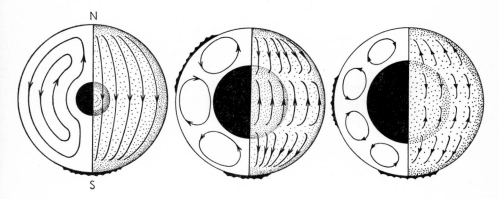

FIG. 26. Convection in mantle with different sizes of core. Left, $n = 1$; middle, $n = 3$; right, $n = 4$. (Reproduced by permission from *Nature*.)

The positions of the continents before the most recent continental displacements occurred can, however, be inferred from palaeomagnetism, not exactly enough to justify an analysis similar to that done by Prey, but sufficiently to see that such an analysis would emphasize the lower harmonics more than does the harmonic analysis of the present topography of the globe. Palaeomagnetic data from South America, Africa, India, Australia, and Antarctica, indicate [23] that these continents, in the mid-Mesozoic, were grouped closely near the South Pole as in Fig. 24. It is evident from palaeomagnetic observations [14] and palaeowind observations [2] that Europe and North America were mainly in the northern hemisphere, in lower latitudes than at present, at the end of the Palaeozoic, as is shown in Fig. 25. Palaeoclimatic evidence also suggests that Asia was closer to the equator during this time than shown. Such a continental distribution would be characterized by the $n = 3$ or 4 harmonics being much more important relative to the $n = 5$ harmonic than at the present day. One may therefore conclude that before the continental drift deduced in the geological record took place the continents were positioned essentially by a convection pattern of the $n = 4$ type, as shown in Fig. 26, and this gave way in the last 200 million years to convection of $n = 5$ type.

The age of the earth is now given as 4,600 million years, based on consideration of uranium–lead ratios in rocks and meteorites [41]. Suppose that initially the earth consists of a mixture of iron and silicate bodies. If it is assumed that the accretion of these bodies has occurred slowly enough, their heat of impact will have been lost by radiation into space and the temperature inside the earth will be the result of compression—the temperature gradient will be the adiabatic one. The heat generated by radioactivity will be equally distributed initially and after the temperature has risen sufficiently to cause creep to become an important process, a slow convection will set in. This convection will be of degree $n = 1$ as shown in Fig. 26 and if it is supposed that the sialic material has already separated or separates while this mode of convection persists, it will be swept to one area of the earth's surface.

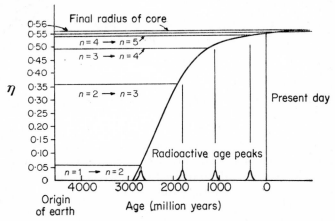

Fig. 27. Growth of the earth's core compared with the radioactive age determination peaks.

Recently Gastil [42] has surveyed the large number of radioactive age determinations which have been made on rocks from all continents (see also [43]). He finds that if the data are represented as a histogram there are peaks at ages 350 m.y., 1100 m.y., 1800 m.y. and 2700 m.y. These peaks are present whatever the elements used in establishing the age and as far as is known occur in all the continents. Because of the absence of suitable minerals in lavas and sediments, ages have been determined almost entirely on metamorphic rocks, which, of course, occur in regions of mountain building. The age peaks have therefore been held to show world-wide upsurges of orogenic activity at various epochs. It would, however, be more correct to say that the times represent times of extensive recrystallization of rocks perhaps involving chemical separation in the upper part of the mantle, adding new sialic material to the continent.

TABLE 1

Values of η for which changes in the n number of the convection pattern in a spherical shell occur

n	Free surfaces at $r = 1$ and $r = \eta$	Rigid surface at $r = \eta$ and a free surface at $r = 1$	Free surface at $r = \eta$ and a rigid surface at $r = 1$	Rigid surface at $r = 1$ and $r = \eta$
	Case of homogeneous sphere			
1– 2	0·22	0·17	0·06	0·02
2– 3	0·44	0·39	0·36	0·31
3– 4	0·57	0·50	0·49	0·46
4– 5	0·62	0·59	0·56	0·53
5– 6	0·68	0·64	0·62	0·59
6– 7	0·76	0·68	0·67	0·64
7– 8	0·77	0·70	0·73	0·69
8– 9	0·78	0·75	0·77	0·72
9–10	0·79	0·76	0·78	0·77
10–11	0·80	0·78	0·79	0·78
11–12	0·81	0·80	0·80	0·79
12–13	0·81	0·80	0·80	0·79
13–14	0·82	0·81	0·81	0·80
14–15	0·85	0·82	0·82	0·80
	Case of sphere with constant gravity			
1– 2	0·24	0·19	0·15	0·06
2– 3	0·44	0·37	0·36	0·33
3– 4	0·56	0·48	0·49	0·46
4– 5	0·65	0·58	0·54	0·52
5– 6	0·71	0·69	0·62	0·58
6– 7	0·75	0·75	0·69	0·67
7– 8	0·77	0·76	0·72	0·70
8– 9	0·79	0·77	0·75	0·73
9–10	0·80	0·78	0·77	0·75
10–11	0·81	0·79	0·78	0·77
11–12	0·81	0·80	0·80	0·78
12–13	0·83	0·81	0·80	0·79
13–14	0·85	0·81	0·81	0·80
14–15	0·86	0·82	0·81	0·80

It may, therefore, be reasonable to identify the radioactive age determination peaks with a reorganization of the convection currents leading to the rise and crystallization at the surface of new sialic material. On the view expressed above of the growth of the earth's core gradually through the earth's life, one would expect that at certain epochs the convection pattern in the mantle would change to a higher harmonic. Chandrasekhar gives the Rayleigh number for different ratios of the radii of core and mantle and for different harmonics of the convection. His data is for two cases, that of constant gravity and that

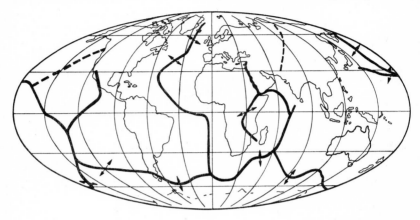

FIG. 28. The world-wide distribution of rifts in the ocean floor. (Reproduced by permission from *Research*.)

of a gravity proportional to radius, i.e. the sphere of uniform density, the latter being better for the case when the core was very small, and the former applicable to the present mantle. Table 1 is derived from Chandrasekhar's calculations and shows the ratio of core to mantle ratio at which the Rayleigh number of a pattern of convection described by a certain harmonic becomes just less than that of the pattern of next lower degree. The correct boundary conditions are a free inner surface and a rigid outer one.

As convection tends to proceed at a rate just adequate to carry the heat which cannot be conducted under the adiabatic gradient, one assumes that on this model the temperature distribution within the earth remains much the same throughout its life and, therefore, the viscosity of the interior and the velocity of the currents will remain nearly constant. As a first step in the problem let us consider the following drastically simplified model, which ignores all effects of pressure.

Let the initial mass of iron in the earth be M, then after time t the amount remaining in the mantle be M minus the mass of the core. Let the radius of the earth be R and the radius of the core at time t be r.

The mass of iron being received by the core per unit time at time $t = 4\pi r^2 \rho \, dr/dt$. The rate of separation of the iron from the mantle will depend on the viscosity of the material and the velocity of the convection, which we are assuming to remain constant, and will be proportional to the area of contact between the convection currents and the core and to the amount of iron remaining in the mantle. Let ρ be the density of iron.

Thus

$$4\pi\rho r^2 \frac{dr}{dt} \propto 4\pi r^2 (M - 4\pi r^3 \rho/3)$$

hence

$$\int \frac{dr}{1 - (r/q)^3} = Kt$$

where

$$q^3 = 3M/4\pi\rho$$

q being the final radius of the core and K a constant.

Integrating

$$\log_e \frac{(r/q - 1)^2}{(r/q)^2 + r/q + 1} + 2\sqrt{3} \tan^{-1} - (2r/q + 1)/\sqrt{3} = Kt + c$$

where c is the constant of integration.

Figure 27 shows a plot of this showing the change of the radius of the core with time. It is initially linear and then asymptotically approaches a constant value.

Figure 27 shows that all the radioactive age histogram peaks are identifiable with times when the core passed through a critical radius. The constants q, K and c are chosen to fit the values of the age peaks and corresponding core radii. This implies that the earth only reached a temperature at which the core could begin to grow about 3000 million years ago and that now 6 per cent of the iron still remains in the mantle.

References

1. NAIRN, A. E. M., "Descriptive Palaeoclimatology". Interscience, New York and London (1961).
2. OPDYKE, N. D., AND RUNCORN, S. K., *Bull geol. Soc. Amer.* **71**, 959–972 (1960).
3. RUNCORN, S. K., *Quart. J. R. met. Soc.* **87**, 282–313 (1961).
4. VESTINE, E. H., LAPORTE, L., LANGE, I., AND SCOTT, W. E., *Publ. Carneg. Instn.* **580** (1947).
5. ELSASSER, W. M., *Phys. Rev.* **69**, 106, and **70**, 202 (1946).
6. ELSASSER, W. M., *Phys. Rev.* **72**, 821 (1947).
7. BULLARD, E. C., AND GELLMAN, H., *Phil. Trans.* **247**, 213 (1954).
8. RUNCORN, S. K., *Ann. Géophys.* **15**, 87–92 (1959).

c

9. RUNCORN, S. K., *Advanc. Phys.* **6**, 169–176 (1957).
10. IRVING, E., *Geophys. J.* Part 1, **3**, 96–111 (1960); Part 2, **3**, 444–449 (1960); Part 3, **5**, 70–79 (1961).
11. GRAHAM, J. W., *J. geophys. Res.* **61**, 735–739 (1956).
12. RUNCORN, S. K., *Advanc. Phys.*, **4**, 244–291 (1955).
13. CREER, K. M., IRVING, E., AND RUNCORN, S. K., *J. Geomagn. Geoelect., Kyoto*, **4**, 163–168 (1954).
14. COLLINSON, D. W., CREER, K. M., IRVING, E., AND RUNCORN, S. K., *Phil. Trans.* **250**, 73–156 (1957).
15. RUNCORN, S. K., *Bull. geol. Soc. Amer.* **67**, 301–316 (1956).
16. COLLINSON, D. W., AND RUNCORN, S. K., *Bull. geol. Soc. Amer.* **71**, 915–958 (1960).
17. IRVING, E., AND GREEN, R., *Geophys. J.* **1**, 64–72 (1958).
18. RUNCORN, S. K., *Proc. geol. Ass. Can.* **8**, 77–85 (1956).
19. RUNCORN, S. K., *J. atmos. terr. Phys.* **14**, 167–174 (1959).
20. WHITE, D., Theory of Continental Drift: A Symposium, 187, American Association of Petroleum Geologists (1928).
21. JEFFREYS, H., "The Earth – its Origin, History and Physical Constitution". Cambridge University Press, London (1952).
22. WEGENER, A., "Die Entstehung der Kontinente und Ozeane". Friedr. Vieweg & Sohn, Brunswick (1941).
23. JEFFREYS, H., Presidential address to International Association of Seismology and the Physics of the Earth's Interior, Helsinki (1960).
24. LOMNITZ, C., *J. Geol.* **64**, 473–479 (1956).
25. JACOBS, J. A., "Handbuch der Physik", 47. Geophysik, I, p. 364. Springer, Berlin, Göttingen, Heidelberg (1956).
26. HILL, M. L., AND DIBBLEE, T. W., *Bull. geol. Soc. Amer.* **64**, 443 (1953).
27. RUNCORN, S. K., *Nature, Lond.* **193**, 311 (1962).
28. CLEGG, J. A., DEUTSCH, E. R., AND GRIFFITHS, D. H., *Phil. Mag.* **1**, 419 (1956).
29. IRVING, E., AND GREEN, R., *Mon. Not. R. astr. Soc. geophys. Suppl.* **7**, 347 (1957).
30. BULLARD, E. C., *Proc. roy. Soc. A.* **197**, 433 (1949).
31. GRIGGS, D. T., *Amer. J. Sci.* **237**, 611 (1939).
32. VENING MEINESZ, F. A., *Proc. Kon. Ned. Akad. Weten.* **55**, 527 (1952).
33. BIRCH, F., *J. geophys. Res.* **57**, 227 (1952).
34. VENING MEINESZ, F. A., "Gravity Expeditions at Sea, Vol. 4" Delftsche Uitgevers Maatschappis, Delft (1923–38) (1948).
35. CHANDRASEKHAR, S., *Phil. Mag.* **44**, 233, 1129 (1953).
36. CHANDRASEKHAR, S., "Hydrodynamic and Hydromagnetic Stability". Oxford University Press, London (1961).
37. HILLS, G. F. S., "The Formation of the Continents by Convection". Arnold, London (1947).
38. PREY, A., *Abh. Ges. Wiss. Göttingen*, **11**, 1 (1922).
39. UREY, H. C., "The Planets". Oxford University Press, London (1952).
40. MUNK, W. H., AND MacDONALD, G. J. F., "The Rotation of the Earth". Cambridge University Press, London (1961).
41. PATERSON, C., *Geochim. et cosmochim. Acta*, **10**, 230–237 (1956).
42. GASTIL, G., *Amer. J. Sci.* **258**, 1–35 (1960).
43. DAVIS, G. L., AND TILTON, G. R., in "Researches in Geochemistry", 190–216. (P. H. Abelson, ed.) John Wiley, New York (1959).

Chapter 2

Palaeoclimatology and Continental Drift

N. D. OPDYKE

I. Introduction 41
   A. Oxygen 18 42
   B. Palaeowinds 42
II. Sedimentary Climatic Indicators 43
   A. Evaporites 43
   B. Bauxites 43
   C. Glacial Deposits 43
   D. Bioherms 44
III. Uniformitarianism and the Study of Palaeoclimates . . 44
IV. Distribution of Cainozoic Climatic Indicators . . . 45
   A. Evaporites 45
   B. Bauxite 46
   C. Bioherms 47
   D. Pleistocene Glaciation 47
V. Discussion of Cainozoic Climate 48
VI. Distribution of Climatic Indicators during the Mesozoic . 52
VII. Distribution of Palaeozoic Climatic Indicators . . . 53
   A. Permian 53
   B. Carboniferous 55
   C. Devonian 56
   D. Silurian 57
   E. Lower Palaeozoic 58
   F. Discussion of Palaeozoic climatic distribution . . 59
VIII. Palaeomagnetism and Palaeoclimatology 60
IX. Conclusions 63
   References 64

I. INTRODUCTION

Palaeoclimatology was one of the original keystones of Wegener's theory of continental drift. He used it as one of his tools in the reconstruction of Pangea particularly in his attempt to locate pole positions relative to his reconstructions. The distribution of the permo-carboniferous glaciation was and has remained one of the strongest arguments in favour of continental drift. The evidence from palaeomagnetism covered in the first chapter by S. K. Runcorn has recently been inter-preted as showing that continental drift of some sort has occurred. Therefore, it will be worthwhile re-examining certain types of palaeo-climatic evidence to determine whether it lends support to the palaeo-magnetic latitudes given by palaeomagnetism.

A. OXYGEN 18

Several approaches to this problem are possible. The most promising technique to be developed in the last decade dealing with palaeo-climatology is palaeotemperature measurements made on fossil material using the $^{16}O/^{18}O$ ratio. This method is based on the fact first recog-nized by Urey [1] that the abundance of the ^{18}O isotope in calcium carbonate is related to its temperature of deposition. Utilizing this fact and working with very sensitive mass-spectrometers, later workers were able to begin reconstructing past climates [2]. Unfortunately informa-tion on past climates have not been forthcoming as rapidly as many might desire because of the many inherent difficulties in the method. Recently, the first paper using this method and dealing with the palaeoclimatology of a geological period has been published; Bowen [3] analysed almost 100 Jurassic Belemnoidea from localities spread throughout the world, but it was possible to come to several important conclusions from this study. The climate of the Jurassic, although very equitable, was zoned with larger tropical and semitropical belts than at present. In a general way the results agree with the lines of latitude derived from palaeomagnetism. Unfortunately, material from several critical parts of the world is missing, so that firm conclusions are not possible at this time. It is hoped that this will be rectified in the future. Until palaeotemperature results are extended into the Palaeozoic in a comprehensive fashion other methods must be attempted.

B. PALAEOWINDS

Another new technique which has appeared in recent years is the study of Palaeowind directions determined from cross-stratification in aeolian sandstones. Opdyke and Runcorn [4] have shown that in the Upper Palaeozoic aeolian sandstones of Europe and North America the directions observed correspond to a trade wind belt if compared with the palaeomagnetic equator.* This method of palaeoclimatic investigation is limited to occurrences of aeolian sandstone which is not very abundant in the geological column; therefore its usefulness is somewhat restricted.

* J. J. Bigarella and R. Salamuni (1961, *Bull. geol. Soc. Amer.* **72**, 1089), in orientation studies on the dune bedding of the Botucatú sandstone of Brazil and Uruguay, regard the deduced wind direction as being in accord with the palaeomagnetic evidence.

II. Sedimentary Climatic Indicators

The palaeoclimate of any particular place on the earth's surface during any geological period is reflected in the fauna and flora that flourished at that time and place and also in the associated sediments. This study is concerned only with the sediments that are considered to be diagnostic of a particular climatic regime. Unfortunately, the climatic and environmental significance of many types of sediment is not understood. Any study of this type is limited by a number of factors which are as follows:

1. Non-deposition of sediments which leaves a gap in the geological column.
2. By the removal through uplift and erosion of large parts of the sedimentary column.
3. By the fact that the geology of some parts of the world is either entirely unknown or known only in its basic outline.
4. Faulty field work coupled with bad or incomplete reporting.

Four types of sediment were chosen as being diagnostic of a particular climatic environment. Those selected for use in the present study are evaporites, bauxites, glacial deposits and bioherms.

A. EVAPORITES

Optimum conditions for the development of evaporites would prevail where high temperature and low precipitation would aid evaporation. Modern evaporites are known to be developing in only two places, at Bacana de Virrila, Peru, at latitude 6°S, which is backed by the Sechura desert, and the Gulf of Karabuga on the Caspian sea, latitude 41°N, whose hinterland is formed by the Kara Kum desert. Types of evaporites are known that do not develop from sea water but, instead, develop from inland drainage in desert areas in salt pans or saline lakes. However, it is most probable that the evaporite deposits that are most important geologically developed in restricted marine basins and relic seas [5].

B. BAUXITES

Bauxite is a product of deep weathering in a tropical or subtropical climate that has contrasting wet and dry seasons [6].

C. GLACIAL DEPOSITS

Glacial action leads to the production of several types of diagnostic deposits and to a special type of eroded surface, all or some of which may be preserved in the geological record. These are tillites, varvites and striated pavements [7].

D. BIOHERMS

Modern reefs are being formed today only in the tropics or subtropics because only in these climates are the optimum conditions for rapid reef growth met. Rankama and Sahama [8] state that "Deposits high in calcareous structures are generally restricted to tropical seas, in which the degree of supersaturation with calcium carbonate is high. More calcium carbonate is separated by organisms in the warm seas of the lower latitudes than in the cold polar seas". Thus the palaeoclimatological significance of bioherms rests on the fact that tropical and subtropical seas provide optimum conditions for the rapid biochemical fixation of calcium carbonate, not on the type of organism that forms the bioherms. Teichert [9] rightly points out that reef-like banks exist at depth in the North Atlantic in very cold water. However, it would seem that the associated facies of the two types of structures would easily enable the geologist to distinguish them from each other.

III. UNIFORMITARIANISM AND THE STUDY OF PALAEOCLIMATES

Hutton's theory of uniformitarianism has been widely and successfully applied in many fields of geology. However, strict application of this theory to the study of palaeoclimatology leads to considerable difficulty. It is apparent to most people that climate is a fluctuating phenomenon and recent research in climatic records shows this to be true [10]. In the geologically very recent past we have the example of the major climatic fluctuations of the Pleistocene, with its alternation of glacial and interglacial maxima, the last major retreat of the ice occurring barely 10,000 years ago.

We can see, therefore, that we are dealing with a phenomenon that is subject to considerable fluctuation in intensity and duration. It can clearly be seen that if we apply the uniformitarian theory to climates in past geological periods using the climatic zones of today we are liable to introduce serious error into any conclusions that we may draw concerning the climates of the past. The present climate is clearly only one point on a curve of climatic fluctuation and any assumptions drawn on the premise that the climate of today is the average climate of the geological past are liable to be in serious error.

From the preceding discussion it is clear that the theory of uniformitarianism in the restricted sense is not applicable to the study of palaeoclimatology. It appears, however, that if a great enough number of geologically recent climatic fluctuations were included in a definition of "present" then a reasonable attempt at interpreting past climates in the light of such a redefined "present" could be made. The most reasonable course to take would be to interpret the past in terms of the latest geological era, the Cainozoic. Several reasons appear to make this course desirable.

1. It is chronologically the closest era to the present.
2. The geology and palaeoclimatology of the Cainozoic is relatively well known.
3. Recent palaeomagnetic studies indicate little if any continental drift or polar wandering during the Cainozoic (with the exception of India).
4. It is a length of time great enough to have allowed significant climatic fluctuations to have taken place and to allow the accumulation of climatically significant sedimentary deposits (60 million years).

IV. Distribution of Cainozoic Climatic Indicators

A. EVAPORITES

Table 1 gives the area of occurrence, formation or age of occurrence, associated sediments and thickness of Cainozoic evaporites.

TABLE 1

Cainozoic

Area	Formation or Interval	Type of Association	Thickness	Kind of Evaporite
Kuwait	Rus	I		Anhydrite
Iraq	Lower Fars Bahrain	I & IV		Anhydrite
Iran, Mtn and Foothill Zone	Lower Fars	I		Anhydrite
Iran, Elburz Mts.	Fars	IV		Anhydrite
Israel	Usdum series	I	600'+	Anhydrite, Halite, Gypsum
Salt Range	Laki Beds	II		Halite, Gypsum, Potassium salts
Algeria	Mellak stage	IV	198'	Gypsum
Algerian Sahara	Eocene (Lutetian)	I		Gypsum

TABLE 1—*continued*

Area	Formation or Interval	Type of Association	Thickness	Kind of Evaporite
Paris Basin	Ludian	IV		Gypsum
Galicia	Saliferous			Halite, Potassium salts
Roumania Carpathians	Cornu beds			
Castelnandary	Aguitanian			Gypsum
Logroño & Burgos	Ludian			Gypsum Halite, Potassium salts
Romagna, Calabria and Sicily	Miocene			Gypsum
Caucasus				Halite
Central Honan N. Hupch	Eocene	IV		Gypsum
Queensland	Eocene			Gypsum
Florida	Palaeocene-Eocene	I		
Horn of Africa	Taleh	I	40′+	Gypsum
Peru	Modern			Halite Gypsum
Caspian Sea, Gulf of Karaboghaz	Modern			

The type of stratigraphic context of evaporites are represented as follows (following Krumbein [25]):

I. Evaporites included within carbonate succession.
II. Evaporites present in a limestone, evaporite, clastic succession with the evaporites preceded by limestone deposition and succeeded by clastic deposition (usually redbeds).
III. Evaporite deposition preceded by clastic (usually redbed) deposition and followed by the deposition of limestone or dolomite.
IV. Evaporite deposition following clastic deposition usually redbeds and succeeded by clastic deposition also normally redbeds.

The preceding are the four broad categories in which evaporites occur in the stratigraphic column although gradations between all the main categories occur. Evaporites are normally associated with the occurrence of redbeds but cases do occur where the clastics associated with the evaporites are black or green.

The thickness of the evaporite succession is always presented as thickness in feet.

B. BAUXITE

Cainozoic bauxite is widely distributed throughout the world with important deposits occurring in North America (Oregon, Arkansas, Mississippi, Alabama and Georgia) and the West Indies (Jamaica,

Haiti and Santo Domingo). Large, commercially important deposits occur in South America mainly in British and Dutch Guiana and in Brazil. Bauxites in Europe occur in Northern Ireland, Germany (the Vogelsberg Mountains), Spain (Barcelona), and the Adriatic area (the Istrian Peninsula, Dalmatia, Herzegovina, southern Montenegro and the Adriatic coast of Yugoslavia). Cainozoic bauxite also occurs in Russia near Akmolinsk, and in two areas of Africa, the larger in the Gold Coast and French West Africa and the other in Nyasaland. Large deposits are scattered throughout peninsular India where they have developed on the Deccan traps and, in extra-peninsular India, in Kashmir [6]. Bauxite occurs throughout south-east Asia and Oceania, principally in Malaya, Indo-China, Borneo, the Caroline Islands and Australia.

C. BIOHERMS

Modern reef development lies principally between latitude 30°N and 30°S going farther to the north of the east coast of North America (Bermuda) and the east coast of Asia (the southernmost Japanese Islands) [11].

Tertiary reefs occur around the margins of the Caribbean and Tethy's seas. The Caribbean occurrences are reported from the Louisiana and Texas Gulf Coast area [12], the Dominican Republic [13] and Venezuela [14]. Bioherms are also developed in France, the Italian Riviera and the Crimea in Europe [14]. A large development of Tertiary reefs occurs in the Middle East [15] in Iran, Iraq, Lebanon, Arabia and Jordan.

D. PLEISTOCENE GLACIATION

The facts concerning the Pleistocene glaciation are reasonably well known but it might be well to recapitulate some of the relevant points. In North America the ice at various times advanced into the heart of the continent as far south as Southern Illinois about latitude 38°N.

Ice during the same period covered most of Northern Europe including the British Isles, with the major centre of accumulation located on the Scandinavian peninsula. The continental ice sheets did not reach as far to the south in Europe as they did in North America. The deepest penetration toward the equator made by the European ice was in the Ukraine at latitude 50°N. This is true only if continental ice sheets are considered, for throughout the Pleistocene glaciers were formed on many mountain chains in response to the general refrigeration; the glaciers that exist and have existed on Mts. Kilimanjaro and Ruwenzori, both practically on the equator, are notable examples.

C*

V. Discussion of Cainozoic Climate

The distribution of these climatic indicators are shown in Fig. 1. A line can be drawn on the map showing the poleward limit of the Cainozoic subtropics as indicated by this study. It is now possible to compare the northern and southern limits of the subtropics with limits obtained by other means. Chaney [16] has made an intensive study of the climatic implications of the Tertiary flora. He was able to outline the probable

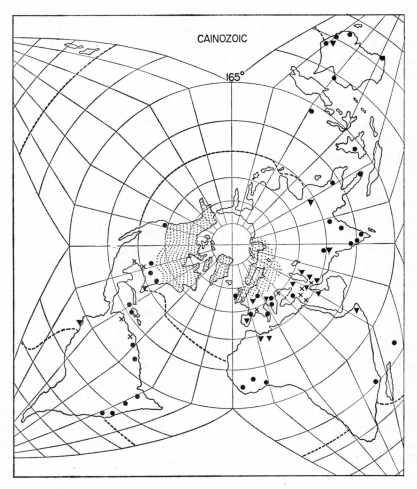

Fig. 1. The distribution of climatic indicators during the Cainozoic. The broken line indicates the limit of modern reef growth. The symbols are as follows: **x** represents Tertiary reefs, filled triangles are evaporite deposits and the filled circles denote occurrences of bauxite. The stippled area shows the maximum extent of the Pleistocene continental glaciation.

maximum extension of the subtropical flora zone: this is shown in Fig. 2. Durham [17], proceeding along lines similar to those of Chaney but using fossil invertebrate fauna instead of flora, arrived at a similar conclusion regarding the poleward limits of the Cainozoic subtropics.

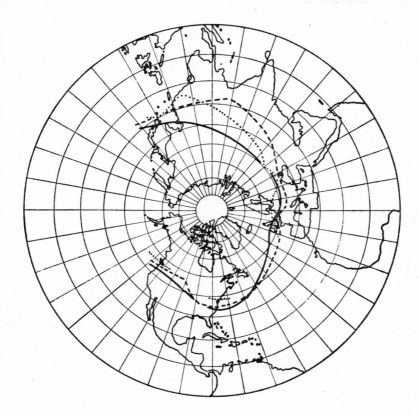

FIG. 2. Maximum extension of the tropic and semi-tropical zone during the Tertiary. The dotted line represents Durham's data, the dashed line Chaney's data, and the solid line the writer's.

Figure 2 shows that the distribution of the Tertiary tropics and sub-tropics using the selected indicators agrees very well with the information obtained from palaeobotany and palaeontology indicating that the approach used is probably valid.

From the distribution of the climatic indicators shown in Fig. 1 several conclusions can be drawn:

    1. The subtropical zone is likely to extend 50° north and south of the equator for any geological period of sufficient length (50 million

years) with a possible maximum extension of 55°, given a favourable combination of geography and ocean currents, e.g. Ireland
during the lower Tertiary.

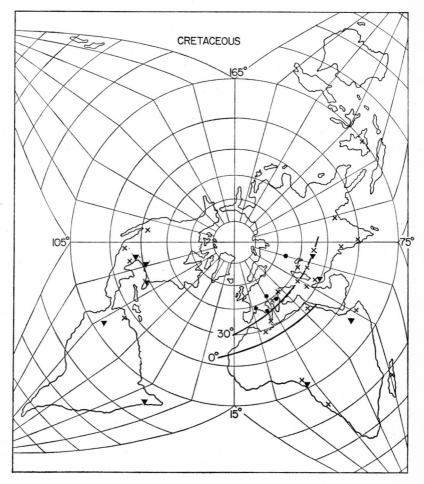

FIGS. 3 to 11. Comparison of palaeomagnetic and palaeoclimatic data. The palaeomagnetic latitudes are represented by solid lines, bioherms by **x**'s, evaporites by filled
triangles, bauxite deposits by filled circles. Glacial deposits are represented by stippled
areas or the letter G. The projections used are polar stereographic.

2. Continental glaciers are unlikely to occur closer than 40° to the
   equator with maximum penetration closer than 38° improbable,
   except by alpine glaciers.
3. It is possible to get overlap in any one period between glacial

conditions and subtropical climate as given by their unique types
of sedimentary deposits. If the Pleistocene glacial maximum from
North America is compared with the Tertiary tropical maximum
of Europe the overlap may be as much as ten degrees. It could be

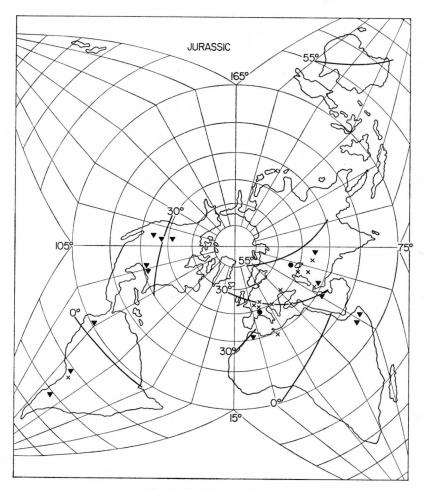

FIG. 4. For key see Fig. 3.

significant that in only one place have continental glaciers actually
passed over a deposit indicating a subtropical climate during the
Tertiary and that is in the bauxites of Northern Ireland. It seems
that the continental glaciation was roughly confined to the temperate and warm temperate zone of Tertiary.

Figures 3 to 11 show the distribution of these climatic indicators through to the base of the Palaeozoic. It must be noted that a study of this type is not very sensitive to small changes in climate; however, any large shift in the geographical pole or of the continents must be reflected sooner or later in the geological column.

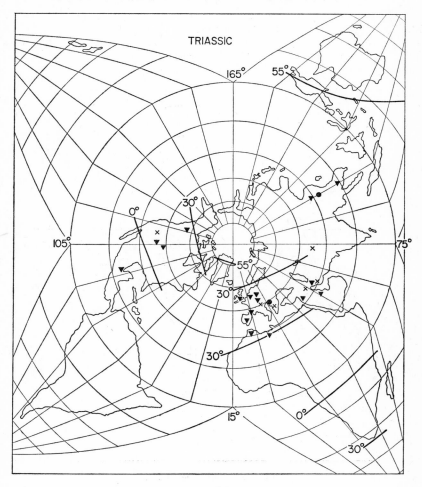

FIG. 5. For key see Fig. 3.

VI. DISTRIBUTION OF CLIMATIC INDICATORS DURING THE MESOZOIC

If we compare Figs. 3, 4 and 5 with Fig. 1, we see that the range of the chosen climatic indicators for the Mesozoic does not greatly exceed the limits taken from the Cainozoic distribution. However, during the

Triassic, evaporites occurred farther north than expected in the Peace River area of Canada and in Western Europe. The Mesozoic distribution demands no significant change in the position of the continents on these climatic criteria alone.

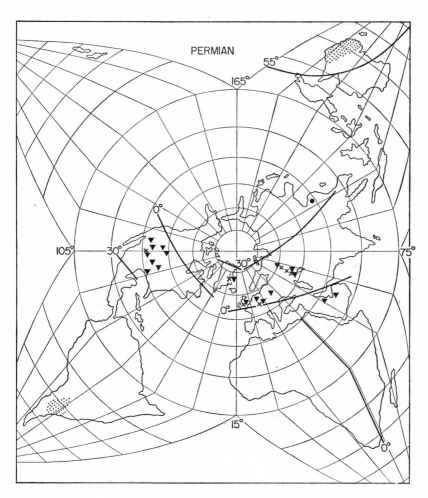

FIG. 6. For key see Fig. 3.

VII. DISTRIBUTION OF PALAEOZOIC CLIMATIC INDICATORS

A. PERMIAN

Figures 6 to 11 show the distribution of the climatic indicators through the Palaeozoic. It can be seen from Fig. 6 that suddenly, in the Permian, grave discrepancies appear in the distribution as predicted from the Cainozoic pattern. In the northern Hemisphere sediments indicating subtropical climate appear north of the maximum range of the Cainozoic subtropical indicators. The most startling is the appearance of evaporites

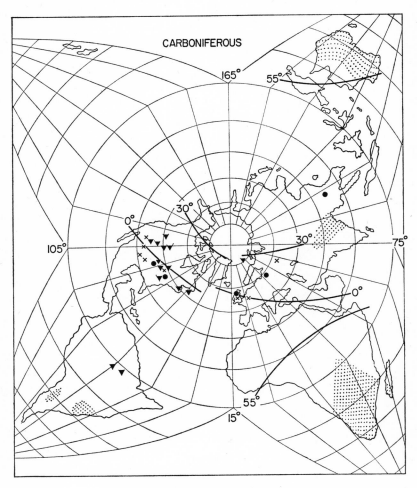

FIG. 7. For key see Fig. 3.

and bioherms on the east coast of Greenland between latitude 70° and 75°N [18] and of evaporites and bioherms along the western slope of the Urals at 60°N [19]. Just as remarkable as this sudden shift to the north of the subtropics in the northern hemisphere is the appearance of continental glaciers on the east coast of Australia [20] at latitude 22°S which is 20° closer to the equator than the nearest approach of the Pleistocene ice. Glacial deposits of this period are found almost as close as this to the equator in Argentina [21].

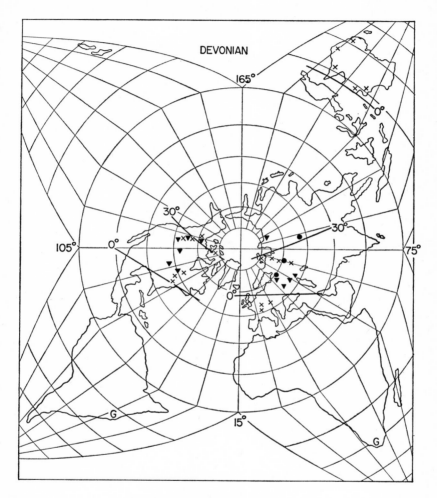

FIG. 8. For key see Fig. 3.

B. CARBONIFEROUS

This discrepancy is found to persist during the Carboniferous when, in the Northern Hemisphere, evaporites are found from this period in Spitzbergen [22] while at the same time the glaciation of the Southern Hemisphere was reaching its peak with the ice actually crossing the equator in Africa [23]. It may be pointed out that the evidence for the Permo-Carboniferous glaciation of the Southern Hemisphere is unimpeachable for one who takes time to investigate the evidence [7].

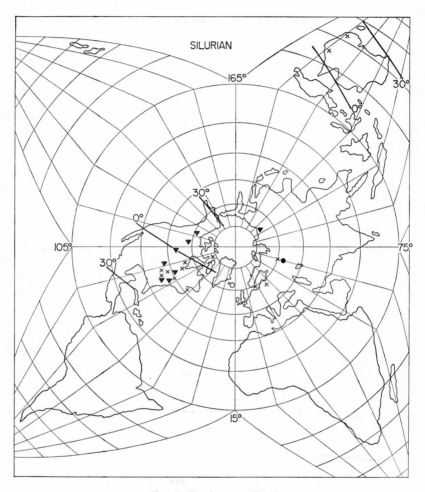

FIG. 9. For key see Fig. 3.

C. DEVONIAN

The distribution of Devonian climatic indicators is no less mystifying, for evaporites are found in this period at 65°N in Canada and within the Arctic Circle in Siberia at Nordvik bay latitude 74°N on the Arctic Ocean [19]. Bioherms extend to the shores of the Arctic Ocean in Europe and far to the north in North America, while evidence indicates that the Cape of Good Hope and South America was experiencing a mild glaciation [23]. Bauxite deposits that are economically important occur at this time along the flanks of the Ural Mountains, the Moscow Basin and the Kusnetz Basin [19].

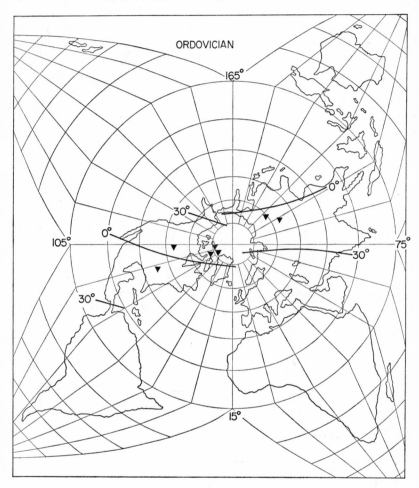

FIG. 10. For key see Fig. 3.

D. SILURIAN

During the Silurian much the same picture emerges as the Devonian. Evaporites and bioherms develop around the periphery of the Canadian shield from West Virginia to south of Great Bear Lake in Canada [24]. In northern Russia important deposits of Silurian gypsum occur on the

Taimyr Peninsula, 76°N [19]. Bauxite also occurs along the eastern slope of the central Urals. South America may have sustained a mild glaciation at this time, according to King [26].

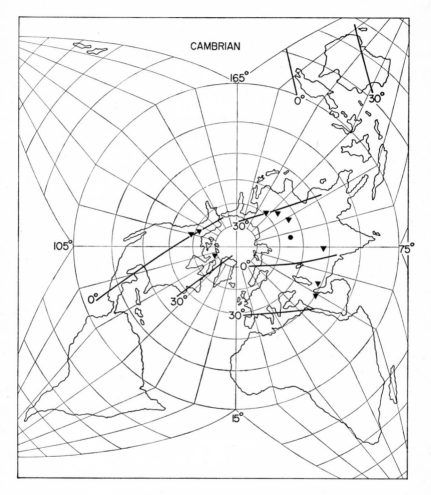

Fig. 11. For key see Fig. 3.

E. LOWER PALAEOZOIC

The Ordovician and Cambrian has much the same type of pattern as that of the rest of the palaeozoic. Again evaporites are present in the Arctic regions and a major evaporite basin developed during the Ordovician in the Arctic Islands of Canada, far to the north above the

80th parallel, composed mainly of gypsum of the order of 1,000 feet in thickness [27]. Cambrian evaporites are also present in Canada, Siberia, the Middle East and India.

F. DISCUSSION OF PALAEOZOIC CLIMATIC DISTRIBUTION

The range in latitude of evaporites, bioherms and bauxites are as follows:

Cretaceous	0–55
Jurassic	0–52
Triassic	0–57
Permian	0–72
Carboniferous	0–79
Devonian	0–77
Silurian	0–76
Ordovician	0–81
Cambrian	0–75

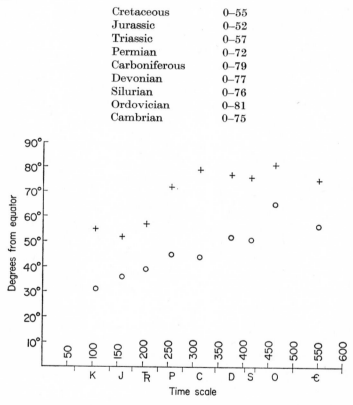

FIG. 12. Distribution of climatic indicators through geological time relative to the present equator. The crosses show the maximum extension from the present equator, and the circles represent the mean distance from the present equator. Time in millions of years before the present.

It can be seen from Fig. 12 that the mean position of the tropical and subtropical climatic data becomes farther from the present equator the farther back in time one proceeds. The vast majority of these climatic criteria are present in the northern hemisphere where an effective northern limit is placed on them by the northern limit of land.

Throughout the Palaeozoic this northern limit is reached in period after period from the Permian to the Cambrian. A phenomenon of this sort can hardly be due to a transitory cause such as warm ocean currents because it is a consistent feature throughout the Palaeozoic.

Thus we can see that the palaeoclimatic evidence is not in accord with what could be expected from the present configuration of continents and ocean basins relative to the present geographical poles and with respect to the orientation of the earth to the sun.

It has often been said by various writers that in the past the earth was much warmer than at present. This hypothesis is often used to explain away the presence of bioherms and evaporites in the Arctic basin and their longitudinal spread. This might be acceptable on the basis of the evidence from North America and Europe but it is entirely incompatible with the concurrent glacial evidence from the Southern Hemisphere.

VIII. Palaeomagnetism and Palaeoclimatology

Since palaeomagnetic studies have refocused attention on the theory of continental drift, the palaeoclimatic evidence must be compared with palaeomagnetic data to determine whether the two are compatible. This has already been done in a general way by Irving [28] and for particular times and places by Schove, Nairn and Opdyke [29], and by Opdyke [30] and Nairn [31].

The palaeomagnetic evidence in support of continental drift has already been covered by Runcorn in Chapter 1. The palaeomagnetic poles presented here have been compiled from a number of sources. The ones selected by the author are those regarded to be most reliable because of positive stability evidence or the absence of concrete evidence of instability such as streaking. In many cases use must be made of the only evidence available. These pole positions are presented in Table 2, along with the sources of the information. If several pole positions are available from a continent for a particular period of reasonable reliability then the mean position was taken to represent the period. A certain amount of subjectivity is almost unavoidable at the present stage of development in palaeomagnetism.

The palaeoclimatic indicators were then placed in their palaeomagnetic co-ordinates using a stereographic net. It has already been shown by Irving [28], that climatic indicators should only be compared with palaeomagnetic results from the same continents. It is clear that palaeomagnetic results from Europe should not be compared with the palaeomagnetic criteria from Australia. Some cases are unfortunately not so unambiguous. The most important is the Urasian landmass. It is not

TABLE 2

Pole Positions

North America	Latitude	Longitude	Source
Jurassic	72·5N	6·5E	32
Triassic	56·5N	105E	32, 33, 34, 35
Permian	37N	111E	32, 35
Carboniferous	36N	134E	36, 32, 37, 38
Devonian	42·5N	144E	38
Silurian	18N	138·5E	39
Ordovician	20N	153E	32
Cambrian	23N	6E	32
Greenland			
Triassic	68N	160E	40
Permian	38N	163E	40
Europe			
Cretaceous	79N	117W	41
Jurassic	56N	120E	42
Triassic	62N	167E	31
Permian	42N	169E	31
Carboniferous	34N	150E	31
Devonian	33N	154E	31
Silurian	28·5N	140E	43, 44
Ordovician	24N	8·5E	44
Cambrian	15·5N	168·5E	45
Australia			
Jurassic	50N	23W	46, 47
Triassic	40·5N	35W	48
Permian	32·5N	8·5W	49
Carboniferous	37·5N	22·5W	49
Devonian	66N	168W	49
Silurian	60N	153W	49
Cambrian	35N	159·5W	49
Africa			
Cretaceous	66·5N	163·5W	50
Jurassic	65N	90W	51, 52
Triassic	84S	172E	52
Permian	2N	118·5E	52
Carboniferous	15S	23E	52
South America			
Jurassic or Upper Triassic	83·5N	112W	53

certain how far results obtained from Western Europe can be extrapolated to the east. Palaeomagnetic results from the Siberian Platform
have tended to confirm the Permian and Triassic results from Europe
but it is not certain that this is true for China or Central Asia. It is
already apparent that results from the Indian subcontinent are widely
divergent from those of Western Europe [54]. Until the position has
been clarified the writer has compared climatic indicators from China
and Central Asia with palaeomagnetic results from Europe, this may
have to be modified as further results are obtained from East Asia.

Difficulties also arise in North America because of the lack of any
well-defined Devonian palaeomagnetic results. The writer has therefore
chosen to compare the palaeoclimatic indicators with the Mississippian
pole from the Barnett Shales [38]. It is hoped that in the future better
information will be available.

The ranges of the tropical and subtropical climatic indicators in their
palaeomagnetic co-ordinates are as follows:

	Range	Average
Cretaceous	0–44	25
Jurassic	0–54	30·4
Triassic	0–41	20
Permian	0–45	12·4
Carboniferous	0–48	9·1
Devonian	0–43	17·8
Silurian	0–39	16·1
Ordovician	0–17	13
Cambrian	0–35	15·6

It can be seen that in *no* case do these limits exceed those of the
Cainozoic and in many cases the higher values are those from China
and the Far East, as could be expected.

The distribution of these indicators in their palaeomagnetic co-
ordinates are also interesting. Figure 13 presents a histogram showing
the densities from the palaeomagnetic equators in class intervals of 10°.
It can be seen that 36·3 per cent of the data fall in the interval from 0 to
10°, 24·1 per cent between 11° to 20°, 22·7 per cent from 21° to 30° and
only 16·4 per cent above 31°. This is the type of distribution which can
be expected from a latitudinally climatically zoned earth. This is the
most reasonable model considering the earth's relationship to the sun.

Let us now consider the relationship of palaeomagnetism to the
Permo-Carboniferous glaciation. The only palaeomagnetic information

from this period of time is from Australia and Africa. There can be no doubt about the Australian palaeomagnetic results, for their magnetic stability has been shown [55]. The results from Africa are of a reconnaissance nature only but the results are indicative [52]. There are no results for this period from India and South America. The Australian poles place the glacial deposits in the Australian Permian and upper Carboniferous above 55° latitude, this is also true of South Africa.These are well within latitudes that continental glaciers could be expected to occur as shown by the Pleistocene glaciation.

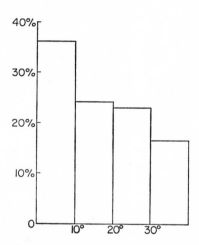

Fig. 13. Histogram showing the distribution of subtropical climatic indicators relative to the palaeomagnetic latitudes.

IX. Conclusions

The distribution of subtropical climatic indicators during the Palaeozoic is not latitudinal with respect to the present equator. These indicators appear north of the Arctic Circle in the Permian and continue in these high latitudes to the Cambrian. This distribution is difficult or impossible to explain given the present relationships of the continents and of the earth to the sun. The existence of a Palaeozoic glacial period makes the existence of a climatically unzoned earth improbable.

It is possible to find the latitudinal spread of these indicators relative to the palaeomagnetic equators. When this is done it is seen that the spread of these indicators becomes latitudinal and in no case do the climatic indicators fall beyond the range expected of them from a study of Cainozoic climates. Glacial deposits are then at high latitudes and bioherms, bauxites and evaporites at low latitudes. It appears, therefore, that the weight of palaeoclimatic information supports continental drift as predicted by palaeomagnetism.

Note added in proof

It has been brought to the writer's attention since the preparation of this manuscript that P. M. S. Blackett [56] has arrived at broadly the same conclusions as those presented here using the same types of evidence.

References

1. UREY, H. C., *Science*, **108**, 489 (1948).
2. EPSTEIN, S., BUCHSBAUM, R., LOWENSTAM, H. A., AND UREY, H. C., *Bull. geol. Soc. Amer.* **64**, 1315 (1953).
3. BOWEN, R., *J. Geol.* **69**, 309 (1961).
4. OPDYKE, N. D., AND RUNCORN, S. K., *Bull. geol. Soc. Amer.* **71**, 959 (1960).
5. GREEN, R., *in* "Descriptive Palaeoclimatology", p. 61. (A. E. M. Nairn, ed.) Interscience Publishers, New York and London (1961).
6. HARDER, E., *Bull. geol. Soc. Amer.* **60**, 887 (1949).
7. FLINT, R. F., *in* "Descriptive Palaeoclimatology", p. 140. (A. E. M. Nairn, ed.) Interscience Publishers, New York and London (1961).
8. RANKAMA, K., AND SAHAMA, Th. G., "Geochemistry". University of Chicago Press (1950).
9. TEICHERT, G., *Bull. Amer. Ass. Petrol. Geol.* **42**, 1064 (1958).
10. LAMB, H. H., *in* "Descriptive Palaeoclimatology", p. 8. (A. E. M. Nairn, ed.) Interscience Publishers, New York and London (1961).
11. LADD, H. S., *Bull. Amer. Ass. Petrol. Geol.* **34**, 203 (1950).
12. ELLISON, A. G., *Bull. Amer. Ass. Petrol. Geol.* **28**, 1355 (1944).
13. YOUNG, G. A., BELLIZZIA, A., RENZ, H. H., JOHNSON, F. W., ROBIE, R. H., AND VALL, J. M., *in* "Symposium sobre yacimientos de petroleo y gas", p. 161. Twentieth International Geological Congress Mexico (1956).
14. TWENHOFEL, W. H., *Bull. Amer. Ass. Petrol. Geol.* **34**, 182 (1950).
15. HENSON, F. R. S., *Bull. Amer. Ass. Petrol. Geol.* **34**, 215 (1950).
16. CHANEY, R. W., *Bull. geol. Soc. Amer.* **51**, 469 (1940).
17. DURHAM, J. W., *Amer. J. Sci.* **250**, 321 (1952).
18. DUNBAR, C. D., *Medel. om Grønland*, **110**, 1 (1955).
19. NALIVKIN, D. V., "The Geology of the U.S.S.R.", International series of Monographs on earth sciences. (S. I. Tomkeieff, trans.) Pergamon Press, London, New York and Paris (1960).
20. DAVID, T. W. E., "The Geology of the Commonwealth of Australia", Vol. 1. Arnold and Co., London (1950).
21. HARRINGTON, H. J., *in* "The Hand Book of South American Geology", *Mem. geol. Soc. Amer.* **65**, 119 (1956).
22. GEE, E. R., HARLAND, W. B., AND McWHAE, J. R. H., *Trans. roy. Soc. Edinb.* **62**, pt I & II, 299 (1951–52).
23. DU TOIT, A. L., "The Geology of South Africa", 3rd edition. Oliver & Boyd, London (1954).
24. LOWENSTAM, H. A., *Mem. geol. Soc. Amer.* **67**, 215 (1957).
25. KRUMBEIN, W. C., *J. sediment. Petrol.* **21**, 63 (1951).
26. KING, L. C., *in* "Descriptive Palaeoclimatology", p. 307. (A. E. M. Nairn, ed.) Interscience Publishers, New York and London (1961).

27. FORTIER, Y. O., *in* "Geology and Economic Minerals of Canada", p. 393. Economic Geology series No. 1. (C. H. Stockwell, ed.) Geological Survey Department, Technical Surveys, Ottawa, Department of Mines (1957).
28. IRVING, E., *Geofis. pur. appl.* **33**, 1 (1956).
29. SCHOVE, D. J., NAIRN, A. E. M., AND OPDYKE, N. D., *Geogr. Ann., Stockh.* **40**, 216 (1958).
30. OPDYKE, N. D., *Int. J. Bioclim. Biomet.* **3**, A, 1 (1959).
31. NAIRN, A. E. M., *J. Geol.* **68**, 285 (1960).
32. COLLINSON, D. W., AND RUNCORN, S. K., *Bull. geol. Soc. Amer.* **71**, 915 (1960).
33. OPDYKE, N. D., *J. geophys. Res.* **66**, 1941 (1961).
34. IRVING, E., AND BANKS, M. R., *J. geophys. Res.* **66**, 1955 (1961).
35. COX, A., AND DOELL, R. R., *Bull. geol. Soc. Amer.* **71**, 645 (1960).
36. NAIRN, A. E. M., FROST, D. V., AND LIGHT, B. G., *Nature, Lond.* **183**, 596 (1959).
37. DU BOIS, P. M., *Nature, Lond.* **184**, 63 (1959).
38. HOWELL, L. G., AND MARTINES, J. D., *Geophysics*, **22**, 384 (1957).
39. GRAHAM, J. W., *J. geophys. Res.* **54**, 131 (1949).
40. BIDGOOD, E. D. T., AND HARLAND, W. B., *Nature, Lond.* **189**, 633 (1961).
41. WILSON, R. L., *Phil. Mag.* **4**, 750 (1959).
42. HARGRAVES, R. B., AND FISCHER, A. G., *Geophys. J.* **2**, 34 (1959).
43. CREER, K. M., IRVING, E., AND RUNCORN, S. K., *Phil. Trans. A,* **250**, 144 (1957).
44. KOMAROV, A. G., *C.R. Acad. Sci. U.R.S.S.* (*Geophys.*), **8**, 1219 (1959).
45. CREER, K. M., *Phil. Trans. A,* **250**, 111 (1957).
46. IRVING, E., *Pap. roy. Soc. Tasm.* **90**, 157 (1956).
47. IRVING, E., AND GREEN, R., *Geophys. J.* **7**, 347 (1957).
48. ALMOND, M., CLEGG, J. A., AND JAEGER, J. C., *Phil. Mag.* **1**, 771 (1956).
49. IRVING, E., AND GREEN, R., *Geophys. J.* **1**, 64 (1958).
50. ROCHE, A., AND CATTALA, L., *Nature, Lond.* **183**, 1049 (1959).
51. GRAHAM, K. W. T., AND HALES, A. L., *Advanc. Phys.* **6**, 149 (1957).
52. NAIRN, A. E. M., *Overseas Geol. Surv. Min. Res. Div.* H.M. Stationery Office, London (1960).
53. CREER, K. M., *Ann. Géophys.* **14**, 373 (1958).
54. CLEGG, J. A., RADAKRISHNAMURTY, C., AND SAHASRABUDHE, P. W., *Nature, Lond.* **181**, 830 (1958).
55. IRVING, E., ROBERTSON, W. A., STOTT, P. M., TARLING, D. H., AND WARD, M. A., *J. geophys. Res.* **66**, 1927 (1961).
56. BLACKETT, P. M. S., *Proc. roy. Soc. A,* **263**, 1 (1961).

Chapter 3

Movements in the Earth's Crust as Indicated by Earthquakes

JOHN H. HODGSON

I. Introduction 67
II. Studies of Earthquake Mechanism 68
    A. Models and Methods 68
    B. Survey of Available Data 74
    C. Models, the Advanced Theory 76
III. Interpretation on the Collapse Model 78
IV. Interpretation on the Fault Model 81
    A. Introduction 81
    B. Nature of Faulting 82
    C. The Null Direction 84
    D. The Kinematic Axes 87
    E. The Direction of Displacement 88
    F. Force Directions Inferred from Fault Directions . . 95
V. Summary and Conclusions 99
    References 102

I. Introduction

Earthquakes may occur anywhere in the world, but most large earthquakes are associated with the two major tectonic zones so well known to geophysicists, the one lying around the boundary of the Pacific, the other reaching from the East Indies, through central Asia, into southern Europe. These zones contain the principal active mountain ranges and island arcs, the principal ocean deeps and volcanoes and zones of very large negative gravity anomalies. No single discipline can solve the puzzle that they pose, but each can contribute some part of a solution.

The principal contribution of seismology to this problem has been through the exact location of earthquakes and, more recently, through information on the rate of energy release. As methods for determining the location and focal depths of earthquakes became refined, it was found that the foci defined zones coincident with the general zones and of about the same breadth. The earthquakes with normal focus lay close to the front of the zone; with increasing depth they were found farther

67

and farther from the front, indicating that the zones were dipping steeply under the continents. It was natural to think of the zones as shear planes, and to suppose that the faults which gave rise to the earthquakes lay in this plane and parallel to it. This assumption became implicit in the thinking of almost all tectonophysicists; it was only in the sense of movement that there was any disagreement. Some writers supposed that movements on the plane were thrust, others that they were normal, still others that they were normal at some depths and thrust at others. No one suggested any appreciable amount of transverse movement, and it was natural that they should not, for it seemed that the linear arrangement of the zones, their mountains and their deeps, could only result from forces normal to themselves. Thrust or normal faulting would be the most logical consequence of such forces.

Shortly after the war a method for determining the sense of movement in earthquakes began to be widely exploited. It was the almost immediate conclusion of this work that movement was neither thrust nor normal, but that in most areas faulting was strike-slip on steeply dipping planes. This concept was so alien to most tectonic theories that there has been a great reluctance to accept it, even among seismologists. In consequence the theory and the methods used in these studies have been examined closely, with the result that, at the time of writing, seismologists are not in agreement about the proper interpretation to be given to the findings. Fortunately the thinking reduces itself to two schools. By discussing the interpretations of both schools we may hope to find some area of agreement which will serve as a guide to other disciplines. We must first, however, say something about methods, in order that the reader may understand the source of the seismologist's difficulty, and the limitations of his findings.

II. Studies of Earthquake Mechanism

A. models and methods

When we examine the initial section of an earthquake record it is usually possible to determine whether the earth moved away from the epicentre (a compression) or towards it (a dilatation). When we examine the records for a single earthquake from many different stations we find that the first longitudinal wave recorded at some of them as an initial compression, at others as an initial dilatation, and that the distribution of compressions and dilatations is arranged in some sort of systematic pattern. Similarly the first shear wave shows a systematic variation of sense from one station to the next. These patterns are related to the mechanism of the earthquake.

In order to understand the observed patterns it is necessary to have some mathematical model of what happens in an earthquake. A very simple model, which will serve to fix our ideas and which has a good deal of historical interest, is illustrated in Fig. 1. The line FF′ is intended to

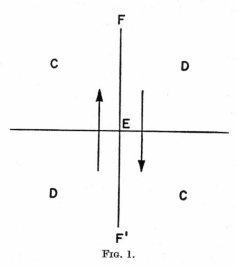

Fig. 1.

represent, in plan, the trace of a vertical fault that undergoes a transverse motion, in the sense shown, at the instant of the earthquake. It is intuitively evident that points ahead of an arrow will be pushed by the earthquake, while points behind an arrow will be pulled, so that the area surrounding the epicentre will be divided into quadrants, alternatively compressional and dilatational with respect to first motion. These quadrants are defined by the traces of the fault plane and of a plane, called the auxiliary plane, drawn perpendicular to the displacement vector through the focus.

The assumptions on which this simple model are based, which are implicit in the thinking of most seismologists, derive largely from studies of the San Francisco earthquake. This earthquake was due to lateral slipping on the San Andreas fault, as if the earth had failed under the action of a couple. Figure 1 thus represents very well what happened in the San Francisco earthquake, but it may be taken to represent the most general case if we suppose that the figure has been drawn on that plane through the focus which lies perpendicular to the fault plane and to the auxiliary plane. On such a plane then we would expect to find a quadrant distribution of compressions and dilatations, the amplitudes of P waves becoming zero on the nodal lines provided by the fault and auxiliary planes, and becoming a maximum on the bisectors of these nodal lines.

1. *Elementary Theory*

The model discussed above is one of three that have received attention; we shall now consider these three models in the light of the elementary theory. The simplest model is that provided by a single force (Fig. 2a). This force may be supposed to be either periodic or impulsive

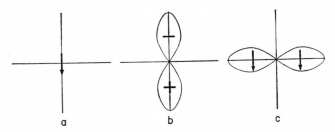

FIG. 2. The radiation pattern for P (2b) and for S (2c) resulting from an isolated force. The same radiation patterns represent strain dislocation on a fault if the extent of the fault and its rate of propagation is taken into account.

and in either case one can work out the motion to be expected at any point. When this is done we find that, as one would expect, points behind the arrow are pulled, points ahead of it are pushed, and there is a line of no P motion at right angles to the arrow. A more useful description of what happens is given in Fig. 2b, which is an idealized radiation diagram. It shows that for P waves the maximum amplitudes are to be expected along the line of action of the force, minimum amplitudes at right angles to this line. For S waves (Fig. 2c) the reverse is expected, minimum amplitudes on the line, maximum at right angles. For any point one can work out the actual direction in which a particle moves under the action of the S wave.

The model of Fig. 3a can be built up by extension from that of a single force by reversing the sign of one of the forces, separating the line of action of the two forces by a small amount, and summing the

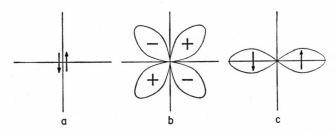

FIG. 3. These radiation patterns for P (3b) and for S (3c) represent the effect either of a couple with moment or a laminar solution, depending on whether the effect of the fault is considered or not.

affect. When this is done the radiation pattern for P (Fig. 3b) provides minima on the line of action of the couple and at right angles to it. For S waves (Fig. 3c) one has maxima (but of course with different signs) on the opposite sides of the line of action of the couple, minima in the line of action.

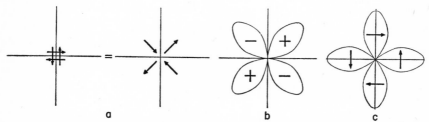

FIG. 4. These radiation patterns for P (4b) and for S (4c) represent the effect either of two orthogonal couples (or equivalently of equal and opposite orthogonal forces) or of a fault, depending on the complexity of the mathematical approach.

The third model, shown in Fig. 4a is provided by couples whose lines of action are at right angles. Elementary theory shows, as the diagram suggests, that this is statically equivalent to pairs of forces, one set drawn inwards the other outwards, along the bisectors of the lines of action of the couples. The radiation pattern for this system (Fig. 4b) is the same for P as for the single couple, but the radiation pattern for S (Fig. 4c) is quite different. Here one finds maxima in the lines of action of both couples, minima on the bisectors, that is to say, maxima on both P minima.

The study of earthquake mechanism involves the examination of the radiation pattern for many earthquakes. In almost all of them the P radiation pattern for Figs. 3b or 4b have been found. The reader will recognize that if the S radiation pattern could be adequately observed it would allow one to select the appropriate mechanism in each case. In practice it is rather difficult to measure amplitudes and to compare them between stations, and therefore most investigators have made use of the direction of P and of S motion rather than its amount. Some investigators compute the direction of the S vector at all points; they find that this allows them to select between models. Other investigators use the combination of senses possible for the P and for the S and find that this allows them to discriminate between the models. In essence, however, they are all using different aspects of the diagrams shown.

2. Extension to Three Dimensions

The elementary approach of the previous section has supposed the problem to be a two-dimensional one, and it may be so treated in areas,

D

such as Japan or California, where there are many stations so close to the epicentre that the curvature of the earth may be ignored. But there are few such areas. A method is required that permits the use of data from distant stations. Such a method was gradually evolved by Byerly between the years 1926 and 1938. While Byerly's method has been extended by various workers there has been no fundamental change in it, and it has been possible to conduct mechanism studies since the mid-1930's.

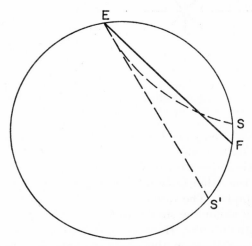

FIG. 5. Cross-section of the earth, showing the complexity introduced into the study of radiation patterns by the curvature of the seismic ray.

We have seen from Figs. 2 to 4 that the essence of the problem is to determine nodal lines. One plots stations in their position relative to the epicentre, and separates those receiving initial compressions from those receiving initial dilatations by a single line (Fig. 2) or more usually by a pair of lines (Figs. 3 and 4). In the latter case one then studies the distribution of S direction and amplitude to select between the single-couple model and the double-couple model. When the technique is extended to three dimensions the two straight lines separating compressions from dilatations become planes and the plotting surface becomes a sphere. The curvature of the seismic ray becomes important, as is illustrated in Fig. 5. Here a station lying to the right of the fault receives its initial motion from a ray originating to the left of the fault; this must vitiate the separation of compressions and dilatations by the fault. This is overcome, as the figure suggests, by substituting the tangent for the ray and plotting the station S in its virtual position S'. This substitution is the essence of Byerly's method.

Another major problem in the use of remote stations is that of mapping. Various projections have been used for this purpose, but all are variations of the stereographic projection. The intersections of the fault-plane and the auxiliary plane with the sphere of the earth form circles; it is a property of the stereographic projection that circles on the sphere project into circles on the map. In any projection normally used for the fault plane work the problem reduces to separating compressions from dilatations by pairs of circles (which may on occasion degenerate into pairs of straight lines). The appropriate S nodal lines may then be computed for each model and the appropriate model selected by comparison with the S observations. Anyone interested in the details of the various projections used is referred to the very complete description given by Scheidegger [1].

3. *Physical Interpretation of the Models*

We shall see in a later section that it has proved difficult to select between the models of Figs. 3 and 4 on seismological evidence. There has therefore been a tendency among some investigators (the writer among them) to adopt one or other model with an almost idealogical fervor. What are the physical models behind the mathematical abstractions which make them so attractive?

It has already been pointed out that Fig. 3a is a very good first approximation to the observations made after the San Francisco earthquake. It was shown in that case that stresses had been building up over a period of perhaps 100 years, due to the northward movement of the western side of the fault relative to the eastern side. This movement continued until the strength of the fault was exceeded; then rupture occurred and the total displacement which had accumulated over the years took place on the fault. In the view of most seismologists it was the fling of the fault which sent the seismic signal to distant stations, not the actual grinding on the fault face, nor the relief of the regional stresses that had set up the strains in the first place. This seems to many a reasonable picture of what happens in a fault, particularly in view of the fact that there have been eleven instances [p. 621 of ref. 2] in which nodal plane solutions have agreed exactly with the observed strike of faulting.

To its devotees the model of Fig. 4a is equally valid physically. Earthquakes are due to stresses within the earth; at any point we can reduce these stresses to an orthogonal triad of principal stresses. For shallow earthquakes one of these stresses is likely to be vertical and to represent hydrostatic stress. The difference of the stresses for the other two axes from the hydrostatic stress, which are usually called the deviatoric stresses, are closely analogous to the forces shown in the right-hand side of Fig. 4a. Under the action of this pair of forces failure suddenly occurs, by the collapse of a volume of rock or by faulting on one or both of a pair of conjugate planes. In the view of some seismologists the nature of the failure is not important; it is the impulsive release of stress which sets up the seismic wave. This model then has the attraction of relating the model to the regional stresses.

It seems desirable to have names for these two models, since we shall have to refer to them frequently. We shall call the model of Fig. 3a a *fault model*, that of Fig. 4a a *collapse model*, the word collapse to be understood in the limited sense outlined above.

B. SURVEY OF AVAILABLE DATA

The data available for analysis in this paper have been supplied by four principal groups, each using somewhat different techniques and each with somewhat different aims. These will now be reviewed. Solutions are becoming available very rapidly; this paper was closed to new solutions in early June, 1960.

Japanese seismologists have been studying mechanism since 1920. In recent years their findings have been collected and analysed by Honda [3] who has been working in this field both personally and as a director of several others. In all, Japanese seismologists have produced solutions for 71 earthquakes, each solution defining a pair of nodal planes for P. In the early days these nodal planes were not very well defined, particularly as to dip, because the data were from nearby stations only. In recent years the Japanese have developed techniques for overcoming this difficulty.

The S radiation pattern has been studied for about 10 of the 71 earthquakes, all of them with deep focus. In each case the radiation pattern has agreed very well with that shown in Fig. 4; thus Professor Honda is the chief proponent of the collapse model. These studies have had the advantage of a very dense network of identical seismographs, and Honda's publications leave little doubt of the radiation pattern.

Soviet seismologists have produced solutions for more than 400 earthquakes; these have been done by two principal groups, one working under the direction of Dr. Keylis-Borok, the other under the direction of Dr. Vvedenskaya. The Soviet studies of mechanism have not been based directly on the study of the radiation pattern, but rather on the study of the various combinations of P and S motions, as outlined in an earlier section. They have shown that this is an equivalent approach to the problem.

The group working under Keylis-Borok [4] has found over three hundred examples of the fault mechanism of Fig. 3, a very few examples of mechanism of Fig. 2, and almost no examples of the collapse mechanism of Fig. 4. Since they have used S they are able to select which nodal plane is the fault in that large number of solutions where a fault mechanism is indicated. They have produced solutions for a number of major earthquakes, but most of their studies have been concerned with swarms of small earthquakes in particular regions. They have accomplished this by setting out large numbers of instruments in the epicentral regions: since these instruments are identical and close to the epicentre they are thus approximating to the technique applied by Honda in Japan. Under these circumstances it is difficult to understand why their conclusions should be so different. To complicate matters, the second Soviet group, working under the direction of Mme. Vvedenskaya [5] has found the collapse model to be appropriate to all the earthquakes they have studied.

This difference of opinion about the appropriate model is thus fundamental; we shall return to this question in a later section.

Ritsema and Veldkamp [6, 7], at De Bilt, have published solutions for 122 earthquakes; the last 64 of these have become available too recently to be included in Fig. 21. All of their solutions are for earthquakes in the East Indies. Whereas other groups have been content to keep up with current earthquakes, they have tried to study old ones as well. In consequence they have produced what is probably the most complete coverage of a single district. Recently they have included the use of S in their studies, but this information has been gathered mostly through questionnaires. Many observers would mistrust this technique for S; in so far as the results are dependable they favour a fault mechanism, and permit the selection of one nodal plane as the fault.

The Ottawa group has solutions for 123 earthquakes published or in press [2, 8]; since 1950 it has attempted solutions for all earthquakes of magnitude greater than 6·8. It is the only group which has attempted broad geographical coverage, and knowledge of mechanism in those areas outside Japan, the East Indies and the Soviet Union and adjacent areas derives chiefly from this coverage. No use whatever has been made of S, so that no decision has been made as to the appropriate model. Assuming a fault model to be the correct one, the Ottawa data are all ambiguous—there is no indication of which of the nodal planes represents the fault.

Finally, there are some 30 fault-plane solutions in the literature made for the most part by investigators who do not specialize in this field of research but who have studied mechanism as part of a general study of a particular earthquake.

C. MODELS, THE ADVANCED THEORY

In the section above, it was pointed out that the Japanese and the Soviets, using what appear to be equally reliable networks and equally advanced techniques, have not been able to agree as to whether the fault or collapse model is the appropriate one. Stauder has studied this matter for several earthquakes and has found examples of all three models [9, 10]. The writer has studied the collected records of three different earthquakes without being able to identify S with certainty, much less come to any conclusion about mechanism. What can be the cause of these difficulties?

It may be observational. S is not an easy phase to observe, and studies made on a world-wide basis suffer because of the difficulty of comparing records obtained on instruments of many different sorts, all with different, and usually indifferent, response to S. However, the Japanese studies have used a network of many stations, all close to the epicentre and all with identical instruments. The Soviet studies have been based partly on the network of identically equipped stations spread uniformly over the Soviet Union, and partly on special networks of identical instruments installed in particular epicentral regions. It is difficult to see how either the Russians or the Japanese could be in error in their observations.

The problem may be interpretative. The diagrams of Figs. 2 to 4 are relatively simple, but when they are extended to three dimensions, and made to take account of the variation of elastic properties within the earth, they become quite complex, and in many instances very similar [11]. But since each group is made up of competent scientists well aware of these interpretative difficulties it seems unlikely that this can be the cause.

Most probably the difficulty is one of the inadequacy of the elementary theory. This possibility is being investigated in two ways, through model seismology and through more advanced theoretical studies.

The work of Press and Healy [12, 13] is typical of the model studies. A slit is cut at the centre of a circular sheet of Plexiglas and pulses are applied to the two sides of this "fault" by crystal transducers. This should simulate very well the conditions of Fig. 3a. The resulting effect is observed at selected points around the periphery of the plate. P amplitudes should be zero in the line of the fault and at right angles to it. This is observed. S should be zero in the fault, a maximum in the direction at right angles. This is also observed if the experiment is done before the slit is cut to represent the fault, but in the presence of the slit a well-defined maximum is found on the line of the fault and the minima are displaced from this line by 25 to 35 degrees. This is still observed if an attempt is made to cement the crack, to simulate a fault long dormant. Apparently the effect of the fault is to inhibit the passage of S and so to vitiate the arguments on which the mathematical theory was based.

A new mathematical treatment of the problem has recently been given by Knopoff and Gilbert [14, 15], using a more sophisticated fault model. They regard an earthquake as due to the sudden vanishing of accumulated strains along a fault plane. They take account of the fact that faulting propagates at a finite rate and they consider two cases— faulting which propagates in one direction from a focus and faulting which propagates in both directions from a focus. In each case they consider all possible types of strain, and for each of these they find the types of body forces that will yield the same motion at a distance. By comparing their results with observation they conclude that only three of the possible models are likely to have physical validity.

The first of these possible models "corresponds to rigid body motion, dislocation, or fault fling in the sense normally given these terms in the literature," the faulting proceeding in two directions from the focus. This produces a radiation pattern such as that shown in Fig. 4. The equivalent body force system is two orthogonal couples in the absence of a fault. It seems very probable that we have here a key to some of the difficulties mentioned earlier. The Japanese observations, interpreted in the light of the work of Knopoff and Gilbert, would correspond to that faulting mechanism which is so consistent with observed geological processes.

The second mechanism which Knopoff and Gilbert regard as reasonable corresponds to a sudden discontinuity in the shear strain between the two sides of the fault, without any relative motion at the fault plane. This produces the two-lobed radiation pattern shown in Fig. 2. The equivalent force system is an isolated force. Knopoff and Gilbert point to one fault-plane solution which could be explained by this mechanism; there are probably two or three others, but there are certainly very few. It is almost certainly not an important mechanism.

The third mechanism which they regard as reasonable is a rather odd one, provided by the sudden release of shear strain in a laminar region. This produces the pattern shown in Fig. 2b, a quadrant solution for P, a two-lobed solution for S; this is the same pattern as was produced by a single couple in the absence of a fault.

The work of Knopoff and Gilbert cannot be regarded as the final word on the subject, for they themselves have assumed a model of a fault; their assumptions are more realistic than previous ones but they are still assumptions. Keylis-Borok has pointed out (personal communication) that in the most general treatment we must start with a statical stress-strain field, explain how this causes fracture to begin, determine the velocity and extent of fracturing and compute the elastic waves resulting from the fracture. In short, the motion on the fault must be derived not prescribed. Keylis-Borok reports that Soviet seismologists have made a beginning on this very difficult general solution and that preliminary results suggest that the appropriate model depends on frequency.

To sum up, it appears that we are on the brink of resolving the difficulties of interpretation which have plagued us. The realistic fault model of Knopoff and Gilbert produces the radiation pattern observed by Honda; this reconciles the Japanese and American points of view. There are still puzzles posed by the Soviet work, for they have in most instances found the radiation pattern of Fig. 2b, which we should otherwise have been prepared to discard. The problem will only be resolved by further theoretical studies supported by much observational work.

The International Seismological Association held symposia on the fault-plane work at both its Toronto and its Helsinki meetings. The proceedings of both have been published in the Publications of the Dominion Observatory [16, 17]. The reader who wishes to inquire in detail into the work is referred to these two references.

It seems premature, for the purpose of the present article, to make a final choice between the collapse and the fault models; we must interpret the available data in the light of both models. This will be done in the two following chapters.

III. Interpretation on the Collapse Model

Studies using the collapse model have been less fruitful than studies using the fault model: there have proved to be fewer aspects to investigate. One obtains two nodal planes in P. The bisectors of these planes are the directions of maximum pressure and of maximum tension, and the sense of each can be determined by inspection of the solutions. One can then plot these directions of maximum pressure and maximum tension and study their relationship to physiography and to geology. Assuming a theory of fault formation one might infer the faulting that should result from the pressure patterns observed, but this would be purely inference since, by hypothesis, we assert that the nodal solutions yield no direct evidence.

The principal worker to interpret his data in this way has of course been Honda. In a paper summarizing the Japanese work [3] he gives two figures which are reproduced herein. Figure 6 shows the direction of maximum pressure for normal focus earthquakes. Figure 7 gives the same information for intermediate and deep-focus earthquakes. It is quite clear from the figures that, for all focal depths, the pressure is normal to the lines defined by the foci themselves.

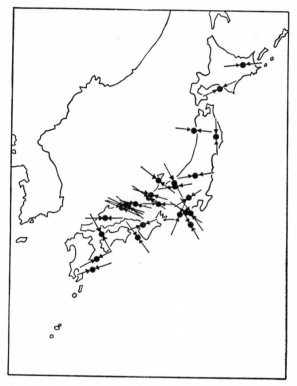

FIG. 6. Direction of maximum pressure, determined on the collapse model, for normal focus earthquakes in Japan (after Honda).

Another group to make interpretations in this sense has been that Soviet group which works under the direction of Vvedenskaya. They have studied a number of earthquakes in the Hindu-Kush and have determined the mean direction of pressure to "form an angle of almost 90° with the trend of the Hindu-Kush mountains". They have also studied a number of earthquakes in the North Pacific; the results for this are shown in Fig. 8, which plots the directions of maximum pressures. Again we see that, in the words of Vvedenskaya, "the axes of pressure are mostly directed perpendicular to the strike of the main structures". In the paper quoted she also illustrates the directions of the maximum tensions, but finds that "the predominant direction cannot

D*

be established for the whole region under consideration" although "a certain coordination in the orientation of tensions is observed at separate areas of the investigated region."

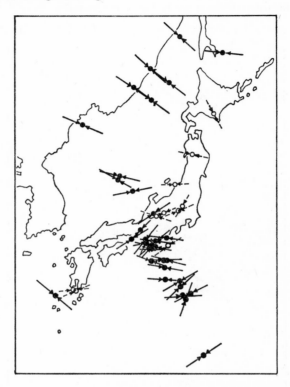

FIG. 7. Direction of maximum pressure determined on the collapse model, for intermediate (dashed lines) and deep-focus (solid lines) earthquakes in Japan (after Honda).

The only other investigator who has made any attempt to analyse his data in terms of the collapse model is Ritsema. In the East Indies he found [6] "a tendency for all maximum pressure components to concentrate in directions about perpendicular to the general trend of the seismic zone. The minimum pressure (or tension) components show a more random distribution, although most of these components are directed in azimuths approximately in the length direction of the zone."

Ritsema has recently prepared a map analysing the world-wide distribution of nodal planes on the collapse model [18]. His findings are shown in Fig. 9. We note in this figure that he agrees with Honda that the forces are normal to the Japanese arc, but that he disagrees with Vvedenskaya in finding that the forces act obliquely to the Kurile arc.

Similarly the forces in the New Zealand–Tonga arc cut the feature obliquely. In California he finds the forces to lie north-south, a direction which has been postulated by several geologists to explain the movement on the San Andreas fault. In Central and in South America the

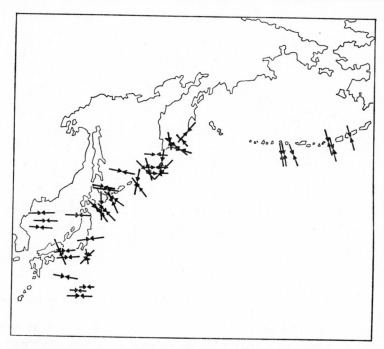

FIG. 8. Direction of maximum pressures in the Pacific, determined on the collapse model (after Balakina, Shirokova and Vvedenskaya).

forces as drawn are approximately normal to the coast. However, there are few solutions in these regions and the arrows represent an average taken over a wide area in each case. It is not clear that the apparent direction should be taken to apply at the exact point the arrow is drawn.

We shall return to a discussion of Figs. 6 to 9 after considering the implications of the fault model.

IV. INTERPRETATION ON THE FAULT MODEL

A. INTRODUCTION

On the collapse model one determines the direction of pressure and infers the type of faulting. On the fault model, on the other hand, one determines the direction and type of faulting and infers the forces that must have caused it. This inference is not easy. In the first place the majority of nodal solutions are unsupported by S data so that it is impossible to remove the ambiguity between the fault plane and the auxiliary plane. In the second place there is no exact theory relating

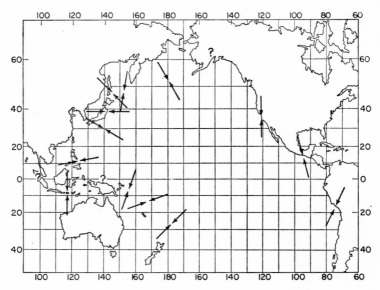

FIG. 9. Direction of maximum pressure for the circum-Pacific (after Ritsema).

faulting and the causative forces, particularly at depths of as much as 600 km at which earthquakes may occur. There have therefore been more speculations about interpretation on this model than on the preceding one.

B. THE NATURE OF FAULTING

In discussing earthquake zones and the associated structural features, tectonophysicists have generally distinguished two sorts of areas. The first of these is typified by California or by New Zealand, where the shearing of massive blocks to produce strike-slip faulting is the obvious feature. The second sort of area is that of the island arc. These features are obviously the result of pressures normal to themselves, and, as we saw in the introduction, it was reasonable to assume that either thrust or normal faulting would be associated with them.

The Ottawa program was the first to produce nodal solutions from a wide variety of areas: in almost all areas these solutions showed steeply dipping, almost perpendicular planes. Interpreted on the fault model this indicated strike-slip faulting and it was apparent from the

TABLE 1

Relationship of Thrust (+) and Gravity (−)
Dip Components to Focal Depth and Geographic Feature

Area	Normal +	Normal −	100 +	100 −	200 +	200 −	300 +	300 −	400 +	400 −	500 +	500 −	600 +	600 −	Total +	Total −
New Zealand to Samoa	4	3	3	1	3	—	2	—	—	—	1	—	1	1	14	5
New Hebrides, Solomon Islands	10	1	2	1	3	1	1	—	—	—	—	—	—	—	16	3
Marianas, Bonins	1	—	—	1	—	1	—	1	—	—	—	—	—	1	1	4
Japan to Kamchatka	2	8	2	—	—	1	1	—	—	1	1	—	—	—	6	10
Aleutians	3	5	—	1	—	—	—	—	—	—	—	—	—	—	3	6
Alaska to Panama	9	9	—	—	—	—	—	—	—	—	—	—	—	—	9	9
Continental North America	1	4	—	—	—	—	—	—	—	—	—	—	—	—	1	4
Caribbean	—	—	1	—	—	—	—	—	—	—	—	—	—	—	1	—
South America	1	3	1	—	—	—	—	1	—	—	—	—	1	—	3	4
New Guinea to Sumatra	8	6	3	1	1	2	—	—	—	1	1	1	—	4	13	15
Central Asia	—	3	—	—	—	—	—	1	—	—	—	—	1	—	1	4
Mediterranean	2	8	—	—	1	—	—	—	—	—	—	—	—	—	3	8
Totals	41	50	12	5	8	5	4	3	—	2	3	1	3	6	71	72

beginning of the program that strike-slip faulting was the rule rather than the exception. It was equally apparent that there was no simple pattern to the strike of these planes; in particular there was no evidence that they lay in and parallel to the earthquake zones in the way that had been expected. As solutions accumulated, the evidence became more striking; other groups produced large numbers of solutions in particular areas, but they all pointed to the same conclusion—strike-slip faulting in almost random strike directions dominates most of the seismic areas of the world. The only important exceptions are the regions of the Hindu-Kush, the Pamirs and the Caspian Sea, in which dip-slip faulting is more important than strike-slip.

Admitting that strike-slip faulting predominates, it is seldom purely strike-slip; there will usually be a component of displacement in the direction of dip. If we adopt the usual point of view that a normal dip component indicates a condition of tension within the earth, while a thrust dip component indicates pressure, we may analyse the dip component to give some clue about the internal conditions of the earth. For example, Wilson has postulated a cooling earth in which tensions at depth are separated from pressures near the surface by a level of no strain at a depth of about 100 kilometres. Is this observed?

This question is examined in Table 1 which shows that for the earth, as a whole, pressures and tensions are almost exactly balanced. There is no indication of any effect of focal depth. Rather there is the suggestion that certain areas, for example the South Pacific, are compressional, while certain other areas, such as the North Pacific, are tensional. It is not clear that one is justified in drawing any conclusion from this table: when faulting is predominantly strike-slip on almost vertical planes the direction of the small amount of dip movement may well be a matter of accident.

C. THE NULL DIRECTION

From the very beginning of the Ottawa program on the mechanism of faulting, the preponderance of strike-slip faulting was a matter of concern. The techniques of the project were unproved, and to have it producing results that were so inconsistent with other lines of evidence was disconcerting. Results from other groups and individuals became available and showed the same tendency, but there was not much comfort to be derived from the similarity of results when all were derived on the basis of the same postulates. Very few earthquakes show surface faulting, so that direct confirmation of the techniques was slow to accumulate. Not only was the preponderance of strike-slip faulting a source of worry. In addition, there seemed to be no pattern to the faulting.

By 1956, for example, enough solutions had accumulated for the South Pacific to permit a study of the strike directions. All the solutions in this area were based on P alone, with the resultant ambiguity between the two planes, but even taking the most favourable combination of possibilities it was clear that strike directions had no simple orientation.

A fault plane solution, even though based on P alone, has one line which is uniquely defined—the line in which the two planes intersect.

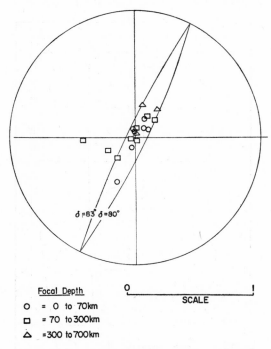

Focal Depth

O = 0 to 70km
□ = 70 to 300km
△ = 300 to 700km

SCALE

FIG. 10. Null directions for the Kermadec–Tonga salient plotted on a polar stereographic net.

Because it is common to both planes, it is perpendicular to the displacement couple whichever plane represents the fault. It is therefore the one line in space which undergoes no displacement during the earthquake. For this reason I called it the *null vector*. McIntyre and Christie [19] have taken exception to the word vector; we shall therefore refer to it as the *null direction*. My colleague P. L. Willmore suggested that the orientation of this null direction be investigated. This proved very fruitful.

In this study the null direction for all the earthquakes of a large area, for example a single island arc, were drawn from a single point. Figure 10 shows an example, for the New Zealand–Kermadec–Tonga trench area, drawn on a polar stereographic projection. As the figure shows, most of the directions lie between a pair of planes, striking N 27°E and dipping almost vertically. This favored direction, N 27°E, is that of the associated geographic feature. The same tendency, for the null directions to lie parallel to a vertical plane having the direction of the associated feature, is noted in many areas. The pattern is often less perfect than that in Figure 10, probably because the areas should be broken into smaller units. An example is provided by South America (Fig. 11).

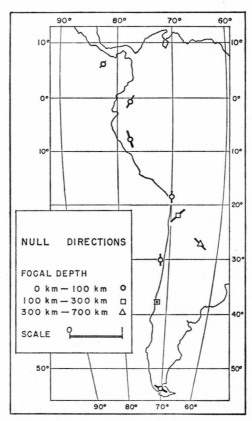

FIG. 11. Null directions in South America. Length of the lines obtained from a polar stereographic projection.

Here the null directions would not produce a simple diagram if plotted in the usual way; when they are plotted on a map it is clear that, with one exception, they are following very closely the tectonic fabric of the country.

The initial interest of the patterns of Figs. 10 and 11 was that they dispelled doubts about the fault-plane techniques. It seemed improbable that results so self-consistent and so readily correlated to the geologic pattern could result from random data. It was most fortunate that the systematic patterns appeared for the earthquakes of the South Pacific and of South America. These are the two areas of the world in which it is most difficult to make fault-plane solutions, since they are so distant from large networks of stations. If the method produces self-consistent results in these areas it must do so everywhere. It remains to seek a physical interpretation for the null direction.

D. THE KINEMATIC AXES

McIntyre and Christie [19, 20] have brought the techniques of structural geology to the interpretation of the null direction. They showed it to be identical with the B Kinematic axis. From the known properties of this axis they forecast that, in those areas where the B axes lie parallel to a plane, one of two things must happen. Either the faults must lie parallel to that plane or the displacements must be perpendicular to it. This led to the very fruitful examination of displacement directions which will be discussed in a later section. McIntyre and Christie attacked the problem in a different way.

Working first with the area covered by Fig. 10 they separated the nodal planes into two sets, one set striking NE, the other NW. Knowing that the null directions lay parallel to a plane, they were then able to determine which of the sets of planes was the more likely to be the faults. They accomplished this in the following way. Taking the A axis to be that of the motion direction in the fault plane, and the C axis to be perpendicular to the A and B axes, they had two possible directions for the A axes depending on which set of planes was assumed to represent the faults. By plotting β-diagrams for all the earthquakes in a selected area that set of planes which gave the β-maximum coincident with the direction of the B axis could be assumed to represent the faults.

In applying these techniques to the fault-plane solutions in the New Zealand–Kermadec–Tonga area they came to the conclusion that faulting is strike-slip on faults that are nearly parallel to the geographic feature; in other words this area would be of the "San Andreas" type outlined in an earlier section. A similar conclusion was later reached for a group of earthquakes in the Philippines–New Guinea area. What was remarkable in each case, however, was that their selected planes were about equally divided between left- and right-lateral strike-slip faulting. This conclusion is very puzzling.

It will be recalled that McIntyre and Christie had forecast that, in those areas where the null directions lie parallel to a plane, one of the principal normals, either the displacement direction or the fault normal, should be perpendicular to the plane. Scheidegger [21] has considered the null directions in a number of limited areas in Asia and has determined the average direction of their normals. This has proved to have a small standard deviation. Since the fault strikes in the same areas are nearly random, it is unlikely that the direction determined is that of the normals to the fault planes. Scheidegger assumes that it represents the average regional displacement. The directions of his determined averages is shown in Fig. 12.

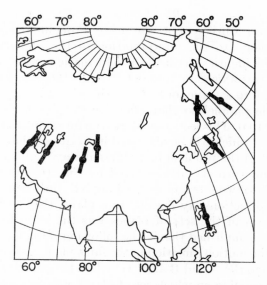

FIG. 12. Mean displacement directions for Asia (after Scheidegger).

E. THE DIRECTION OF DISPLACEMENT

Following the suggestion of McIntyre and Christie the writer made an earlier study [22] of the direction of displacement in earthquakes of the Western Pacific. The direction of displacement may be determined very simply from the fault plane solutions, since it is the direction normal to the auxiliary plane. The majority of the solutions in the areas considered were ambiguous, since S had not been used in their solution; in each case there were thus two directions of displacement possible. In the North Pacific, however, there was a large number of solutions made by Kogan in which S had been used and in which the direction of displacement could therefore be uniquely determined. When these directions were plotted on a map of the area [see Fig. 2a of ref. 22] it was quite clear that, in general, displacements were perpendicular to the associated features. It was then shown that the ambiguous results could be similarly interpreted but that, alternatively, displacements could be

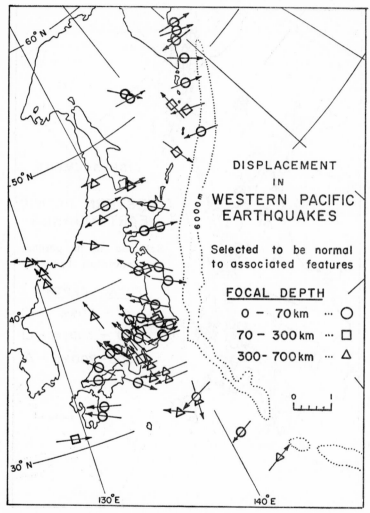

FIG. 13. Displacement directions in the north-western Pacific selected to be normal to the associated features. See text for explanation of scale and sense of displacement.

interpreted as parallel to the associated feature. Only in the North Pacific where we were guided by Kogan's unique solutions was there some justification for choosing the perpendicular displacements.

I have since extended this study to include all fault-plane solutions which were known to me as of June, 1960, and I have plotted the displacement directions in Figs. 13 to 22. In plotting these displacements, a unit vector has been drawn on the hanging-wall side of the

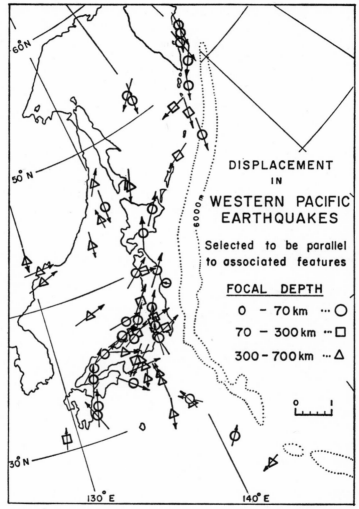

FIG. 14. Displacement directions in the north-western Pacific selected to be parallel to the associated features.

fault in the direction of the actual displacement and this has been projected on to a horizontal plane. Where the projected arrow has unit length it indicates that the displacement was purely horizontal; where the projected arrow is very short, it indicates that the motion was nearly vertical. *The lengths of the vectors are not in any way related to the magnitudes of the earthquakes.*

The displacements in all earthquakes in the North-western Pacific for which solutions are available, with the exception of the Soviet solutions, are shown in Figs. 13 and 14. The Soviet solutions have already been given in the earlier paper and, as already mentioned they showed displacement to be everywhere normal to the associated geographical feature. In Fig. 13 the ambiguous solutions from other sources have been plotted with the displacement direction most nearly normal to the

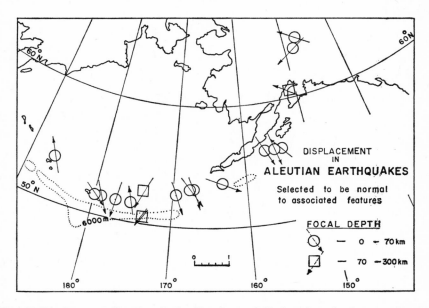

FIG. 15. Displacement directions in the Aleutians and Alaska selected to be normal to the associated features.

feature being selected in each case. In the light of the Soviet work this seems the more probable arrangement. In Fig. 14 the other possible displacement has been plotted. It is apparent that these are, on the whole, parallel to the features. It must be allowed, of course, that the true picture might be made up of a mixture of the two, with some earthquakes giving displacements normal to the features, others parallel to them, but this does not seem very plausible.

Equivalent data for the Aleutians are given in Figs. 15 and 16, and again it seems clear that displacements may be either normal to the arc, or parallel to it. There have been a very few Soviet solutions in this area, all of which have favoured the normal displacements. Note that a new symbol has been introduced in Fig. 16, where one of the displacements has been shown by a broad arrow. This indicates that this displacement is uniquely determined, in this case from field observation, but the same symbol will be used when the displacement has been uniquely defined through the use of S.

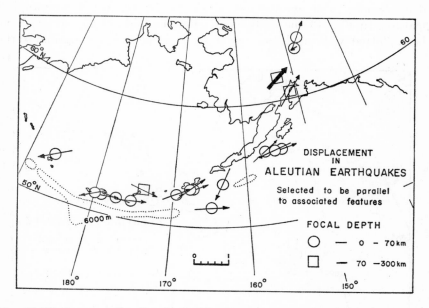

FIG. 16. Displacement directions in the Aleutians and Alaska selected to be parallel to the associated features.

In the case of North America (Fig. 17) there are so few solutions that it has not been necessary to plot separate diagrams for the normal and the parallel vectors. They have been shown on the one map, the normal vectors being indicated by solid lines, the parallel ones by dashed lines. The same technique has been used for South America (Fig. 18). In both cases there has been considerable success in selecting normal and parallel vectors.

Figures 19 and 20 give the two possible sets for the South-West Pacific. These areas had already been discussed in the earlier paper [22] although with fewer data.

The fault-plane solutions in Fig. 21, for the East Indies, derive almost completely from Ritsema. He has used S to select the fault plane and the solutions are therefore unique. Ritsema finds that where the faults are strike-slip they strike perpendicular to the features, where they are normal or thrust they strike parallel to it, so that, with few exceptions, the displacements are normal to the features.

Finally we present the data for the Mediterranean area in Fig. 22. Again, as for North and South America, the data are so few that we have been able to show both of the possible displacement directions on a single map.

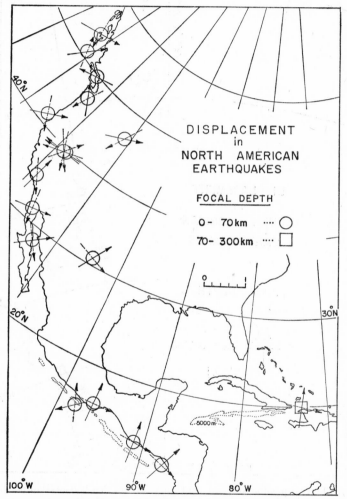

FIG. 17. The two possible displacement directions in North American earthquakes.

Considering all the maps, it seems fair to say that in most areas possible displacement directions can be separated into two sets, one representing displacements perpendicular to the features, the other displacements parallel to them. In the two areas where unique solutions are available in large numbers, they yield the perpendicular displacements. It is tempting to assume that the perpendicular displacements

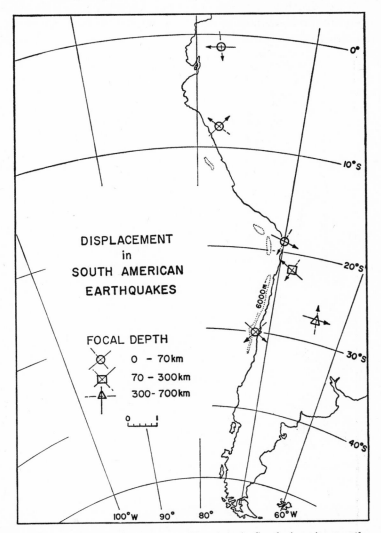

FIG. 18. The two possible displacement directions in South American earthquakes.

should be chosen everywhere. However, considering the theoretical and interpretative doubts mentioned in Section II, it would be unwise to jump to this conclusion. We shall return to a discussion of these results in a later section.

F. FORCE DIRECTIONS INFERRED FROM FAULT DIRECTIONS

For many years geologists have believed that one could infer the directions of the principal stresses in an area from the observed patterns of faults. The leader in this field has been Anderson [23] who published a very detailed tectonic study of Great Britain, tracing the changes in major tectonic force throughout geologic time by tracing the changes

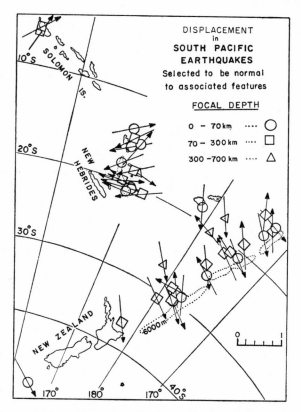

FIG. 19. Displacement in south-western Pacific earthquakes, selected to be normal to the associated features.

in fault directions and types. Since that time Anderson's methods have been applied with great success in other parts of the world, particularly in the Canadian Shield by Wilson and in the South-Western Pacific by Wellman and by Lensen. The techniques have been applied by various authors to the interpretation of the fault-plane results. The most recent, and the most complete effort in this direction has been made by Lensen [24].

Lensen has extended Anderson's methods somewhat and has found two equivalent ways of determining the principal horizontal stress (PHS in the diagrams) from observed faults or from fault-plane solutions. The first of these depends on the ratio between the horizontal and

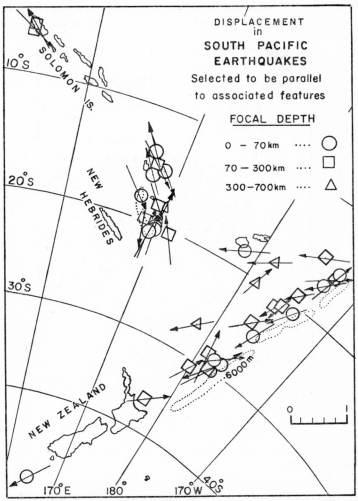

FIG. 20. Displacement in south-western Pacific earthquakes, selected to be parallel to the associated features.

vertical movement on a fault, the second on the angle between conjugate systems of transcurrent faults. He has shown that these two approaches give consistent results.

In his most recent paper he has applied his techniques to the entire boundary of the Pacific, using geologic information as well as all available fault-plane solutions. Figure 23 is typical of the diagrams he has produced. It shows the principal horizontal stress directions for each fault-plane solution and contours these to find the mean regional directions; in interpreting these contour lines we are to understand that

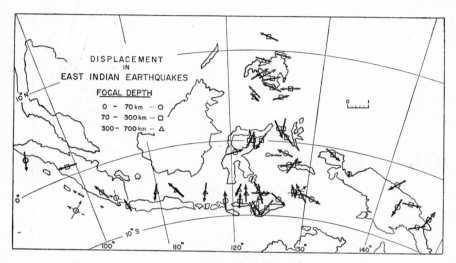

FIG. 21. Displacement directions in the East Indies. The heavy arrows indicate that the directions have been uniquely determined through the use of S.

the principal stresses act parallel to them. In this particular region Lensen finds that the principal horizontal stresses generally act normally to the geographic features, but with some complexities which are still incompletely documented.

Figure 24 summarizes Lensen's findings for the entire circum-

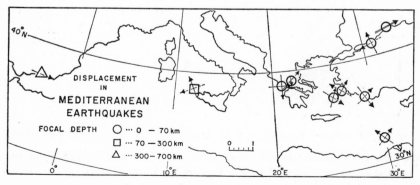

FIG. 22. The two possible displacement directions in Mediterranean earthquakes.

Pacific. The map is limited to normal focus earthquakes. Lensen believes that the forces may be different at depth, but there are still too few fault-plane solutions at the various depths to allow definite conclusions.

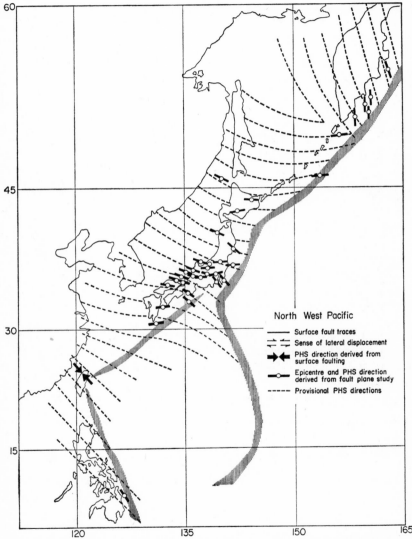

FIG. 23. Principal horizontal stress in the north-western Pacific (after Lensen).

The figure suggests that in most of the island arcs the principal horizontal stresses are normal to the features, whereas north-south stresses prevail in North America and in most of South America.

It should be mentioned that Lensen's interpretation of the forces active in the Pacific do not agree at all with forces postulated, for example, by Benioff [25] or by St. Amand [26]. Both these authors suppose that the entire Pacific basin is rotating in a gigantic counter-clockwise motion with respect to the continental masses.

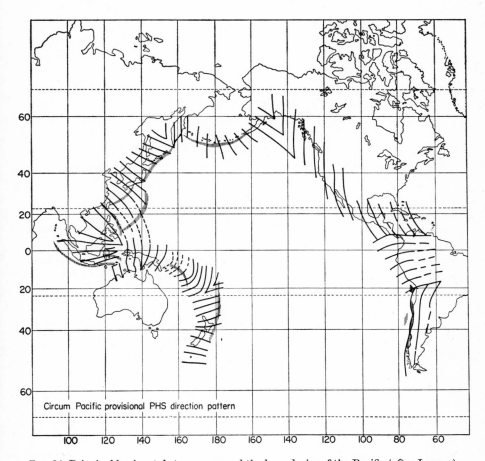

FIG. 24. Principal horizontal stresses around the boundaries of the Pacific (after Lensen).

V. SUMMARY AND CONCLUSIONS

It will be apparent from the foregoing that seismologists are not in a position to supply any final, hard-and-fast rules by which to judge a theory of continental drift. In this section I shall try to define the common ground on which most seismologists would agree, the major facts which must be accounted for.

The first of these concerns the location of large earthquakes and of deep earthquakes. Most of the former and all of the latter are in the two tectonic zones already described. Because of this, most continental boundaries are not seismically active. We may list those that are: the Pacific boundaries of South and North America; the Pacific boundaries of Asia and of Oceania; the Mediterranean boundary of Europe; the line, which may be regarded as a continental boundary in a special sense, in which the Eurasian mass presses up against the subcontinent of India; and finally the East Indian area in which the circum-Pacific zone and the Asiatic zone meet in great complexity. Aside from these there are many areas of minor seismic activity in the world, but none of them is particularly connected with continental boundaries. For details the reader is referred to the monumental work of Gutenberg and Richter, "Seismicity of the Earth" [27].

Within these zones the earthquakes tend to align themselves in a systematic way, with the shallow earthquakes toward one side, the deep ones toward the other, so that the zones have the appearance of dipping planes. The dip is almost always under the continent. The alignment of earthquake foci in this way is not nearly as co-planar as some investigators have supposed; the data suggest a zone of failure rather than a plane. Earthquakes do not occur at all depths throughout this zone. In many places there are no earthquakes with deep foci, in others certain depths may be missing. Again the reader is referred to Gutenberg and Richter [27] for the details.

Beyond these facts, our conclusions must be related to one or other of the models. If one assumes the collapse model one has the pressure directions shown in Figs. 6 to 9. These are normal to most island arcs, but cut the very important New Zealand–Kermadec–Tonga feature obliquely. They act north-south in California. If we assume a fault mechanism, we have a variety of methods of analysis, but all of them point in the same direction. Displacements, where uniquely known or where determined statistically, are normal to the geologic features; where the solutions are ambiguous one displacement can usually be selected normal to the feature, the other parallel to it. The determination of principal horizontal stress shows that this acts normal to most island arcs but is north-south throughout most of the Americas.

These conclusions from the collapse model and the fault model show considerable similarity and a very reasonable correlation with geological observation. As I pointed out earlier, tectonophysicists usually have one of two type areas in mind when discussing these matters. The first type is provided by the San Andreas fault in which the observed motion is strike-slip and nearly parallel to the coast. The second type is

CARL A. RUDISILL LIBRARY
LENOIR RHYNE COLLEGE

the island arc, in which the folds lie parallel to the length of the arc. These have always been regarded as the results of pressures normal to themselves. It is informative to compare Fig. 9 (based on the collapse model) with Fig. 24 (based on the fault model) for these two type areas.

Both figures agree on the direction of the principal pressure in California, the one classical example of a "San Andreas" area, but agree less well in the New Zealand–Kermadec–Tonga sector, which is the other classical example. The agreement in the latter case may in fact be better than it appears, for the arrows in Fig. 9 are averaged over a very long arc; Fig. 24 shows that the direction varies considerably over the length of this arc. In both areas the directions are approximately those demanded by the observed faulting.

In most of the island arcs the two figures are in substantial agreement. There are apparent differences in the East Indies and in the Kuriles, but again these are areas of very rapid change in Fig. 24, and the arrows in Fig. 9 represent averages over very great lengths. In either interpretation the forces are predominantly normal to the island arcs; we have seen that this is a reasonable finding.

We conclude then, that so far as forces are concerned, the seismic results are reasonable and consistent with geological observations, whichever model is assumed.

One final puzzle remains on the fault model. We saw that in most areas the faulting is strike-slip on planes which do not usually have a very consistent strike direction, and which almost never coincide with the plane of the zone of failure. Such information as is available suggests that the strike-slip faults of a particular area are not all in the same sense but seem to be equally divided between left-lateral and right-lateral motion. This entire pattern of faulting is puzzling.

An analogy may be available in the field of engineering. Bijlaard pointed out many years ago [28] that the zones of failure observed in the East Indies are very similar, except in scale, to the bands of plastic flow observed in the failure of steel plates. These bands of flow intersect at an angle which is a function of the major and minor stresses to which the plates are subjected; Bijlaard showed analogies in the structures of the East Indies which suggest that the broad zones along the continental margins are zones of plastic failure. The bands in the steel plates result from the summation of an infinite number of sub-microscopic failures. Is it possible that earthquakes are the scaled-up equivalent of these sub-microscopic failures, so that the zones of plastic failure around the continents are the summation of the displacements in an infinite number of earthquakes? If this were so, it would not be unnatural that the orientation of the fault planes should be statistically random.

CARL A. RUDISILL LIBRARY
LENOIR RHYNE COLLEGE

References

1. SCHEIDEGGER, A. E., *Bull. seismol. Soc. Amer.* **47**, 89 (1957).
2. HODGSON, J. H., *Bull. geol. Soc. Amer.* **68**, 611 (1957).
3. HONDA, H., *Sci. Rep. Tôhoku Univ.* (e), **9**, Suppl. 1 (1957).
4. BESSONOVA et al., *Trud. Geofiz. Inst., Mosk.* **40**, 166 (1957), *translated in* "Soviet Research in Geophysics", Vol. 4. American Geophysical Union, Washington (1960).
5. BALAKINA, L. M., SHIROKOVA, H. I., AND VVEDENSKAYA, A. V., *Publ. Dom. Obs., Ottawa,* **24**, 321 (1961).
6. RITSEMA, A. R., *Publ. Dom. Obs., Ottawa,* **20**, 341 (1959).
7. RITSEMA, A. R., AND VELDKAMP, J., *Meded. ned. met. Inst.* **76** (1960).
8. HODGSON, J. H., *Publ. Dom. Obs., Ottawa,* **20**, 369 (1959).
9. BYERLY, P., AND STAUDER, W., *Earthq. Notes,* **29**, 17 (1958).
10. STAUDER, W., *Bull. seismol. Soc. Amer.* **50**, 347 (1960).
11. STAUDER, W., AND BYERLY, P., *Earthq. Notes,* **29**, 24 (1958).
12. PRESS, F. *Publ. Dom. Obs., Ottawa,* **20**, 271 (1959).
13. HEALY, J. H., AND PRESS, F., *Bull. seismol. Soc. Amer.* **49**, 193 (1959).
14. KNOPOFF, L., AND GILBERT, F., *Bull. seismol. Soc. Amer.* **49**, 163 (1959).
15. KNOPOFF, L., AND GILBERT, F., *Bull. seismol. Soc. Amer.* **50**, 117 (1960).
16. HODGSON, J. H., ed., *Publ. Dom. Obs., Ottawa,* **20**, 251 (1959).
17. HODGSON, J. H., ed., *Publ. Dom. Obs., Ottawa,* **24**, 301 (1961).
18. RITSEMA, A. R., *Publ. Dom. Obs., Ottawa,* **24**, 355 (1961).
19. MCINTYRE, D. B., AND CHRISTIE, J. M., *Bull. geol. Soc. Amer.* **68**, 645 (1957).
20. MCINTYRE, D. B., AND CHRISTIE, J. M., *Publ. Dom. Obs., Ottawa,* **20**, 385 (1959).
21. SCHEIDEGGER, A. E., *Publ. Dom. Obs., Ottawa,* **24**, 385 (1961).
22. HODGSON, J. H. In "Contributions in Geophysics", Vol. 1, p. 69. (H. Benioff, M. Ewing, B. F. Howell and F. Press, eds.) Pergamon Press, New York and London.
23. ANDERSON, E. M., "The Dynamics of Faulting and Dyke Formation with Applications to Britain". Oliver and Boyd, Edinburgh and London (1942).
24. LENSEN, G. J., *Publ. Dom. Obs., Ottawa,* **24**, 389 (1961).
25. BENIOFF, H., *Publ. Dom. Obs., Ottawa,* **20**, 395 (1959).
26. ST. AMAND, P., *Publ. Dom. Obs., Ottawa,* **20**, 403 (1959).
27. GUTENBERG, B., AND RICHTER, C. F., "Seismicity of the Earth and Associated Phenomena". Princeton University Press (1949).
28. BIJLAARD, P. P., *Trav. Sect. Géod. Un. géod. int.* **13**, Fasc. 2 (1936).

Chapter 4

Movements on Major Transcurrent Faults*

HUGO BENIOFF

I. General Considerations 103
   A. Large Earthquakes and Transcurrent Faulting . . 103
   B. The Extent of Faulting in Large Earthquakes . . 104
   C. The Complexity of Earthquake Strain Systems . . 105
II. Circum-Pacific Shallow Faults 106
   A. The San Andreas Segment 106
   B. The Chile Segment 118
   C. The Peru–Ecuador Segment 123
   D. The Central America–Mexico Segment . . . 124
   E. The British Columbia–Alaska Segment . . . 124
   F. The Aleutian Segment 126
   G. The Kurile–Kamchatka Segment . . . 127
   H. The Japan–New Zealand Segment . . . 128
   I. Résumé and Conclusions 129
III. Other Large Transcurrent Faults 131
   A. Anatolia 131
   B. The Eastern Pacific Basin Faults . . . 131
IV. Deep Faults of the Circum-Pacific Margins 132
   A. General Characteristics 132
   B. Origin 132
   C. Direction of Slip 133
   D. Relation to Shallow Faults 133
   References 133

I. GENERAL CONSIDERATIONS

A. LARGE EARTHQUAKES AND TRANSCURRENT FAULTING

As a result of the work of Hodgson [1] and others, using Byerly's method for deriving fault plane characteristics from seismogram first motions, it has come to be recognized that roughly three-quarters or more of all tectonic earthquakes are generated on predominantly transcurrent or strike-slip faults. The reason for this late recognition of the preponderance of strike-slip movements is chiefly that the majority

* Division of the Geological Sciences, Contribution No. 1061.

E

of great shallow earthquakes occur off the coast along the circum-Pacific arc and, consequently, their generating faults are thus not available for direct field study. Figure 1 is a plot of epicentres of major

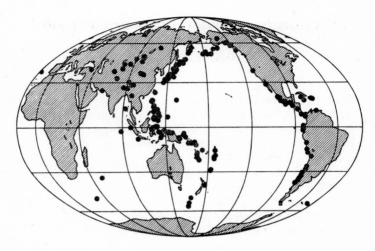

FIG. 1. World distribution of great shallow earthquakes of magnitude 8 and larger recorded between 1904 and 1954 (after Gutenberg and Richter).

earthquakes of the world for the interval 1904 to 1952, taken from Gutenberg and Richter [2], showing the preponderance of Pacific marginal sources with a smaller number located in continental Asia and other places.

B. THE EXTENT OF FAULTING IN LARGE EARTHQUAKES

It should be emphasized that plots such as Fig. 1 are inadequate as representations of earthquake locations, either as sources of seismic wave energy, or as indicators of tectonic activity, since an epicentre is a point only on the surface vertically above the focus (hypocentre) where faulting is initiated. Earthquakes of magnitude 8 and larger involve active faulting segments extending to 1,000 km or more. From the point of view of earthquakes as tectonic manifestations or sources of seismic energy a map of earthquakes should, therefore, exhibit active faulting segments rather than epicentres. Unfortunately, the available data on active segments for past earthquakes are limited. This situation will improve substantially, since recently two methods have been found for determining instrumentally the extent of faulting in large earthquakes. These will be mentioned later. This chapter represents an attempt to assemble available information on the great transcurrent faults and, although it is much less than adequate for a full understanding of them, it does represent our present state of knowledge (or ignorance).

C. THE COMPLEXITY OF EARTHQUAKE STRAIN SYSTEMS

Although first-motion fault plane studies have been invaluable as an introduction to world fault movements, they have raised a number of problems. One of the difficulties in attempting to interpret first-motion fault plane solutions in terms of tectonic mechanism arises from the circumstance that in a given extended region tectonic processes are seldom simple, i.e. derived from a single dynamic system. Thus, as indicated later, portions of the circum-Pacific arc exhibit tectonic activity in at least three distinct faulting patterns—a general tangential dextral transcurrent system, a local radial transcurrent system and a general radial dip-slip faulting system, which may include a strike-slip component. In places these interact with each other to form local strain patterns and secondary faults which cannot be interpreted without knowledge of the general patterns. The White Wolf fault on which the Kern County, California, earthquake of 1954 occurred, is an example of such a secondary fault [3].

Another difficulty in connection with the interpretation of first-motion fault plane solutions stems from a circumstance that initial slip on a fault may not coincide with the final motion as pointed out in Section II,A,11. It is unsafe to attempt to derive general tectonic stress patterns from first-motion fault plane solutions because the fault rupture may follow an earlier plane or zone of weakness, such as a contact, and thus depart substantially from the direction of break in an amorphous homogeneous body. The stress pattern which gives rise to a fault may change with time but until the change is radical the original fault will continue to be the principal relief mechanism. A large earthquake on one fault might be triggered by a smaller one on a different neighbouring fault, in which case the fault plane solution would be that of the minor fault. A number of seismologists attempt to deduce the mechanism of earthquake generation from initial motion studies. Thus, Honda [4], finds that the source frequently has the form of a double-couple, rather than the single-couple of the elastic rebound mechanism of Reid. This mechanism is acceptable as an explanation for the first-motion transient of a large earthquake or for the whole of a very small one in which, from the point of view of the seismograph, the whole shock is a transient. But, for the main energy-releasing mechanism in

E*

large earthquakes with breaks extending up to a thousand kilometres or more, the double-couple is untenable. Consequently, this chapter will be concerned principally with conclusions based on field and instrumental data from large earthquakes.

Fig. 2. Air photograph of a branch of the San Andreas system looking north from vicinity of Indio, California. *Photograph by Spence Air Photos.*

II. Circum-Pacific Shallow Faults

A. THE SAN ANDREAS SEGMENT

1. *Atypical Characteristics*

The portion of the North American Pacific margin between the mouth of the Gulf of California and Alaska differs from the remaining segments of the arc in that it has no oceanic trench, no deep earthquakes, it is the least active segment of the arc and in the interval from the California–Mexico border to Point Arena (1,150 km), the principal fault, known as the San Andreas, lies inland. The San Andreas fault is the only major Pacific marginal fault segment with large earthquakes that has been available for field study. Consequently, more is known about it than any other, and for this reason it will be treated first in this article in order to help interpret the less adequate data on other faults. It is a vertical transcurrent fault with dextral polarity.*

2. Earthquakes of 1857 and 1906

The great 1906 San Francisco earthquake was generated by a slip on this fault. The resulting rift was visible from Point Arena south to San Juan, a distance of 310 km (Fig. 3). The break presumably continued

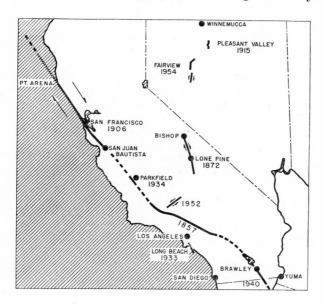

Fig. 3. San Andreas and associated fault systems. Breaks associated with recent earthquakes shown as solid lines.

northward under the sea an undetermined distance. In the 1857 Southern California earthquake on the same fault, the active segment extended approximately from San Bernardino through Gorman a distance of 120 km and on north an undetermined distance. The northern limit was not observed owing to absence of inhabitants in the area, but it is assumed that faulting did not extend as far north as San Juan, the southern terminus of the 1906 shock. Consequently, there probably exists a segment between the two which has not slipped since the white settlers arrived in the region.

* A dextral transcurrent fault is defined as one in which, viewed from above, a horizontal line crossing the fault rotates clockwise during slip.

E**

3. *The Length of the San Andreas Segment*

From San Bernardino north the fault is essentially a single break. In the vicinity of San Bernardino, a branch known as the San Jacinto fault takes off in a S.W. direction, and farther south the fault becomes a zone of approximately parallel faults extending into the Gulf of

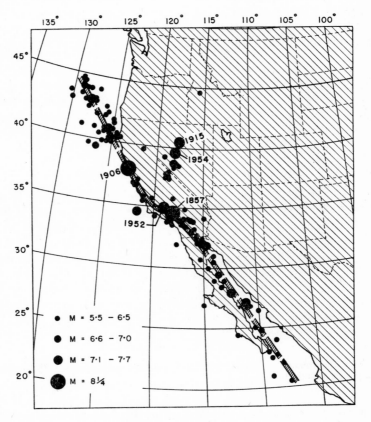

FIG. 4. San Andreas fault zone outlined by earthquake epicentre pattern.

California. Assuming that the fault* can be defined by the pattern of earthquake epicentres, its extension south into the Gulf of California and north into the Pacific Ocean, can be traced as shown in Fig. 4. The total extent of this fault is thus some 3,400 km.

* The term "fault" is used in this article in the megascopic sense denoting a region of contact between two great blocks moving relative to each other. The position of the slip surfaces at any given time varies with the strength, friction and cementing in the contact region and consequently the fault is, in effect, a zone of fracture and not a single surface.

4. *Slip during Earthquakes of 1857, 1906 and 1940*

During the 1906 San Francisco earthquake the maximum relative slip was 6·4 m, and that of 1857 was presumably roughly the same. In the 1940 Imperial Valley shock on one of the southern branches the maximum relative slip was 5·8 m on a break some 65 km in extent.

5. *The Secular Rate of Fault Block Movement*

Geodetic measurements carried out by Whitten [5] have indicated a relative movement of the fault blocks of approximately 5 cm per year. The geodetic method of measurement is rather insensitive and consequently, in order to obtain meaningful results, measurements have to be made over time intervals of 20 years or more. Consequently, it is not known whether the strain accumulation continues at a uniform rate or not.

6. *The Frequency of Earthquakes*

The repetition rate of major earthquakes on the fault is directly related to the rate of strain accumulation. If the strain rate of accumulation is constant at 5 cm per year and if the fault slips at the same strain value each time, then taking the 1906 displacement of 6·3 m as the critical value for rupture, the earthquake should repeat at intervals of 630/5 = 126 years. Since at this writing (1961) the elapsed time since the 1857 shock is 104 years, we cannot as yet say whether or not the interval between shocks is in accordance with this crudely calculated value.

7. *Total Accumulated Slip*

A rate of 5 cm per year is very fast, geologically speaking. It represents 50 m per 10^3 years or 50 km per 10^6 years. If the fault has been moving constantly at this rate for a long geologic time, the total relative offset should be quite large. Unfortunately, the field evidence for the maximum offset is not satisfactorily clear, as the effects of various geological processes tend to obliterate the evidence for the older movements. Hill and Dibblee [6] offer observations indicating a possible offset of at least 560 km. Crowell [7] has reported convincing across-the-fault correlations separated 260 km dating back to earliest Miocene. On the other hand, Higgins [8] could find no definite correlations older than Pleistocene with a displacement of 24 km.

The mouth of the Gulf of California facing the ocean can be conceived as having been formed by a 480 km dextral slip of the San Andreas fault at its southern terminus, as suggested by Hamilton [9]. However, an expected corresponding north-west projection of the western face of the fault into the ocean at Point Arena is absent. Thus, if the 5 cm per year rate is continuous, the moving fault structure in the northern segment at least must be a relatively thin layer gliding over a deeper surface whose contours define the continental coastal relief.

8. *Depth of Faulting and Aftershock Mechanism*

Other dilemmas arise in connection with estimates of the depth of faulting. The epicentres of San Andreas earthquakes are quite shallow, 15 km or so. Byerly and De Noyer [10] have shown that the rate of

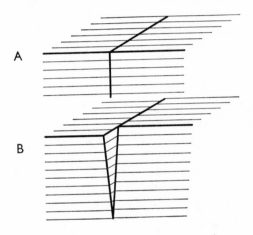

A

B

FIG. 5. Transcurrent fault in continuous medium before (A) and after (B) a slip.

decrease of seismic wave energy with distance from this fault for the 1906 and 1940 earthquakes is consistent with an effective faulting depth not greater than about 12 km. For any one shock this presents no problem. However, if we envisage a succession of shocks on a given fault segment in a continuous medium, all having the same direction of slip, it follows that with each succeeding shock the effective depth must increase, as can be deduced from consideration of Fig. 5. As the relative displacement of the blocks increases, the depth of the vertex of the triangle forming the active fault surface must also increase. For a total displacement of 560 km as given by Hill and Dibblee [6], the depth should be some hundreds of kilometres. One way out of this difficulty is to assume that faulting extends downward only to some discontinuity, as represented in Fig. 7, which acts either as a lubricated contact or else as an additional horizontal fault surface, making the San Andreas a dihedral fault with two-dimensional strain accumulation and relief. In the latter case, the radiation pattern of the shock differs from the form usually accepted, and consequently this condition probably does not exist. An effective lubricated contact for the slow 5 m per century block movement might be conceived as resulting from flow in a thin layer of weak or viscous material. For short-period strains the material behaves as an elastic solid and forms a firm contact for the transmission of seismic waves. A lubricated contact of this kind will result in

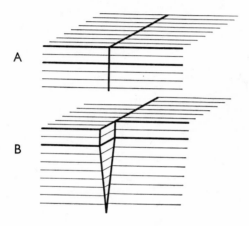

FIG. 6. Transcurrent fault with relaxation discontinuity before (A) and immediately after fault slip (B).

a particular form of aftershock mechanism. Thus assume that, owing to flow or lubrication, secular strains in the crust in the vicinity of a transcurrent fault are not effectively transmitted across a horizontal discontinuity at some depth such as 12 km which can be termed the relaxation discontinuity. Accordingly, during the time the secular strain accumulates in the upper layer, flow at the discontinuity prevents accumulation in the lower, so that at the moment before an earthquake occurs the upper layer is strained but the lower one is unstrained. During the short interval of time the fault slips the viscous coupling across, the relaxation discontinuity effectively binds the upper and lower layers together, with the result that strain relief in the upper induces strain and possibly a fault break in the lower as shown in Fig. 6. This in turn produces an opposing stress which prevents the strain in the upper layer from being fully relieved. Following the earthquake the viscous coupling across the discontinuity permits the lower layer strain to relax slowly and this leaves a slowly increasing portion of stress in the upper layer opposed by fault friction only. When at some point along the fault this increasing stress exceeds the reduced fault frictional constraint, the fault slips again and thus generates the first aftershock. This process repeats until substantially the whole original strain increment is dissipated. The final configuration then is shown at B of Fig. 7.

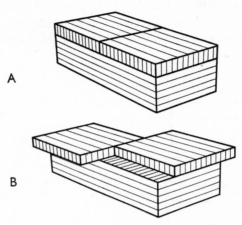

Fig. 7. Transcurrent fault with relaxation discontinuity before a slip (A) and after completion of aftershock sequence (B). This also represents a fault with a lubricated lower contact.

With this hypothesis the faulting activity is confined to the crust above the assumed relaxation discontinuity. It also offers an alternative explanation to the author's original aftershock hypothesis [11], in which the aftershock strain is derived from elastic afterworking of the fault rocks. On the basis of the 12 km depth of faulting found by Byerly and De Noyer, the relaxation discontinuity in California lies at least 20 km above the Mohorovičić discontinuity.

9. *Horizontal Fault Strain Pattern*

The word "strain" in this article with reference to earthquakes, is used to refer to strain increment since as in electric potential absolute measurements are not possible. Using measurements carried out by the U.S. Coast and Geodetic Survey, Byerly and De Noyer [10] showed that the horizontal strain displacement pattern on the San Andreas fault just after an earthquake is given by the empirical form

$$Y = A \cot^{-1} BX \tag{1}$$

where Y is the horizontal displacement parallel to the fault of a point distant X from the fault, and A and B are constants. This equation is given in terms of a co-ordinate system laid out on the strained fault pattern immediately prior to an earthquake. By differentiation we obtain the strain

$$\sigma = \frac{dY}{dX} = \frac{AB}{1 + B^2 X^2} \tag{2}$$

Figure 8 is a plot of equation (2) with constants given by Byerly and De Noyer for the 1906 San Francisco earthquake. It is indeed surprising

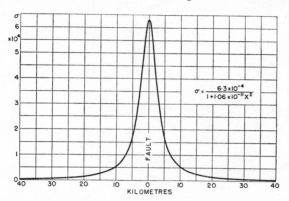

Fig. 8. Plot of the San Andreas fault strain immediately preceding the 1906 San Francisco earthquake. Adapted from Byerly and De Noyer [10].

to find that in a fault of great linear extent, the strain is confined to such a narrow zone. At a distance $X = 10$ km from the fault, the strain is reduced to 0·086 of maximum. It has been suggested [12] that the horizontal concentration of strain so near the fault indicated by the slope of the strain displacement curve is a result of a reduced rigidity of the blocks in the vicinity of the fault. Such a reduction may be caused by numerous minor fractures in the fault zone. As a working hypothesis, it may be assumed that the aftershock epicentre pattern corresponds roughly with the width and length of the earthquake-generating strain zone. Unfortunately, the distribution of aftershock epicentres of no large San Andreas earthquake is known, since adequate seismograph networks were not available in 1906 and earlier. We have, therefore, no aftershock pattern for comparison with the geodetically derived strain pattern by Byerly and De Noyer. We do have observations of after-shock distributions in several other earthquakes discussed later (Kamchatka, 4th November, 1952; Aleutians, 9th March, 1957; Chile, 22nd May, 1960), but for these shocks the corresponding geodetic or other field measurements of the strain patterns are not available for comparison.

10. *The Bend of the San Andreas Fault*

The fault is fairly straight from the northern terminus to the region of the San Emigdio Mountains, where it is deflected sharply eastward some 35°. Farther south in the vicinity of Whitewater it curves westward and becomes nearly parallel to the northern straight segment; from there on south it continues in a roughly straight line. In the vicinity of the sharp bend the projection of the Garlock fault intersects the San Andreas fault at angles of approximately 40° (see Fig. 9). This is a

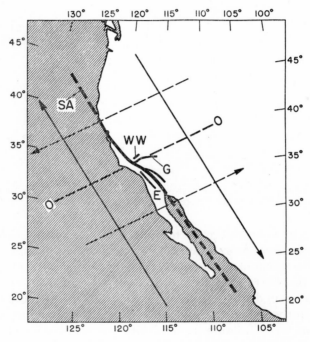

Fig. 9. San Andreas and associated faults showing dual dynamic system. SA, San Andreas fault; G, Garlock fault; E, Elsinore fault; WW, White Wolf fault.

sinistral transcurrent fault. It has been argued that the Garlock fault is a conjugate fracture with the San Andreas fault produced by a north–south linear horizontal stress [6]. However, this concept meets with difficulties. Thus at shallow depths (less than 50 km or so), fractures occur at angles less than 45° with the direction of the greatest principal stress, whereas in the San Andreas–Garlock intersection the angle is nearly 90°. Moreover, conjugate fractures must occur nearly simultaneously. Otherwise, the occurrence of the first break alters the stress pattern in such a way as to prevent the second fracture from developing.

If the San Andreas fault has undergone the large (560 km) total displacement posited by Hill and Dibblee, then the Garlock component is of later origin and must, therefore, have developed in response to a later and different stress system from that which produced the San Andreas fracture. The bend in the San Andreas fault, together with direction of slip of the Garlock fracture, suggests that these are expressions of a movement of the block north of the Garlock fault in a westerly direction relative to the southern block, as shown by the dashed arrows in Fig. 8, and that this movement started after the San Andreas fault was developed [3]. The region in the vicinity of the Garlock–San Andreas intersection is thus one of severe distortion, since the two fault movements being nearly at right angles to each other must ultimately be incompatible if they both continue without reversals.

The existence of the San Jacinto and Elsinore faults aligned approximately along the southern projection of the northern segment of the San Andreas fault may thus be evidence that this primary incompatibility is being resolved by the production of new fractures capable of taking over the linear San Andreas movement. The distortion of that portion of the eastern block of the San Andreas fault moving southward along the curved restraint of the great bend must arise principally from a compression oriented approximately north–south. The White Wolf fault is thus a mechanism for relief of this localized stress.

11. *The Origin of the Transverse Couple*

The origin of the transverse couple indicated by the curvature of the San Andreas fault is assumed by the writer to be a north–south gradient in the rate of oceanwards expansion of the continental margin [13]. In addition to its oceanwards or radial expansion, the continental margin is also moving tangentially along the San Andreas fault—the moving contact between the Pacific Basin and the continent.

12. *Inland Extension of Dextral Marginal Strain*

(a) *Owens Valley Fault*

The Owen's Valley fault lies parallel to the San Andreas fault inland at a distance of about 300 km. A 20 km segment of this fault centring on Lone Pine was active in the earthquake of 26th March, 1872. The movement was principally vertical, but had a substantial strike-slip component. The western side moved up relative to the eastern, a maximum of about 6 m. Unfortunately, the polarity of the strike-slip component is open to some doubt, since the original observers were not interested in this aspect of the earthquake. H. O. Wood (personal

E***

communication) was positive that the movement was right lateral.
V. Gianella [14] found dextral slip on some segments and sinistral on
one. P. C. Bateman [15] interprets an earlier paper by W. J. Johnson as
convincing evidence for dextral slip.

(b) *Fairview–Dixie Valley Fault*

Farther east in Nevada, 500 km from the coast, another fault was active
on 16th December 1954, during the Fairview–Dixie Valley earthquake.
This is a normal fault dipping to the east with a strike approximately
N 20° E. Figure 10 is a photograph of the scarp taken on 26th December,

Fɪɢ. 10. Fault scarp at Fairview Peak, Nevada earthquake of 16th December 1954,
looking south.

1954, looking south. The maximum dip offset was about 5 m and the
break was visible over a distance of 104 km. In addition to the dip-slip,
the displacement had a substantial dextral transcurrent component as
shown in Fig. 11, taken on the same day as the preceding photograph
looking west toward the uplifted face of the fault at a point where the

displacement was largest. The direction of slip is clearly indicated by grooves and striations cut by small rocks entrapped between the surfaces and by irregularities in the fault surfaces as they slid past each other. It will be noticed from the curved shape of the grooves that

FIG. 11. Fault scarp at Fairview Peak, Nevada earthquake of 16th December 1954, looking west. The grooves produced by rocks and fault surface irregularities are shown.

during the fault movement, the horizontal component of slip increased substantially from its initial value. The appearances of the grooves also strongly indicates that the fault movement was unidirectional without oscillations.

It appears, therefore, from these two cases that the San Andreas dextral shear-stress system extends inland at least 500 km, and is superimposed on the local stress patterns. Similar inland extensions of dextral shear-stress have been observed in other parts of the circum-Pacific arc, particularly Chile and Alaska, mentioned later.

B. THE CHILE SEGMENT

1. *Dextral Transcurrent Land Faults*

Until recently, data concerning the nature of the faulting associated with the high level of seismic activity of the Chile segment were very sparse. However, instrumental observations of the great earthquake of 22nd May 1960, together with field observations of the land faults by St Amand [personal communication, 1958] and by St Amand and Allen [16] have served to elucidate clearly this interesting section of the circum-Pacific arc. They found a system of dextral transcurrent land faults lying parallel to the coast and extending over the length of Chile. These indicate that a dextral shear strain exists throughout the strip between the Andes and the coast, similar to the pattern associated with the eastern California and Nevada faults.

2. *Marine Fault and the Great Earthquake of 22nd May, 1960*

(a) *Direction and Extent of Faulting from Aftershock Pattern*

Convincing evidence for the location of the principal fault offshore and that it is similar to the San Andreas fault is derived in part from the aftershock distribution pattern of the earthquake. A map of the region is shown in Fig. 12 with epicentres taken from the United States Coast and Geodetic Survey cards. The principal shock was preceded by five large foreshocks. Owing to the ground disturbance caused by the last two which occurred within 15 minutes of the principal earthquake, the epicentre location of the latter shown on the map may not be precise. Assuming that the aftershock epicentre distribution pattern coincides roughly in length with the active fault segment and is symmetrical about it [17], we conclude that, in the principal earthquake, faulting was propagated a distance of approximately 1,000 km southward from the focus. The pattern is roughly rectangular in form as shown by the dashed lines. Assuming symmetry, a mid-line dividing the rectangle lengthwise thus defines the position of the fault at the average depth of foci represented by the epicentres. It is clear that the surface expression of the fault lies off the coast. Moreover, if the fault dips eastward 30° in conformity with the deeper marginal fault [18], the scarp must lie west of the midline and thus be farther from shore. A further argument for the submarine location of the scarp is the absence of surface faulting on land [19].

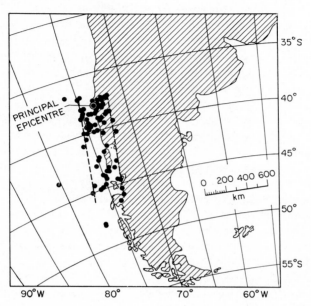

FIG. 12. The epicentre of principal shock and aftershocks of the Chilean earthquake of 22nd May 1960.

(b) *Speed and Extent of Faulting from Rayleigh Waves*

Additional evidence for the extent of faulting in this shock has been obtained from observations of Rayleigh waves. In a theoretical study of the radiation pattern from a finite source with a finite rupture speed, Ben-Menahem derived a spectral directivity function which relates the spectrum amplitude ratios of Rayleigh waves propagating in opposite directions from the source, to the speed, direction, and extent of faulting [20]. As predicted earlier by the writer [17] Ben-Menahem found that waves travelling in the direction of faulting are shorter in period and have greater amplitudes than those travelling in the opposite direction. In this method the rupture speed and extent of faulting are not independent. In applying it to the recorded waves of this earthquake the best fit was obtained with a faulting speed of 4·5 km per sec and an active segment of 750 to 800 km. In his theoretical calculation Ben-Menahem assumed the fault slip to be uniform throughout the length of the active segment. Since, as observed in the San Francisco 1906 earthquake, the slip varies from a maximum near the middle of the active segment to zero at the end, Ben-Menahem's method must indicate a segment somewhat shorter than the actual value. His findings are, therefore, consistent with a 1,000 km break.

Another way of deriving the length of active faulting and faulting progression speed, suggested by Frank Press, depends upon the phase relation between the vertical and horizontal components of the Rayleigh wave-free oscillations of the earth [21]. In a single travelling Rayleigh wave the phase difference between the vertical and horizontal ground displacement is 90°. In a standing Rayleigh such as one of the free oscillations of the earth, the phase difference is either 0° or 180° if the source is a point. For a progression source of finite length and finite speed the phase takes on values between 0° and 180° depending upon the wave length, the fault length and the progression speed. In this method, as in Ben-Menahem's, the fault length and progression speed are not independent. Using this method in a study of the spheroidal free oscillations of the earth excited by the same earthquake, the best agreement between observed and calculated values was obtained for a progression speed in the range of 3 to 4 km per sec with an active fault segment of 960 to 1,280 km [21].

All three methods for determining the length of active segment in this earthquake are in good agreement for a value of approximately 1,000 km. The two depending upon Rayleigh wave characteristics also show that for this transcurrent fault the progression speed was in the range 3 to 4 km per sec. This is a reasonable value, since in this type of fault the speed of rupture must be less than longitudinal wave speed. In a dip-slip fault the horizontal rupture speed must be less than the shear wave speed [17].

(c) *Evidence from Strain Seismogram*

Additional evidence that this earthquake involved transcurrent faulting and that faulting progressed southward from a northern focus, is available from inspection of the seismogram written with the strain seismograph at Isabella, California, reproduced in Fig. 13. G-waves are horizontally polarized long-period transverse surface waves and are generated by horizontal fault movements. The very large amplitudes of the G-waves on the seismogram demonstrate the transcurrent nature of the source. In addition, the amplitudes of the even numbered G and Rayleigh waves are much larger than those of the odd-numbered waves. The odd-numbered waves left the source in a direction toward Isabella, whereas the even left in the opposite direction and travelled around the earth before reaching Isabella for the first transit. In an extended

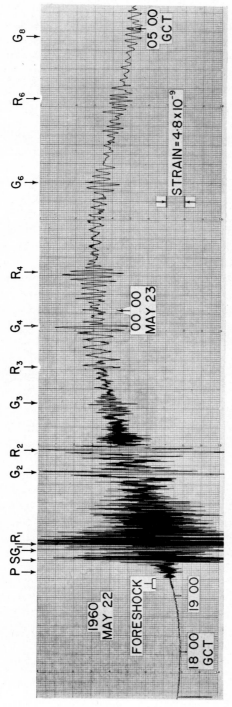

FIG. 13. Seismogram of the Chilean earthquake of 22nd May 1960, from the fused quartz strain seismograph at Isabella, California. The large amplitudes of the G-waves are evidence for transcurrent faulting and the greater amplitudes of the even-numbered G and Rayleigh waves indicate that faulting progressed southward from the focus.

faulting source, surface waves which travel in the direction of faulting acquire greater energy than those travelling in the opposite direction. Since in this seismogram the even-numbered waves are much larger and since Isabella is northwest of Chile, the fault break must have progressed southward from the focus, in accordance with other evidence mentioned earlier.

3. *Polarity of Slip*

The polarity of slip in this earthquake has not been determined from the seismograms of the principal shock and, owing to the disturbance caused by the immediate foreshock, it may never be recovered from P-wave data. The dextral polarity of the adjacent land faults cited earlier is presumptive evidence that the marine fault is also dextral. However, convincing evidence for a polarity of slip in the great earthquake has come from a study by Aki [22] of 15 of its aftershocks. His procedure is to subject the Rayleigh wave seismogram to a digital inverse equalization procedure, whereby the effects of the dispersive path between the source and the seismograph are eliminated. In this way he recovers the source function in the form of a single pulse. Since the pulse shape and polarity depend upon the entire faulting motion at the source, this approach is much more reliable than the one depending upon longitudinal wave first motions for reasons given earlier. Aki found that 6 of the 15 aftershocks were primarily dip-slip movements. The remaining 9 shocks indicated dextral transcurrent slips.

4. *Rate of Seismic Tectonic Activity*

The map (Fig. 1) shows 7 earthquakes of magnitude 8 or greater which have occurred along the Chilean segment in the half century represented thereon. This indicates a higher rate of tectonic activity than that of the San Andreas segment—possibly as much as 10 times greater. Since these observations represent such a short interval of time, they may mean only that the rates were not the same for the half century covered. This inequality may be temporary only.

5. *Width of Strain Zone*

In the 1906 San Francisco earthquake of the San Andreas system, the observed ground displacements mentioned in II,10, indicated a rate of decrease of strain with distance in either direction from the fault such that at 21·8 km the strain was reduced to 2 per cent of the maximum. Defining the strain zone width as twice this distance to include both sides, the width comes out 43·6 km. Geodetic measurements of the displacements are not available for the Chilean shock. Assuming that the strain zone outlined by the aftershock epicentres is rectangular in shape and symmetrical about the fault [17], the width is 270 km as measured between the dashed lines of Fig. 12, less twice the value of the average maximum error in locations. The maximum error is taken because the dashed lines are drawn through extreme locations. It is difficult to assign extreme values of error for these locations but 50 km is an acceptable estimate, in which case the strain zone can be taken to be about 170 km wide.

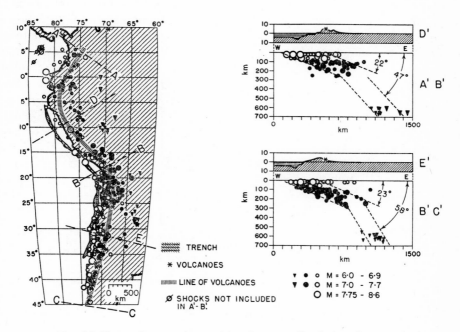

FIG. 14. Map and composite sections of western South America.

C. THE PERU–ECUADOR SEGMENT

1. *Characteristics*

The Peru–Ecuador margin of South America is strikingly similar to the Chile segment in many ways. The rates of strain release for each of the three earthquake depth classifications is very nearly identical with the corresponding rates of the Chile segment [13]. The profiles and the spatial distributions of the earthquakes are also very nearly identical, as may be seen in Fig. 14. There can be little doubt that the two segments are parts of a single system. They have been treated separately in this chapter as a result of the information recently obtained from the earthquake of 22nd May, 1960, for the Chile segment without corresponding observations for the northern part.

D. THE CENTRAL AMERICA–MEXICO SEGMENT

1. *Parallel Marine Fault*

This portion of the circum-Pacific arc has an oceanic trench, a parallel range of high mountains and many large earthquakes with foci extending to a depth of 200 km. It has no deep earthquakes. The foci outline a parallel marine fault dipping under the continent at about 35° and cutting the surface within the oceanic trench [18]. A map and composite section are shown in Fig. 15. The available instrumental data on

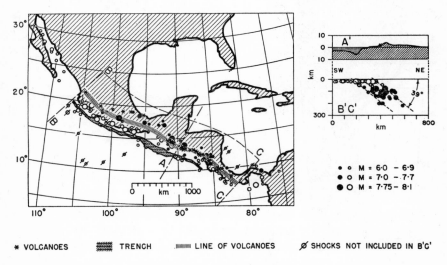

★ VOLCANOES   ▨ TRENCH   ⅲ LINE OF VOLCANOES   ⌀ SHOCKS NOT INCLUDED IN B'C'

Fig. 15. Map and composite section of the Mexico–Central America segment.

these earthquakes is inadequate to establish the character of the fault, although the similarity of this segment to others is strong presumptive evidence that its movements are mostly transcurrent and probably dextral.

E. THE BRITISH COLUMBIA–ALASKA SEGMENT

1. *Evidence from Three Large Earthquakes*

The British Columbia–Alaska segment, as outlined by earthquake epicentres, extends from a point about 47°N off the coast in the vicinity of Vancouver Island northward to about 60°N where it crosses inland

(Fig. 16). Here the line of epicentres terminates, although St Amand [23], shows the fault continuing as a land feature and curving sharply to the south-east. This segment has been the site of a number of large earthquakes. Of these, at least three are known to involve dextral transcurrent movements parallel to the margin. The first-motion fault plane

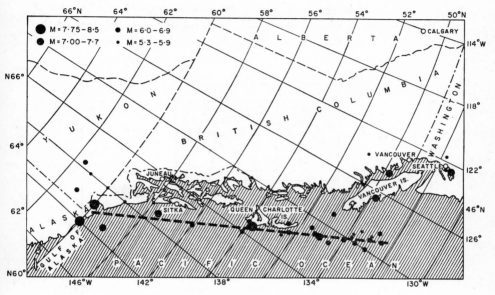

Fig. 16. Map of the British Columbia–Alaska segment.

solution indicated that the Queen Charlotte earthquake of 22nd August 1949, magnitude 8·1, was generated by a dextral slip striking N 29°W [24]. The earthquakes of 24th October 1927, magnitude 7·1 [25] and 10th July 1958, magnitude 8·0 [26], studied by Stauder using first-motions and S wave data, yielded fault plane solutions showing strikes N 30°W and N 25°W respectively, with dextral transcurrent slip. A fault plane solution derived from Rayleigh waves by Brune [27], and field observations of ground displacements by Tocher [37], for the 10th July 1958 shock both indicated the same characteristics as found by Stauder. Other large earthquakes in the region such as the Yakutat shock of 1899, have involved possibly large dip-slip components. However, even though in the latter, vertical offsets up to 14 m were observed, St Amand [23] is of the opinion that these may have been secondary phenomena. This segment, like the San Andreas, has no trench and no intermediate or deep earthquakes. It is definitely a marine dextral transcurrent fault.

F. THE ALEUTIAN SEGMENT

1. *Evidence from the Earthquake of 9th March 1957*

The Aleutian segment forms an exceptionally accurate circular arc.
Its level of seismic activity is very high, with many great shallow earthquakes and a smaller number of intermediate depth [18]. Instrumental
data on the fault have come principally from the great earthquake of
9th March 1957. A map showing the location of the epicentres of the
principal shock and the aftershocks is shown in Fig. 17. The position of

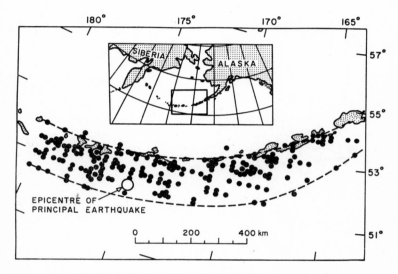

FIG. 17. Map showing the epicentre of the Aleutian earthquake of 9th March 1957 and
aftershock.

the principal earthquake epicentre within the pattern shows that
faulting progressed horizontally in opposite directions away from the
focus, although the eastern break was more than twice as long as the
western. The total extent of the break was 1,100 km. The pattern
accurately follows the curvature of the adjacent Aleutian Island arc
and clearly outlines a marine fault. The pattern width of 160 km un-
corrected for epicentre location error, corresponds to an actual strain
zone width of about 100 km. The great length of the break is strong
evidence that the motion was predominantly transcurrent. The energy
densities involved in dip-slip faulting are greater than in strike-slip
faulting, since in the former the generation of relief involves gravitational energy in addition to elastic energy, and the gravitational
contribution is generally greater than the elastic [28]. Thus, unless the

slip is small, the length of break in a dip-slip fault must be less than that of a strike-slip fault of equal energy release. The pattern of after-shocks can be accepted as proof of the existence of a large marine fault parallel to the Aleutian arc and, although the evidence favours trans-current faulting, it is not compelling. The only evidence as to polarity comes from the inland extension of the fault in Alaska, where the faults are dextral [23].

G. THE KURILE–KAMCHATKA SEGMENT

1. *Structure*

A map and composite section of the Kurile–Kamchatka segment is given in Fig. 18. This segment represents the most general form of the

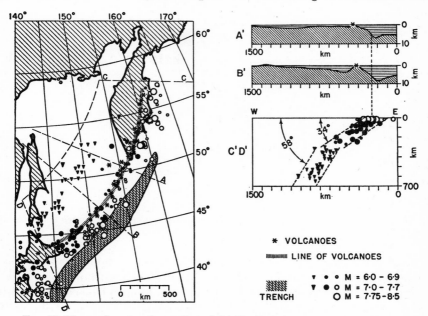

FIG. 18. Map and composite section of the Kurile–Kamchatka segment.

circum-Pacific margin [18]. It has the deep trench, the adjacent uplift carrying the line of volcanoes along the ridge, the shallow and inter-mediate earthquake foci lying on a fault plane dipping 34° inland, and the deep foci lying on a fault plane dipping 58° inland and intersecting the intermediate plane at a depth of approximately 300 km. The un-corrected widths of the fault zones of the intermediate and deep foci are about 200 km. Subtracting a focal location error of 50 km radius leaves a value of 100 km.

2. *Evidence from the Earthquake of 4th November 1952*

A number of great earthquakes have originated on this segment in recent years. The one with the best instrumental data is the shallow Kamchatka shock of 4th November 1952 (magnitude 8·25), the epicentre of which is shown plotted together with those of its aftershocks on the map Fig. 19. The long dimension of the aftershock pattern is

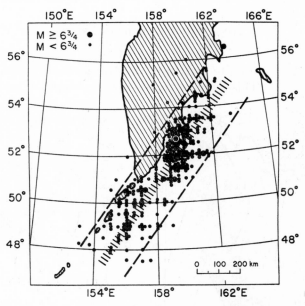

FIG. 19. The epicentre map of the Kamchatka earthquake of 4th November 1952, and its aftershocks.

parallel to the continental margin and shows a faulting progression length of about 1,000 km on a marine fault. The width of the pattern is 220 km which, with a correction of 100 km for epicentre errors, indicates a probable strain zone of about 120 km width. Using the strike of the fault given by the aftershock pattern to distinguish between the fault and auxiliary planes, Hodgson's fault plane solution [29] indicates a dextral slip on a transcurrent fault striking N 10°E.

H. THE JAPAN–NEW ZEALAND SEGMENT

1. *Land Faults*

The data for the segment from Japan to New Zealand are quite incomplete. For the Japanese Islands we have inadequate observations as yet on large marine shocks, although the continuity of the Japan

Trench with the Kurile Trench is presumptive evidence for continuity of fault movements. The land faults parallel to the coast exhibit dextral polarity according to Tsuboi (personal communication) and, consequently, it may be assumed that the parallel marine faults are also dextral pending further observations. The same is true for the New Zealand segment where the Alpine, a large parallel dextral transcurrent land fault, shows a total offset of 480 km since the Jurassic according to Wellman [30].

2. *Slip Polarities*

For the remaining portion of the arc from Japan to the Kermadec Islands, the only significant faulting information is given by Aki's studies of the source functions derived from phase equalization of Rayleigh waves from a large number of small circum-Pacific earthquakes, magnitudes $5\frac{3}{4}$ to $6\frac{3}{4}$, located in this region [31, 32]. Since this method depends upon the whole movement of the source, it should be more reliable than the first-motion methods which operate on the beginning transients only. For 38 shocks interpreted as being due to horizontal movements, he found 26 with dextral and 6 with sinistral polarizations. Since many small shocks do not conform with the principal regional movements, the large preponderance of dextral movement in these studies is strong, but not conclusive, evidence for dextral transcurrent slip of the principal fault system.

I. RÉSUMÉ AND CONCLUSIONS

1. *The Faults*

The data of the preceding paragraphs as to the nature and extent of the circum-Pacific marginal faults are summarized graphically on the map, Fig. 20. The segments for which the data appear convincing, are shown as solid lines and those for which there is doubt, by dashed lines. It thus appears that around the circum-Pacific margins the majority of large shallow earthquakes are associated with. great transcurrent parallel dextral marine faults which, with the exception of the San Andreas segment, intersect the surface under the ocean roughly 50 km from the coasts. Three of the great earthquakes which have occurred on the margin since 1952 have involved fault breaks of some 1,000 km in extent. It is highly probable that most of the great circum-Pacific earthquakes of the past were similar to these in character. The rate of accumulation of strain on the principal faults is known only for the San Andreas, where it is roughly 5 m per century. Several other segments exhibit substantially greater seismic activity and on these the accumulation may be 10 to 15 m per century. The data are inadequate to

determine whether or not the strain accumulation rate at any one
segment is constant in time, since the available measurements have
extended over a few decades only. The question as to the total accumulated slip on these faults is thus unanswered. In addition to the principal parallel faults there are a number of minor transcurrent faults

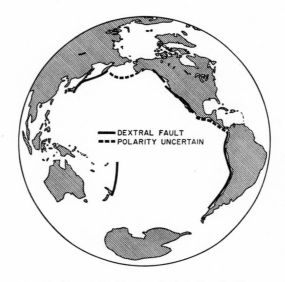

FIG. 20. Circum-Pacific marginal shallow faults.

oriented more nearly radial to the arcs which exhibit both dextral and
sinistral polarities. These are considered to be expressions of secondary
shear stress systems generated by differential seawards spreading of
the continental margins mentioned in IV,B.

2. *Are the Continents Rotating about the Pacific Basin?*

When it first became evident that a large segment of the circum-
Pacific arc was dominated by parallel dextral faults, a simple overall
kinematical description seemed obvious. Thus, St Amand [33] and
Benioff [28] both suggested that the Pacific Ocean basin was rotating
as a whole relatively to the surrounding continental mass with the
marginal faults representing the contact between the two moving
systems. This simplification is not without difficulties. The majority
of the segments are convex toward the Pacific, and in the East Indies
region from the Philippines to Samoa and on to New Zealand, the
margin is grossly distorted inward to such an extent that the length of

the segment from Samoa to New Zealand is directed radially with reference to the major portion of the arc. A rigid relative rotation of the system as a whole would thus produce motions across portions of several of the segments instead of along their arcs. Furthermore, many of the successive segments are not only separated and radially offset at their ends by fairly large seismically inactive and presumably unfaulted portions of the margins but, in addition, their projections frequently meet at angles substantially less than 180°. Thus, for example, the Aleutian and Kamchatka segments meet at an angle of about 90°. All of these departures from circular symmetry make the concept of a simple rotation of the continental mass relative to the oceanic mass difficult, if not perhaps untenable. It may be possible that plastic flow of the marginal rock masses is adequate to accommodate the very irregular outline in a common rotation of the system but in most portions of the arc evidence for such flow is lacking. We are thus left with a series of separate transcurrent fault segments without a satisfactory explanation as to how they may be integrated into a single simple system. The problem of origin of the forces which drive the faults is left as an exercise for the reader!

III. Other Large Transcurrent Faults

A. ANATOLIA

Evidence for transcurrent faulting outside of the circum-Pacific arc is scanty. A series of shocks beginning with the large earthquake of 26th December 1939, have outlined a dextral transcurrent fault system in Anatolia, Asia Minor [34]. After the 26th December 1939 shock the break was visible for some 400 km. Other shocks ending with one on 18th March 1952 exhibited shorter breaks. The combined length of the active segments for this series was roughly 1,200 km. Information as to rate of secular strain accumulation and total offset is lacking.

B. THE EASTERN PACIFIC BASIN FAULTS

The recent discovery of several very long faults in the Eastern Pacific Basin lying nearly east–west and ending at the margin of the North American continent, has added further complexity to the circum-Pacific tectonic problems. These faults are treated in detail in another chapter in this book and, consequently, are considered only briefly here. Although the total offsets on these faults exceed the maximum known offsets for the circum-Pacific faults, they are now seismically inactive except a small segment of the Mendocino scarp extending 220 km westward from the San Andreas fault. The earthquakes on this segment are small and undoubtedly represent an activity induced by the adjacent San Andreas fault. The San Andreas fault exhibits no departure from linearity where it crosses the line of the Mendocino scarp, indicating that the latter is either inactive or that the two systems join on a horizontal lubricated contact [35]. Evidence for the continuation inland of these marine faults is lacking. The Murray fracture is approximately collinear with the Garlock fault, but its polarity is dextral whereas the Garlock is sinistral. The collinearity must, therefore, be fortuitous.

IV. Deep Faults of the Circum-Pacific Margins

A. General Characteristics

In addition to the shallow earthquakes, deeper shocks are also found associated with most of the circum-Pacific margin except that portion extending from Lower California to Alaska. The epicentres of the deeper shocks are generally distributed inland in relation to the shallow epicentres. Composite profile plots of their foci have shown that they define great faults lying parallel to the margins and dipping under the continents at average angles of 33° down to about 300 km for all segments [18]. In those segments having deep foci the dip steepens at approximately the 300 km level to 60°. Figure 18 is a map and composite section of the Kurile Kamchatka segment which has the most general form. In addition to the earthquake epicentres and foci it exhibits all of the marginal orogenic structures, including the line of volcanoes, the oceanic trench and the adjacent uplifted region. It appears from studies of the strain-release characteristics that tectonic movements associated with each of the shallow intermediate and deep earthquake sequences proceed independently [13].

B. Origin

On the basis of the geometry of the marginal profiles, the writer assumes that orogenic characteristics were generated by a relative encroachment of the continental margins on the ocean basins. This may have been a result of a mass movement of the continents toward the Pacific Ocean described as continental drift. However, the writer prefers the hypothesis in which the spreading or encroachment is a result of accelerated continental growth at the margins by accretion from below either as a physical change or chemical differentiation [37]. As the continental margin grows and so increases in volume, the upper portion is forced to over-ride the adjacent denser oceanic mass by gravitational forces. Consequently, the contact between the two becomes a fault dipping under the continent. The oceanic trench and the parallel mountain range are expressions of this marginal faulting activity.

C. DIRECTION OF SLIP

During the time when the relief is increasing, the direction of slip is up on the continental side and down on the oceanic. In recent years observations of the direction of slip of deep earthquakes have indicated both normal and reverse faulting as well as transcurrent movements. The existence of normal faulting thus indicates that the growth of the continental marginal mass may be a reversible process and, in those areas where normal faulting predominates, the marginal relief is returning to equilibrium, possibly as a result of ablation of the underside of the continent. The presence of substantial transcurrent movements of the deep faults is evidence of radial horizontal or tangential vertical stress gradients in addition to the orogenic forces.

D. RELATION TO SHALLOW FAULTS

The evidence is at present inadequate for determining the relationship of the intermediate and deep faults to the great system of shallow dextral transcurrent faults. As mentioned earlier we do know that the rate of seismic strain relief of the deeper faults is less than that of the shallow and that the intermediate and deep earthquake sequences follow time patterns very nearly independent of each other and of the shallow sequences.

The form and dimensions of the deep faults forming the circum-Pacific oceanic continental contact appear to the writer to be strong, if not convincing, evidence that the continents extend downward at least to the 300 $\pm$ km angular discontinuity and possibly to the 650 km level.

References

1. HODGSON, JOHN H., "Direction of Faulting in Some of the Larger Earthquakes of the North Pacific, 1950–1953". Publication of the Dominion Observatory, Vol. XVIII No. 10, pp. 219–252 (1956).
2. GUTENBERG, B., AND RICHTER, C. F., "Seismicity of the Earth", 2nd edition. Princeton University Press (1954).
3. BENIOFF, HUGO, Bull. Calif. Min. Bur. 171, 203 (1955).
4. HONDA, HIROKICHI, "The Mechanism of Earthquakes". Publication of Dominion Observatory, Vol. XX No. 2, pp. 295–340, Ottawa (1957).
5. WHITTEN, C. A., "Measurements of Earth Movements in California", Bull 171, pp. 75–80. State of California, Division of Mines, San Francisco (1955).
6. HILL, M. L., AND DIBBLEE, T. W., Bull. geol. Soc. Amer. 64, 443–458 (1953).
7. CROWELL, JOHN C., Science, 134, 1429 (1961).

8. HIGGINS, CHARLES G., *Bull. geol. Soc. Amer.* **72**, 51 (1961).
9. HAMILTON, WARREN, *Bull. geol. Soc. Amer.* **72**, 1307 (1961).
10. BYERLY, PERRY, AND DE NOYER, JOHN, *in* "Contributions in Geophysics in Honor of Beno Gutenberg", Vol. 1, pp. 17–35. Pergamon Press, New York and London (1958).
11. BENIOFF, HUGO, *Bull. seismol. Soc. Amer.* **41**, 31 (1951).
12. BENIOFF, HUGO, *Bull. geol. Soc. Amer.* **62**, 1526 (1951).
13. BENIOFF, HUGO, *Bull. geol. Soc. Amer.* **60**, 1837 (1949).
14. GIANELLA, VINCENT, *Bull. geol. Soc. Amer.* **68**, 1827 (1957).
15. BATEMAN, P. C., *Bull. seismol. Soc. Amer.* **51**, 483 (1961).
16. ST. AMAND, PIERRE, AND ALLEN, CLARENCE, *Bull. geol. Soc. Amer.* **71**, 1965 (1960).
17. BENIOFF, HUGO, *Bull. Calif. Min. Bur.* **171**, 199 (1955).
18. BENIOFF, HUGO, *Bull. geol. Soc. Amer.* **65**, 385 (1954).
19. ST. AMAND, PIERRE, "Los Terremotos de Mayo – Chile 1960". Michelson Laboratories, U.S. Naval Ordnance Test Station NOTS TP2701, China Lake, California (1961).
20. BEN-MENAHEM, ARI, "Radiation of Seismic Surface-Waves from Finite Moving Sources". Thesis in partial fulfilment of the requirements for the degree of Doctor of Philosophy, California Institute of Technology, Pasadena, California (1961).
21. BENIOFF, HUGO, PRESS, FRANK, AND SMITH, STEWART, *J. geophys. Res.* **66**, 605 (1961).
22. AKI, KEIITI, *J. geophys. Res.* **65**, 4165 (1960).
23. ST. AMAND, PIERRE, *Bull. geol. Soc. Amer.* **68**, 1343 (1957).
24. HODGSON, J. H., AND MILNE, W. G., *Bull. seismol. Soc. Amer.* **41**, 221 (1951).
25. STAUDER, WILLIAM, *Geofis. pur. appl.* **44**, 135 (1959).
26. STAUDER, WILLIAM, *Bull. seismol. Soc. Amer.* **50**, 293 (1960).
27. BRUNE, JAMES N., "Radiation Pattern of Rayleigh Waves from the Southeast Alaska Earthquake of July 10, 1958". Publication of the Dominion Observatory, Vol. XXIV No. 10, pp. 1–11 (1961).
28. BENIOFF, HUGO, "Circum-Pacific Tectonics". Publication of the Dominion Observatory, Vol. XX No. 2, pp. 395–402 (1959).
29. HODGSON, J. H., "Direction of Faulting in Some of the Larger Earthquakes of the North Pacific, 1950–1953". Publication of the Dominion Observatory, Vol. XVIII No. 10, pp. 219–252 (1956).
30. WELLMAN, H. W., *Geol. Rdsch.* **43**, 248 (1955).
31. AKI, KEIITI, *J. geophys. Res.* **65**, 2405 (1960).
32. AKI, KEIITI, *J. geophys. Res.* **65**, 4165 (1960).
33. ST. AMAND, PIERRE, "Circum-Pacific Orogeny". Publication of the Dominion Observatory, Vol. XX No. 2, pp. 403–411 (1959).
34. RICHTER, C. F., "Elementary Seismology". W. H. Freeman and Co., San Francisco (1958).
35. TOCHER, DON, *Bull. seismol. Soc. Amer.* **46**, 165 (July 1956).
36. KENNEDY, GEORGE C., *Amer. Scient.* **47**, 491 (1959).
37. TOCHER, DON, *Bull. seismol. Soc. Amer.* **50**, 267 (1960).

Chapter 5

Magnetic Evidence for Horizontal Displacements in the Floor of the Pacific Ocean

VICTOR VACQUIER

One of the standard objections to the concept of continental drift is the implied difference in mechanical properties between oceanic and continental crusts. The rigidity of the continental crust is illustrated by the phenomenal fit obtained by Carey [1] of the 2,000-metre contours lying off the coasts of Africa and South America. The continents appear to have drifted apart without resistance and without plastic distortion in the perfectly liquid sima underlying the oceans. For most authors writing on continental drift, except Carey who invokes a several-fold expansion of the whole earth, the crust under the oceans accommodates the motion of the continents and is largely forgotten, as little is known about it. We now have evidence of lateral displacements in the oceanic crust which rival in magnitude the proposed displacements of the continents, and in the course of which the oceanic crust seems to have behaved with comparable rigidity.

During the last six years the Scripps Institution of Oceanography under the sponsorship of the Office of Naval Research has been conducting total magnetic intensity surveys in the north-eastern Pacific Ocean. Figure 1 shows the area surveyed on trips aboard the U.S. Coast and Geodetic Survey ship *Pioneer* during which the ship steamed along east–west lines about five miles apart, the ship's position being determined by a ground-wave radio locating system with beacons on the coast. This detailed survey was extended from 1958 to 1960 by three cruises of Scripps ships, also shown in Fig. 1, which covered the area with east–west lines spaced on the average about 20 miles apart, during the course of which the ship was located by ground-wave loran and, when out of range of the loran stations, by astronomic sights and dead reckoning. It is estimated that the average error in locating the Scripps ships was between one and two miles.

The outstanding characteristic of the magnetic intensity contour charts obtained in the course of these surveys is a persistent north–south alignment of magnetic anomalies of several milligauss in ampli-

F
135

tude. This general pattern extends from 32° to 52°N latitude and at latitude 40°N it has been followed from the edge of the continental slope to 151°W longitude. The north–south lineation is known to exist over all of the surveyed area of Fig. 1. A small representative portion of

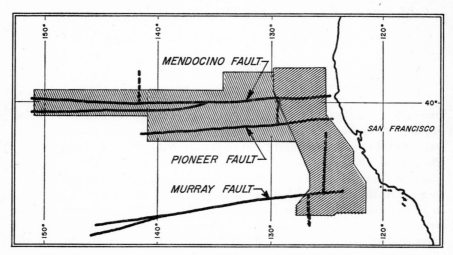

Fig. 1. Location of the magnetic survey relative to the Mendocino, Pioneer, and Murray Fractures. The dashed vertical line represents the axis of a north–south magnetic anomaly which was continuous before slipping started.

the magnetic contour chart is reproduced [2] in Fig. 2. This chart carries the suggestion of an 84 nautical mile (154 km) right-lateral slip along the Murray Fracture Zone, one of the great east–west transcurrent fault zones of the north-eastern Pacific Ocean[3].

The anomalies depicted in Fig. 2 represent small departures of the magnetic intensity from its mean value measured in the direction of the earth's magnetic field. The contour interval used on the chart of Fig. 2 is about 0·1 per cent of the earth's total field. The largest anomaly on the chart is smaller than 2 per cent of the earth's field, so that the direction along which the anomalous field is measured changes little over the area of a particular feature. For this reason it is customary to regard the charted values as the variations of a magnetic intensity vector directed along the average direction of the earth's magnetic field prevailing in the area of the survey.

Anomalies in the magnetic field roughly delineate bodies of rock within the floor of the ocean which have contrasting intensity of magnetization with respect to the surrounding material. The magnetism of the rock depends mostly on two factors, the amount of magnetite it contains (0 to 6 per cent) and the degree to which it is magnetized. It is possible for two adjacent rock masses of the same mineralogical composition to produce a large magnetic anomaly because one rock mass is magnetized differently in both magnitude and direction from the other.

The magnetite in oceanic basalts, which is most probably the rock that concerns us, occurs in the ground mass surrounding the coarser-grained minerals. In its pure state, magnetite loses its magnetism at about 585°C, its Curie temperature. If the rock contains some titanium its Curie temperature is lowered to possibly 100°C. Very broad magnetic anomalies may be caused by both local differences in geothermal gradient and by differences in the Curie temperatures due to minor mineralogical impurities such as titanium.

The magnetization of the rock consists of two parts, that induced by the Earth's field and the permanent or remanent magnetization that is acquired as the rock cools from the Curie temperature in the earth's field. From measuring the direction and the strength of the magnetization of rocks and bricks it has been found that the earth's magnetic field changes radically in direction and magnitude in both geologic and historic time scales [4, 5, 6]. Thus adjacent lava flows of the same composition separated in time by 500 years can produce substantial magnetic anomalies. Since we have no information on their direction of magnetization, it is customary to assume that the rock masses constituting the ocean floor are magnetized in the direction of the present earth's field, and that the anomalies arise from differences in the strength of their magnetization, be it caused by mineralogical composition or by differences in amount of thermoremanent magnetization.

The maximum sharpness of the north–south trending magnetic anomalies sets a limit to the maximum depth to which a thin plate of infinitely magnetic material magnetized in the direction of the earth's field can be placed in order to reproduce the magnetic anomaly. Figure 3 [2] shows the magnetic intensity profile A–A' located in Fig. 2. The profile is accurately reproduced by a thin infinitely magnetic plate 1·5 km below the ocean floor. A magnetic plate of actual material such as basalt would have to be about 1 or 2 km thick to produce the observed anomaly, as shown in Fig. 3. This calculation suggests that the top of the more magnetic material is close to the surface of the ocean floor. There are, of course, an infinite number of distributions of magnetized matter that would reproduce the magnetic anomaly but those of which the upper surface is deeper than 6 km are excluded. This is true only of the particular anomaly which was chosen because it was one of the sharpest on the chart. The ones that are less sharp may be buried deeper.

A seismic refraction station near the site of the anomaly of Fig. 3 gave the crustal section shown in Fig. 4. A reasonable origin for the north–south trending magnetic anomalies are thus tabular bodies of lava which either replaced both sediment and the intermediate velocity layer or which got covered by the latter so that their presence is not

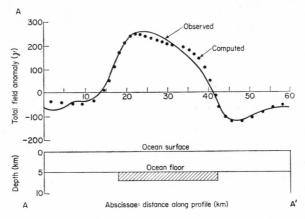

FIG. 3. Two-dimensional interpretation of magnetic profile A–A′. The dots represent the anomaly which would be produced by an infinite north–south block, of susceptibility 0·0109, computed for a field of 50,000 dip 59°, declination 17°E.

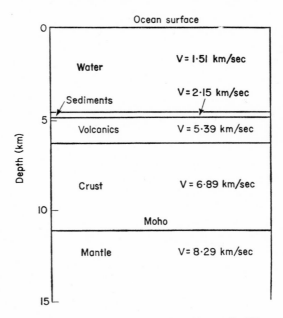

FIG. 4. Interpretation of seismic refraction profile "Cusp L".

obvious on the echogram. It has been suggested [7] that the lavas could have filled depressions due to block faulting of the crust. Seismic profiles shot in the north–south direction so as to be over nearly their whole length in either a magnetic intensity high or in a magnetic intensity low did not yield different velocities for these two locations [R. W. Raitt, personal communication].

Regardless of their origin, the magnetic anomalies provide a pattern which can be matched across the east–west fractures [3]. The magnetic observations on Scripps ships were made along east–west lines parallel to the fractures, as shown in Fig. 5. The magnetic intensity profiles in this figure are drawn approximately in their actual location in latitude. The north–south alignment of the anomalies is indicated by the similarity of the profiles as long as there is no fault between them. When a fault is crossed, the magnetic features are different on the other side, and one has to slip the profiles along the fault until correspondence is restored. Figure 6 shows the profiles of Fig. 5 after they have been translated so as to produce the best fit to the eye [8]. The scales of longitude indicate the amounts of shift across the Pioneer and the Mendocino Faults. Some of the magnetic features have been joined by dashed lines. They indicate some distortion caused by local differences in the width of the anomalies as well as by departures from north–south orientation. Occasionally the north–south anomalies terminate where there is no fault and thus cause a difference in the pattern. The uppermost profile on Fig. 6 has been redrawn as a dotted line south of the Pioneer Fault to facilitate comparison with the adjacent solid-line profiles.

The significance of a new fact of observation in geology is usually discussed from the author's personal bias. This reporter is not a geologist and has at this time no all-embracing system for which lateral displacements of 1,500 km in the ocean floor provide the missing keystone. It is likely that enough factual information of this kind will be added in the next ten years for starting meaningful speculations. In the meantime we can review some logical implications without attempting a final synthesis. Two possible points of view can be adopted. One postulates that the lateral displacements in the ocean floor propagate into the continent at the time of their occurrence; the other assumes that although there is some alignment of the oceanic fractures with continental features of the present day, the displacements do not propagate into the continent.

If the lateral displacements in the oceanic crust extend into the continent at the time of their occurrence, the present absence of these displacements on the continent can be accounted for by the right-lateral displacement along the San Andreas Fault. If one takes the simple view

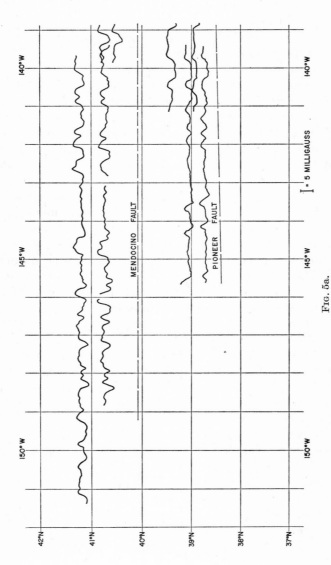

FIG. 5a.

FIG. 5. Profiles of anomalous total magnetic intensity along east—west tracks.

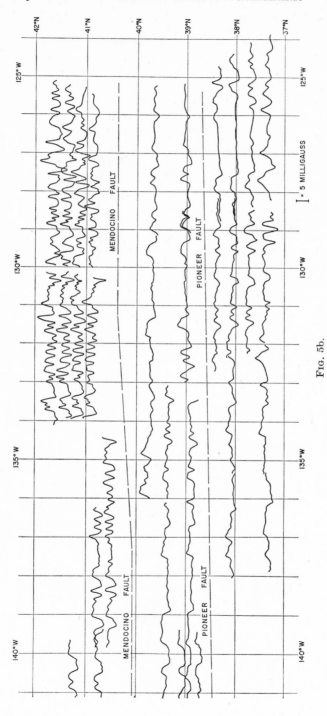

Fig. 5b.

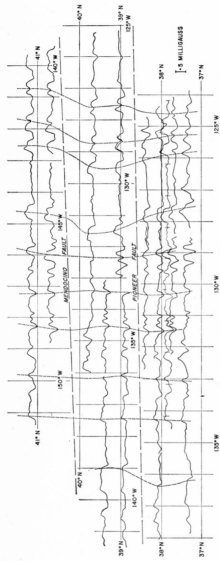

FIG. 6. Interpretation of the anomalous total magnetic intensity profiles of Fig. 5 in terms of left-lateral displacement of 265 km along the Pioneer Fault, and 1,150 km along the Mendocino Fault.

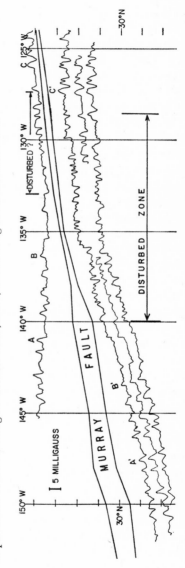

FIG. 7. Magnetic intensity anomaly profiles on opposite sides of the Murray fault are plotted over the ship's tracks with the magnitude of the anomaly at right angles to the track line. A matches A′ and C matches C′.

that the San Andreas Fault separates the Pacific Ocean from North America, and that the right-lateral slip along this fault is more recent than the displacement along the Mendocino Fault, one should be looking for the continuation of the latter on the continent at least 640 km to the south [9] from its position at sea. Now the motion of the San Andreas Fault has been traced to Jurassic time, and its average rate is about 1 cm per year. Assuming the same rate of slip for the Mendocino Fault, the latter must have started slipping 100 million years before Jurassic time. One would hardly expect the record of such an ancient event to have been preserved on the continent, although some east–west lineations 640 km south of Cape Mendocino are present. In any event the age of the San Andreas Fault does imply that the displacements along the oceanic faults are old and that the floor of the north-eastern Pacific has remained relatively quiescent since the Paleozoic, because the geomagnetic anomalies that permit us to measure the displacements have not been appreciably disturbed.

The discussion of the preceding paragraph is discarded if it be assumed that the continental block does not partake in the displacements of the oceanic crust, but that the latter can slip under or out from underneath the continental mass, causing only mild geological and geophysical disturbances to appear on the continent opposite the Mendocino and the Murray Faults [8]. The depression of the oceanic crust that carries the anomalous magnetic properties under the continent is suggested by the smoothing out of the magnetic field as one proceeds shoreward over the continental slope and shelf. As expected, this area of smooth magnetic field at the continental margin is much narrower along the Pacific Coast of North America [10] than it is along shores of the Atlantic Ocean [11, 12]. Obviously, if the displacements in the oceanic crust are independent of continental geology, nothing can be said about their age until rock cores from the oceanic crust are dated paleontologically and geochemically.

The existence of displacements in the ocean floor of magnitude comparable to the distances that continents are presumed to have drifted, indicates that there must be a mechanism for lubricating, so to speak, these displacements so that whole continents and, in the present case, stretches of oceanic crust several hundred kilometres long remain virtually undistorted by the motion.

Because the displacements measured in the ocean do not propagate onto the continent, the oceanic crust must be regenerating at different rates by a process of the kind postulated by Carey for the formation of rift valleys and rift oceans, or perhaps by the rise of mantle material along the northern extension of the East Pacific rise. The north–south

F*

lineation of the magnetic anomalies would be the record of the regenerative process. Therefore, a band of strong magnetic lineations should run parallel to the great oceanic rises. If the north-east Pacific is representative of this postulated general rule, we may expect the band of magnetic anomalies to be generally over 2,000 km wide.

The hypothesis of convection currents in the mantle has been advanced without proof to permit continents to move through the more rigid material of the ocean floor. Now the measurement of displacements in the floor of the ocean has demonstrated the existence of a kind of mobility of the crust that disposes of the objection that the strength of the oceanic crust prevents the continents from moving.

Note added in proof

Recently [13] a right lateral displacement of 750 km (Fig. 7) has been measured at the western end of the Murray fault. This is a larger displacement than the one at its eastern extremity, which is only 154 km. Between the eastern and the western regions there is a disturbed region which does not have a lineation that can be fitted. This disturbed region, especially the one south of the fault, is characterized by higher abyssal hills than the surrounding topography. It should also be noted that the depth contours are offset concordantly with the displacement of magnetic features.

The magnetic anomalies occurring in bands parallel to the oceanic rises can very well be caused by the hydration of the olivine of the peridotitic mantle [14] into serpentine and magnetite by juvenal water.

References

1. CAREY, S. WARREN, "Continental Drift: A symposium". University of Tasmania, Hobart, Tasmania (1958).
2. MASON, R. G., *Geophys. J.*, 1, 320 (1958).
3. MENARD, H. W., *Bull. geol. Soc. Amer.* 70, 1491 (1959).
4. THELLIER, E., AND THELLIER, O., *Bull. Acad. Sci. U.R.S.S. geophys. Ser.* 1296 (1959).
5. BLACKETT, P. M. S., CLEGG, J. A., AND STUBBS, P. H. S., *Proc. roy. Soc.* 256, 291 (1960).
6. COX, A., AND DOELL, R. R., *Bull. geol. Soc. Amer.* 71, 645 (1960).
7. MENARD, H. W., AND VACQUIER, V., Office of Naval Research, Research Reviews, June, p. 1–5 (1958).
8. VACQUIER, V., RAFF, A. D., AND WARREN, R. E., *Bull. geol. Soc. Amer.* 72, 1251 (1960).
9. HILL, M. L., AND DIBBLEE, T. W., Jr., *Bull. geol. Soc. Amer.* 64, 443 (1953).
10. MASON, R. G., AND RAFF, A. D., *Bull. geol. Soc. Amer.* 72, 1267 (1960).
11. HEEZEN, B. C., AND THARP, M., 1959. *Geol. Soc. Amer. Special Paper* No. 65.
12. Project "Magnet" Unpublished data, U.S. Navy Hydrographic Office, Washington 25, D.C.
13. RAFF, A. D., *J. geophys. Res.* 67, 417 (1962).
14. HESS, H. H., *in* "The Sea—Ideas and Observations", in press. (M. Hill, E. D. Goldberg, C. O'D. Iselin and W. H. Munk, eds.) Interscience Publishers. London and New York.

Chapter 6

Thermal Convection in the Earth's Mantle

F. A. VENING MEINESZ

I. Introductory and Summary 145
II. The Constitution of the Mantle 146
III. Arguments in Favour of Convection Currents in the Mantle. 153
IV. Convection Currents in a Plane Crystalline Layer . . 156
V. Spherical Harmonics 159
VI. Convection Currents in the Crystalline Mantle . . . 162
VII. Spherical Harmonic Development up to the 31st Order of the
Earth's Topography 164
VIII. Interpretation of the Spherical Harmonic Development of the
Topography: Convection Systems in the Mantle; Origin of
Continents; Relative Displacements of Continents . . 169
References 176

I. Introductory and Summary

Before taking up the principal subject of this chapter, that of convection currents in the earth's mantle, we shall, in Section II, deal with the constitution of the mantle. A paper by Meijering and Rooymans of the Philips Physics Laboratory at Eindhoven is of great importance for this subject. It seems that the mantle consists mainly of $(Fe,Mg)_2SiO_4$ with some $(Fe,Mg)SiO_3$ and other metal ions. In the upper 500 km the $(Fe,Mg)_2SiO_4$, in the olivine phase, has the orthorhombic modification. From 900 to 2,900 km depth it is probably in the cubic or spinel phase. Between 500 to 900 km depth we may suppose a gradual transition between these two phases.

In Section III, p. 153, we shall take up our main subject and argue in favour of convection currents in the mantle. In Section IV, p. 156, we shall deal with thermal convection currents in a plane layer of crystalline character which has, therefore, a yield point. Because of this the convection current only makes a half turn, after which a period of rest ensues before the next half turn occurs. This is the property that gives the convection currents in the mantle their episodic character. Because the matter is crystalline, it is likely that the currents have the property that the central part of each cell makes a half turn round a horizontal axis without much permanent deformation.

In Section V, p. 159, we shall introduce the subject of spherical harmonics, which in the following Section will allow us to deal with convection currents in the mantle. In Section VII, p. 164, we shall treat of a spherical harmonic development up to the 31st order of the earth's topography recently made by Hofsommer and Potters of the Mathematical Centre in Amsterdam and made possible by a subsidy of the Netherlands Organization for Pure Research. The results show a correlation of the earth's topography and mantle currents.

In the last Section, p. 169, this correlation is tentatively interpreted. The conclusion is that, as well as convection cells through the whole mantle, smaller cells probably occur which fill up the whole mantle and are responsible for the subsidence of deep basins inside island arcs. In this Section we shall likewise study the origin of the continents and the problem whether in the latter part of the earth's history relative displacement of continents has been and still is possible.

In this chapter the word "crust" is used to denote the rigid outer layer of the earth. Under the oceans, where this layer below a depth of less than 10 km probably consists of the same crystalline olivine as the upper mantle, the transition between crust and mantle depends on temperature and on the stress applied.

II. The Constitution of the Mantle

Views on the constitution of the mantle have mainly been derived from two sources: seismic velocities and the constitution of basic eruptives and meteorites.

The seismic velocities in the mantle, after reduction is made for the effects of pressure and temperature [2], give a constant density of 4·0 from a depth of 900 to 2,900 km. After the same reduction the upper 500 km of the mantle probably has a constant density of about 3·3. From 500 km depth to 900 km depth the indications point to a gradual transition of the density from 3·3 to 4·0.

The basic eruptives show a preponderance of pyroxenes and olivine, and so this seems to point to their forming an important part of the upper mantle layer. The constitution of the non-ferrous meteorites is not in contradiction with this result. The presence of a transition layer between 500 and 900 km depth and, below it, of a layer of a thickness of 2,000 km of constant (reduced) density 4·0, combined with the strong evidence in favour of the existence of convection currents throughout the whole mantle, seems to point towards the supposition made as early as 1936 by Bernal [1], that the olivine is changed to a denser form, probably in the cubic state in the lower part of the mantle, and that, above this, a transition is found stretching from 500 to 900 km depth.

Important light on these problems is provided by a valuable study by Dr. J. L. Meijering and Dr. C. J. M. Rooymans of the Philips Physics Laboratories at Eindhoven, communicated by Dr. E. J. W.

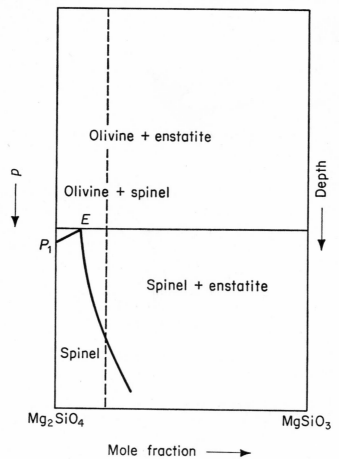

Fig. 1. Tentative schematic transformation diagram of $MgSiO_4$–$MgSiO_3$.

Verwey, director of these Laboratories, to the Proceedings of the Kon. Ned-Akademie van Wetenschappen of Amsterdam, Ser.B,61,5, 1958, from which we quote the following:

Silicates in the Mantle Treated as a System which is at least Ternary

The composition of the mantle probably deviates appreciably from the overall formula $(Metal)_2SiO_4$. In other words, there will be silicates present which either cannot dissolve in the lattice, or only with formation of defects, *inter alia* vacancies. The former will be expected for the olivine lattice, but the latter for the spinel lattice, as it is known that deviations from the stoichiometric formula often occur; Ringwood [7] remarks that, therefore, the extra components of the system will stabilize the spinel phase and thus decrease the transformation pressure spinel–olivine, as Fe_2SiO_4 does already.

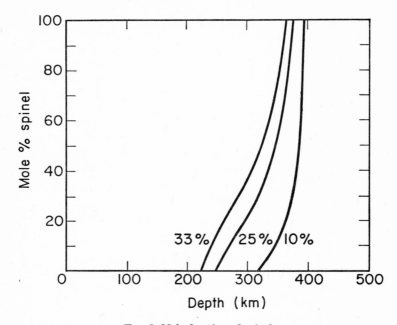

Fig. 2. Mole fraction of spinel.

However, we think it quite possible that the solubility of these components in the spinel phase is still small at the conditions prevailing at, say, 400 km depth, gradual solution taking place with increasing depth.

For example the binary system Mg_2SiO_4–$MgSiO_3$ might be like that of Fig. 1. The olivine and enstatite phases are assumed to show negligible solid solubility. The (extrapolated) transformation pressure enstatite→spinel of $MgSiO_3$ may be quite high. Therefore the eutectoid concentration E in Fig. 1 can be low and, for moderate $MgSiO_3$ concentrations, complete homogeneity may only be reached at a pressure considerably higher than P_1, the transformation pressure olivine→spinel of Mg_2SiO_4. The solubility increase sketched in Fig. 1 will be partly due to the temperature rise with depth but also to the increasing pressure itself. There is no doubt that dissolution of enstatite in spinel leads to a volume decrease, cf. the dissolution of Al_2O_3 in $MgAl_2O_4$ [4]. Hence this gradual dissolution with increasing depth will contribute to the density increase in the transition zone. In the binary system of Fig. 1 a monovariant three-phase equilibrium is passed; but in the ternary system Mg_2SiO_4–Fe_2SiO_4–SiO_2 the three-phase equilibrium olivine–spinel–rhombic pyroxene (enstatite with Mg partially substituted by Fe) is di-variant. The phase regions from great depths upward would be: spinel, spinel + pyroxene, spinel + olivine + pyroxene, olivine + pyroxene. The two middle regions then form together the transition zone, which thus contains a kink at a pressure below P_1. Not only can the bottom of the zone be shifted to, say, 900 km, but the "tail" of the volume effect may become much more gradual than was found for the binary system in Fig. 2, in conformity with the "experimental" curve*.

In this picture the part of the mantle *above* the transition zone is not single-phase. But the olivine/pyroxene ratio would not change with depth, and most physical properties in this region would be simple averages of those of two phases of roughly constant composition.

The treatment of the mantle as a ternary system is still an over-simplification. Also other high-pressure phases may well play a role. The transition zone may accordingly contain several kinks.

Conclusion

We conclude that the treatment of the mantle as a one-component system is unsatisfactory for interpreting the limits of the transition zone. A treatment based on the binary system Mg_2SiO_4–Fe_2SiO_4 is much better in this respect, but fails in predicting further details, namely the distribution of the volume effect over the zone. Unless the "experimental" data for this distribution are discarded as too un-certain, the system must be treated as being at least ternary, which it probably is. Then fair agreement can be expected in a plausible way.

Being physical chemists—and no geologists—we can say only a few words on the possible consequences for the convection theory. The loss of balance between rising and subsiding columns in the convection-currents would presumably be a gross effect. Integrated over the transition zone the specific heat and volume effects depend only on the conditions at the boundaries of this zone and not on the course of the transformation in it. Thus the treatment of the mantle as a system of more than one component does not appear to entail

---

* Birch [3] has suggested that $MgSiO_3$ might adopt a structure of the corundum type (Al_2O_3), or that SiO_2 might exist at high pressures in the rutile (TiO_2) structure. It must be remarked, however, that Si has a strong preference for tetrahedral surrounding, which is accomplished in the assumed spinel structure but not for the two structures named above. Recently it has been found that the high-pressure form of SiO_2—coesite—[6] has not the rutile structure, but still contains Si in tetrahedral surrounding.

difficulties in this respect. Another essential point is that if the heat of transformation is larger than about 100 cal/gram, convection currents cannot be expected to break through the transition layer [10].

Nieuwenkamp's estimate [11] that the heat of transformation will be smaller, probably even less than 25 cal/gram, agrees with our estimate of the transformation entropy. Vening Meinesz's conclusion [11] that the transition layer is a strong source of instability in the mantle, leading to convection-currents, is therefore not affected by our paper.

The above passage from the last part of the paper, shows that the constitution of the mantle is not solely $(Fe,Mg)_2SiO_4$, in the olivine phase for the upper part and in the spinel phase for the entire lower part of the mantle, but that it is likely that other constituents are present, which in the spinel can easily be present in solution. This picture of the mantle appears not only acceptable, but decidedly more likely than the old view that it would only consist of $(Fe,Mg)_2SiO_4$.

The second conclusion they come to, that the mantle is unstable and that convection currents are likely to occur, is of the greatest importance for the geophysical history of the earth. The cooling of the earth by heat radiation at the surface has a similar effect; it causes the upper mantle layer to have a lower temperature than the layer below and, therefore, higher density, which evidently means instability. In the following way we can see that for the olivine-spinel constituent of the mantle this latter instability is much weaker than the former one.

We shall start by considering the subsiding column of a convection current. Examining a particle of mass 1 gram and having a downward velocity w_0, we must assume that a certain percentage of the light phase in it is changed to the heavy phase, such that the heat K set free, in calories per gram, by this phase-change raises the temperature of the particle sufficiently to restore the phase equilibrium of the two phases at the higher pressure reigning at the depth attained. If we indicate the phase equilibrium temperature at a depth z by the function F of z, a subsidence of the particle of w_0, occurring during one second requires a temperature rise of $w_0 \delta F/\delta z$; and, if we denote the specific heat of the mantle matter by c, this needs a production of heat by the phase change of $cw_0 \delta F/\delta z$ calories per gram per second. So this requires a percentage of the particle to change from the light phase to the heavy one of $(cw_0/K)(\delta F/\delta z)$ per second.

A part of this phase change increases the percentage of the heavy phase, which we henceforth shall denote by q, to the value of q present at the depth attained, which after a subsidence over a distance w_0 is

$w_0 \delta q/\delta z$ larger; the remaining part of the increase of q serves for increasing q at the depth attained by $\delta q/\delta t$. For this increase we thus find

$$\frac{\delta q}{\delta t} = \left(\frac{c}{K} \frac{\delta F}{\delta z} - \frac{\delta q}{\delta z} \right) w_0 \tag{1}$$

For the rising column we obviously find the same formula. The sign of w_0, however, is here reversed and so $\delta q/\delta t$ is negative.

If the increase of density by the phase change is $\Delta \rho$ we can conclude that the vertical velocity w_0 brings about a change of density given by

$$d = \Delta \rho \frac{\delta q}{\delta t} = \left(\frac{c}{K} \frac{\delta F}{\delta z} - \frac{\delta q}{\delta z} \right) w_0 \Delta \rho \tag{2}$$

We can carry out a rough integration of the density change over the full height of the transition layer, and for this purpose we shall assume that the specific heat c, the transition heat K, the vertical velocity w_0 and the density change $\Delta \rho$ caused by the phase transition are constant over the entire height of the transition layer. Indicating the temperature difference between top and bottom of this layer by $\Delta \theta$, our integration gives

$$D = \left(\frac{c \Delta \theta}{K} - 1 \right) w_0 \Delta \rho \tag{3}$$

For the subsiding column, i.e. for positive values of w_0, the value of D is positive and, therefore, represents the excess of matter in this column. The gravity attraction gD on this excess of matter represents part of the driving force of the convection current. The second half of this force is provided by the upward gravity effect gD on the mass deficiency, represented by the same formula (3) for the rising column of the current and, therefore, for a negative value of w_0. Both parts together give the total contribution to the driving force of the current by the transition layer.

From formula (3) we can derive that the contribution by the transition layer to convection in the mantle becomes negative for values of K larger than $c \Delta \theta$. We can conclude that for this case the transition layer practically prevents convection in the mantle. So we can state that the condition for the possibility of mantle convection over the entire height of the mantle is given by

$$K < c \Delta \theta \tag{4}$$

We shall now investigate the driving power for normal convection, which is provided by normal thermal expansion. Denoting the thermal volume expansion coefficient by α_t and the mantle density by ρ, a change of temperature ν of a unit of volume gives a volume expansion of $\nu\alpha_t$. This diminishes the density ρ by an amount of $-\rho\nu\alpha_t$. If β is the downward temperature gradient, a downward velocity w_0 of the subsiding column of the current, which in 1 sec displaces a particle over a distance w_0, gives a temperature difference per second of $-w_0\beta$ with regard to the temperature reigning normally at that depth and, therefore, an increase of density at that depth of d' given by

$$d' = \alpha_t\beta w_0\rho \tag{5}$$

Integrating over the entire height of the subsiding column we obtain approximately

$$D' = \alpha_t\Delta\theta w_0\rho \tag{6}$$

in which $\Delta\theta$ again denotes the temperature difference between top and bottom. The weight of the excess of matter D' in the subsiding column represents, for this case of normal thermal convection, half of the driving force of the current. The second half of this force is provided by the weight of the deficiency of matter in the rising column, which is given by the same formula (6); the rising velocity w_0 of this column has the same magnitude as that of the subsiding column but it has opposite sign.

By taking the ratio of formula (3) for D and formula (6) for D' we obtain the ratio between the roughly computed driving forces for convection in layers between the same differences of temperature at top and bottom, which in the first case is caused by a phase change as previously described, and in the second case by the temperature gradient in the way it acts for normal convection. We obtain

$$\frac{D}{D'} = \frac{\Delta\rho}{\rho\alpha_t\Delta\theta}\left(\frac{c\Delta\theta}{K} - 1\right) \tag{7}$$

We can introduce $\Delta\rho = 0\cdot7$, $\rho = \frac{1}{2}(3\cdot3 + 4\cdot0) = 3\cdot65$, $c = 0\cdot20$ and $\alpha_t = 2 \times 10^{-5}$. This gives us

$$\frac{D}{D'} = \frac{9590}{\Delta\theta}\left(0\cdot2\frac{\Delta\theta}{K} - 1\right) \tag{8}$$

Assuming $\Delta\theta = 500°$ the condition (4) for the possibility of convection becomes

$$K < 100 \text{ calories per gram}, \tag{9}$$

as is mentioned by Meijering and Rooymans. They agree with Nieuwenkamp's estimate that K is equal to or smaller than 25 cal/gram.

Introducing this value, combined with the above-mentioned value for $\Delta\theta$, in (8) we obtain

$$\frac{D}{D'} = 57 \cdot 5 \tag{10}$$

We may conclude that the presence of the transition layer, where the change with depth of olivine into spinel and the reverse are possible, is a much stronger source of instability than the downward temperature gradient brought about by the cooling of the mantle at the surface. The value obtained in (10) is, however, not acceptable without further discussion. According to Meijering and Rooymans the constitution of the mantle must be more complicated and this diminishes D/D' to 4·4. Nevertheless, our conclusion remains true.

This leads to the view that the convection currents, which episodically occur in the mantle, are mainly caused by the instability of the mantle in the transition layer. It even appears possible that without this layer they would not occur, or, in other words, that the instability brought about by the cooling would not be strong enough to exceed the yield point and would not, therefore, lead to flow. If this is true the cooling of the earth, which gradually lowers the temperature of the mantle and thereby increases the thickness of the deeper mantle layer, where the spinel modification dominates, and thus raises the transition layer, could lead eventually to the whole mantle being in the spinel state of the lower layer. The transition layer would then have disappeared and, thereby also, the main cause of the mantle convection currents; the episodic periods of orogeny could no longer occur and the history of the earth would have entered a more quiet phase. The writer must, however, emphasize that these speculations cannot be considered as solidly founded; they do not represent more than a tentative hypothesis.

In the next section we shall examine the many arguments pointing to the episodic occurrence of mantle convection currents.

III. ARGUMENTS IN FAVOUR OF CONVECTION CURRENTS IN THE MANTLE

In this section we shall give many arguments in favour of the hypothesis that slow convection currents occur episodically in the mantle of the earth. As the mantle is probably crystalline, these currents must be extremely slow; they are not likely to have a velocity of more than 10 cm per year. They further must have the property that the stress deviator causing them must exceed a yield point before they can set in. We shall see that this renders them episodic and gives them a half-turn character; they are separated by long periods of rest.

The first argument can be derived from the crustal deformations in island-arc areas. As mentioned on previous occasions [8, 9, 12], the pattern and type of deformation of the Indonesian island arc can be explained by a field of uniaxial horizontal compression of the crust, which can be accounted for by a mantle current exerting a drag on the crust in a SSE direction. The contraction theory cannot explain this stress field. This argument is further strengthened by similar evidence found in the Caribbean and Japanese island arcs and also by such facts as are known about other island arcs. In these areas geosynclines are in a state of formation.

A second argument is provided by older geosynclines, e.g. the Alps, where the amount of compression of the crust at right angles to the strike of the geosynclinal belts is too large to be accounted for by the contraction theory; for the Alps this may be estimated at some 250 km during a period of about 100 million years. It is clear that mantle currents can easily explain such figures.

A third argument from the geosynclinal belts can be found in the regression to which the continents are subject during the first half of the compressional period, and in the transgression following during the second half and during the long period of rest before another cycle of crustal compression comes about. We can explain this by the fact that during the first quarter of the current's rotation the high temperature matter of the deepest mantle layer is transported in the rising column and by its thermal dilatation makes the crust above it rise; as the continental crust is richer in radioactive constituents than the oceanic crust, the temperature must be higher below the continents than below the oceans and so we must expect most of the rising columns of the mantle current system to be located below the continents. So in general the continents must show the regression. This must be increased by the fact that the subsiding column below the adjacent ocean parts must at that time contain most of the low temperature matter originally found in the upper mantle layer; the crust above it must, therefore, show the subsidence corresponding to the thermal contraction of this low temperature matter. The mid-ocean ridges are probably situated above rising mantle currents and, according to recent views (H. H. Hess and others), they have been rendered higher by the same cause.

After the next quarter-turn the current may be expected to come to a stop; the mantle matter of low temperature and higher density is then down and the high-temperature matter of lower density on top; dynamic equilibrium is restored. In this short review of the current phenomenon thermal conduction has been neglected and this is no doubt warranted by the extremely low values of heat conduction in the mantle. At this period the above-mentioned difference of temperature in the rising and subsiding columns of the current has vanished and, therefore, the regression from the continents must also have disappeared while the mid-ocean ridges must have subsided to much lower depths; in the continents transgression takes place until in the next period of mantle currents the regression from the continents and the rise of mid-ocean ridges occurs again. This, however, will not occur before a long time-interval of several hundreds of million years has elapsed; during this interval the heat of the core must by conduction have heated up the lower mantle layer and the upper mantle layer must have lost its heat by radiation towards the outside.

A fourth argument in favour of mantle currents is provided by the possible explanation offered for the "Mittelgebirge" in Europe and elsewhere. We must assume that gradually the geosynclinal down-buckled mountain-root was heated by the surrounding mantle matter, into which it was pushed down, and assumed the same plastic properties. This crustal matter then must have been carried along by the mantle current and distributed along the lower boundary of the crust, raising up this crust large distances from the geosynclinal mountain range, as was the case for the Alpine arc where the French, Belgian, Dutch and German "Mittelgebirge" came into being. Without assuming mantle currents this explanation could not be advocated.

Another point in favour of mantle currents is the development in the same period of geosynclines, which indicate crustal compression, and of "graben" and "horsts", which are evidence of crustal tension. The drag on the crust exerted by mantle currents can simply account for these facts, while the contraction theory would fail.

A strong argument for mantle convection currents is provided by Bowen's theory of the origin of basalt. He assumes that release of pressure causes selective fusion of peridotite, giving basaltic magma and olivine, the latter remaining in the solid state. The selective fusion of peridotite in the upper layer of the mantle must soon exhaust this layer and, as we know that the formation of basalt has continued throughout the earth's history, we have to assume mantle currents for bringing new peridotite to the surface, thus producing new basaltic magma.

In two ways geomagnetism provides arguments in favour of convection currents in the mantle. In the first place it is difficult to understand how, without convection currents, cooling can have penetrated down to the core sufficiently to cause in the core the current systems needed for bringing about the geomagnetic phenomena.

In the second place the study of the direction of magnetization of rocks has not only led to the hypothesis of polar shift, but also to the supposition that even in recent periods the relative position of the continents has varied. For both phenomena it is difficult to find another explanation than the presence of mantle currents. For accounting for polar shift it is sufficient to assume that the drag forces exerted by the currents on the crust have a resultant moment which rotates the entire crust around the earth and which thus causes a relative movement of the poles and the crust. For the other phenomenon it is necessary to admit that these drag forces can still change the relative positions of the continents. We shall come back to this point and mention that such relative movements are also required for explaining the facts known about the Permian glaciation.

There are still more arguments in favour of convection currents in the mantle, which come to light by the development of the earth's topography in spherical harmonics. We shall deal with them in Section VIII.

In conclusion, the relatively quick subsidence to great depth of the deep basins inside the island arcs, e.g. the Banda basin and the Celebes basin inside the Indonesian island arcs and the Mediterranean basin between the Riviera and Corsica [5], in the last one or two million years is difficult to explain without assuming small-scale currents in the upper part of the mantle.

Taken together, the evidence in favour of mantle convection currents given in this section seems compelling.

IV. Convection Currents in a Plane Crystalline Layer

We shall start by dealing with the problem of convection in the mantle by treating it as a plane layer, for which the mathematical problem is simpler. After introducing spherical harmonics (p. 162) we can adapt our solution to the mantle; for this purpose we can treat the earth and its equipotential surfaces as spheres. A great many of our discussions are directly applicable to the sphere. This is in particular true for the following considerations regarding the half-turn character of the current.

Before entering in this subject, it may be mentioned that the discussion (in Section VIII) of the spherical harmonic development of the earth's topography will show that in the beginning of the earth's history the mantle convection currents must have had the character of currents in a purely viscous medium so that their breadth must have been considerably larger than their height. (The equations for such currents have already been considered by the writer [12, chapter 11].)

The mantle must have become crystalline since that period and the mantle convection currents in recent periods must have had a breadth more or less equalling the height; their centre parts must have had the character of rolls. Here we shall treat of the latter type of current.

There is a yield point in crystalline substances that has to be over-come before flow is possible. Although there is a downward temperature gradient, which causes lower temperature and, therefore, higher density at the top of the mantle than farther down, the particular instability which arises therefrom cannot lead to a flow and overturn of the mantle before a trigger effect of a sufficient size is present to overcome the yield strength. This trigger effect could be a horizontal temperature gradient, which causes a pressure gradient that fulfils this condition.

In this type of convection current, the thermal conduction must be so small, that in most cases it can be neglected. Hence the current carries its temperature along with it and similarly the density deviations corresponding to temperature deviations.

We may thus conclude that, if the current is started by some secondary phenomenon, subcrustal matter of lower temperature caused by the cooling enters the subsiding column, and higher temperature matter of the lowest mantle layer enters the rising column. The mean densities of these two columns begin, therefore, to differ more and more; the subsiding column becomes heavier and the rising one lighter. This favours the flow and so the velocity increases.

The whole phenomenon has, therefore, an accelerating character up to the moment when the current has made about a quarter turn. At that time the upper mantle matter of lower temperature and higher density is for the major part located in the subsiding column and the lower mantle matter of higher temperature and lower density for the greater part fills the rising column. The difference in density of these two columns and, therefore, the current velocity also are then at their maxima.

From this moment on, the velocity gradually decreases until after the second quarter-turn the low-temperature matter is entirely in the lower mantle layer and the high-temperature matter in the upper. The stability of the mantle is then readjusted and the current stops. The convection current has made a half-turn.

It is interesting to note that at this stage dynamical stability has been re-established, but the thermal conditions are strongly disturbed. The lowest temperatures are in the bottom of the mantle which is in contact with the high-temperature core, while the hottest part of the mantle is touching the colder crust. In both boundary areas strong heat conduction must take place, which, though extremely slow, will gradually change the situation; it must lead to convection currents of a smaller type than here discussed. They must eventually bring back the old conditions which led to the half-turn mantle convection, viz. a mantle with lower temperatures in the upper part and higher temperatures in the lower part. Some secondary phenomenon must then bring forward a second cycle of half-turn convection. From geological evidence we can deduce that these periods of strong tectonic activity have a fitful character and last some 100 million years. The periods of rest are longer, probably of the order of 300 million years.

So we see that the geological evidence of episodic periods of tectonic activity can well be accounted for by the half-turn convection theory. They are separated by periods of temperature readjustment, which themselves are accompanied by smaller convection. These latter periods prepare the dynamic instability leading to the new cycle of half-turn convection over the whole thickness of the mantle.

This continuous system of half-turn convection, separated by longer temperature readjustment phases is, therefore, a dominating phenomenon during the history of the earth's mantle.

We shall now study the half-turn convection in somewhat more detail for the plane crystalline layer dealt with in this section. The fact that the layer is crystalline implies that there is a yield point which the stress deviator causing the flow must exceed before flow can take place. This must tend to cause parts of the mantle to move as a solid body. In our case this probably produces a rotation as a solid body of the central part of a convection-cell. In this area the velocity gradients of purely viscous flow would differ only slightly from those produced by such a rotation and so the maximum stress difference would remain below the yield point. In making this statement about purely viscous flow the convection-cell is supposed to have a square vertical cross-section. This supposition finds support in the spherical harmonic development of the earth's topography, which we shall deal with in Section VIII.

We shall consider the rotation of the central part of the convection cell as the main phenomenon and start our discussions by neglecting the pseudo-viscous phenomena around, with this important exception that we shall assume the current to exert strong drag on the crust above, on the core below, and on the neighbouring parts of the mantle which, because of this, must tend to move around in contrary direction. We shall suppose the drag forces exerted by the rotating central part to be proportional to the velocity of rotation.

In Fig. 3 our rotating convection-cell of circular cross-section is represented. O is its centre and M its centre of gravity before the rotation starts. The distance OM depends on the way the temperature increases downwards and is denoted by d. Assuming the whole phenomenon to be two-dimensional and denoting the weight of the cell per length unit of the third dimension by G, the moment of force working on the cell during the rotation is given by

$$M = Gd \sin \theta \qquad (11)$$

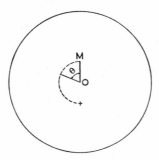

FIG. 3. Half-turn rotation of cell, caused by downward temperature gradient which gives upward density gradient; M is the centre of gravity.

We shall indicate the product Gd as the "moment of instability" M_i; it is the maximum value of M, which acts on the cell after a quarter-turn. When the value of M sinks below the value corresponding to the yield point of the mantle matter, the rotation stops; the half-turn is, therefore, not entirely attained. If, however, the earth's cooling proceeds, the moment M may increase again and the rotation can continue till it stops when the yield point is no longer exceeded. This fitful character towards the end of an orogenic cycle seems in good agreement with the geological evidence.

V. Spherical Harmonics

For applying our results to the mantle of the earth, we use spherical harmonics. For our problems about mantle convection currents we can neglect the flattening of the earth and treat the mantle as a spherical shell. Spherical harmonics express an arbitrary quantity distributed over a sphere as a function of the spherical polar co-ordinates r, the radius, ν, the angular distance to the poles, and λ, the geographical longitude, as shown in Fig. 4. The formulae (12) express the orthogonal co-ordinates x, y and z in these polar co-ordinates.

$$\begin{aligned} x &= r \sin \nu \cos \lambda \\ y &= r \sin \nu \sin \lambda \\ z &= r \cos \nu \end{aligned} \qquad (12)$$

A development in spherical harmonics of a quantity on a sphere which we wish to express in ν and λ means that we want to write this quantity as the sum of a series of terms, beginning with a zero order term, which is the mean value of the quantity over the sphere, and continuing with terms of the first order, second order, etc., which are each functions of ν and λ of which the mean over the sphere vanishes.

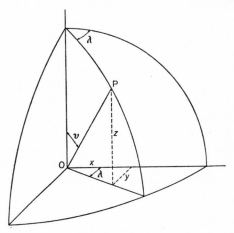

Fig. 4. Change of co-ordinates.

For giving an idea of these harmonic terms, we shall start with a more simple problem, viz. the development of an arbitrary quantity on a circle, with radius r, in a Fourier series, which expresses our quantity F as a function of the angle φ between the radius of our quantity and a fixed radius of our circle. The zero order term of this series is again the mean value of the quantity over the whole circle. The following terms have again harmonic character and the mean of each over the circle is zero. The Fourier series has the following form

$$F = A_0 + A_1 \cos \varphi + A_2 \cos 2\varphi + \ldots + A_n \cos n\varphi + \ldots$$
$$B_1 \sin \varphi + B_2 \sin 2\varphi + \ldots + B_n \sin n\varphi + \ldots \qquad (13)$$

We see that this development fulfils the conditions mentioned, and also the condition which obviously is necessary, that the introduction of the angle $\varphi + 360°$ instead of φ, or of the angle $\varphi + 720°$ etc., gives the same result for each term and, therefore, also for the sum F. The coefficients A_0, A_1, B_1, A_2, B_2, $\ldots A_n$, B_n, $\ldots$ depend on the quantity F and can be found from the formulae

$$A_n = \int_0^{2\pi} F \cos n\varphi \, d\varphi; \quad B_n = \int_0^{2\pi} F \sin n\varphi \, d\varphi \qquad (14)$$

We see that this Fourier development has the advantage of revealing periodic properties of the function F; if for a special value of n the value of $\sqrt{A_n{}^2 + B_n{}^2}$ is large, the function shows a strong wave of the period $2\pi/n$.

The development in spherical harmonics of a quantity on the sphere has the same important property; it reveals periodicities in the distribution of F on the sphere. Thus in Section VIII we shall in this way discover regularities in the distribution of the continents over the earth's surface. Because the distribution now depends on two variables, the polar distance ν and the longitude λ, the spherical harmonic development is considerably more complicated than the development in a Fourier series. We shall not go deeply into this subject but refer to treatments elsewhere [see especially ref. 12, section 3–2 for a succinct one] or, for a more fundamental one "A Course of Modern Analysis" by Whittaker and Watson. There are many other excellent expositions of the subject. Here we shall confine ourselves to the following short treatment.

The term of the order n has the following shape

$$Y_n = a_n P_n + a_{n1} P_n^1 \cos \lambda + \ldots + a_{np} P_n^p \cos p\lambda + \ldots a_{nn} P_n^n \cos n\lambda +$$
$$+ b_{n1} P_n^1 \sin \lambda + \ldots + b_{np} P_n^p \sin p\lambda + \ldots b_{nn} P_n^n \sin n\lambda \quad (15)$$

We see that, in general, Y_n consists of $2n + 1$ sub-terms, in which the functions P are functions of the polar distance ν only; they are given by the formulae (16). The coefficients a and b are adapted in such a way to the function F that (15) gives the nth order term of F; they are found by integration; they are comparable to the coefficients A and B of formula (13). [See form (17)]. Putting $\cos \nu = t$, we have

$$P_n = \frac{1}{2^n n!} \frac{d^n (t^2 - 1)^n}{dt^n} \quad \text{and} \quad P_n^p = \frac{1}{2^n n!} (t^2 - 1)^{p/2} \frac{d^{n+p}(t^2 - 1)^n}{dt^{n+p}} \quad (16)$$

If dS is a surface element of the earth and $S = 4\pi r^2$ its surface area, we have

$$a_{np} = \frac{2n+1}{4\pi r^2} \int_0^s F . P_n^p \cos p\lambda \, dS \qquad b_{np} = \frac{2n+1}{4\pi r^2} \int_0^s F . P_n^p \sin p\lambda \, dS \quad (17)$$

We shall now discuss the functions aP and bP of the different sub-terms. As they are independent of the longitude, the first term $a_n P_n$ only depends on ν; it is, therefore, constant along parallels. It is called a "zonal" or "Legendre" spherical harmonic. The equation $P_n = 0$ determines n parallels on which it is zero; they separate positive and negative zones of this first sub-term. For our further discussions it has special significance.

The same is true for the last sub-term, consisting of the terms $a_{nn}P_n^n \cos n\lambda + b_{nn}P_n^n \sin n\lambda$, which is called the "sectorial" spherical harmonic. It is zero along n equidistant meridians, which separate sectors between the two poles of alternatingly positive and negative signs. The value of P_n^n is given by

$$P_n^n = (2n-1)(2n-3) \ldots 3 \sin^n \nu \qquad (18)$$

It has the same sign over the whole meridian and has its maximum value at the equator; it is zero at both poles. This sub-term, therefore, has the character of an orange; the cross-section with the equator-plane, i.e. for $\nu = 90°$, has the shape given by formula (13).

The other sub-terms, viz. those for values of p of 1, 2, ... $(n-1)$, are called "tesseral" spherical harmonics; they are zero along p meridians and $n-p$ parallels and so they chess-boardwise divide the sphere into fields, which alternately have positive and negative signs.

The higher order terms represent the more detailed topography.

VI. Convection Currents in the Crystalline Mantle

We again base our considerations on the supposition that, because of the crystalline character of the mantle, great parts must tend to rotate as a solid, while the other parts flow as a pseudo-viscous fluid. This leads to the hypothesis that the rotating solid parts must imprint a pattern on the movement and that we, therefore, are not too far from the truth in starting with the distribution and rotation of these solid parts and in treating the pseudo-viscous flow as a secondary pheno-menon.

In dealing with this problem, we may probably assume that the distribution of the solid parts in the spherical shell of the mantle has the character of a zonal or a sectorial spherical harmonic, in which the axes of the rotating parts are perpendicular or parallel, respectively, to the axis of the spherical harmonic system. This last axis need not coincide with the earth's rotation axis; their relative orientation may be entirely at random. The axes of rotation of the currents may be fairly long and reach over a great part of a parallel or meridian, respectively, of the spherical harmonic system and they must, therefore, have a curvature. So the rotation around these axes must be accompanied by some distortion.

We shall now, for the second of our two cases, examine the distribu-tion of the rotating circular current cross-sections in the equator-plane of our spherical harmonic system; they must evidently be comprised in the cross-section of the mantle. As it is schematically shown in Fig. 5, we must assume that there are ten cells over the whole cross-section, which means that the current is distributed according to a fifth order spherical harmonic.

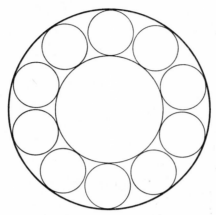

Fig. 5. Schematic picture of ten rotating convection cells in the mantle.

The following computation shows that, if we assume the cells to have a diameter equalling the full thickness of the mantle, they leave a gap between them of about 6 per cent of their diameter. In reality the solidly moving parts must be smaller and must be surrounded by pseudo-viscously deforming matter, which at the mantle's surface exerts a drag on the crust obeying the spherical harmonic of the sectorial type given by $a_{nn}P_n^n \cos n\lambda + b_{nn}P_n^n \sin n\lambda$.

The thickness of the mantle is $2,900 - 35$ km $= 2,865$ km and so the radius of the rotating cells, as drawn, must be $1,432$ km. As the total earth radius is $6,371$ km, the distance of the cell's centre to the earth's centre is $6,371 - 35 - 1,432$ km $= 4,904$ km. The angle φ, subtended by half of the cell at the earth's centre is, therefore, given by

$$\sin \varphi_1 = 1,432/4,904$$

and so

$$2\varphi_1 = 33° 58'. \tag{18}$$

This value for the whole cell is $2° 2'$ less than $36°$, i.e. $5 \cdot 65$ per cent less than one-tenth of $360°$. As the sectorial spherical harmonic mentioned in the last terms of (15), depends on λ through the factors $\cos n\lambda$ and $\sin n\lambda$, the number of cells over the whole circumference of the equator is $2n$, and so the above result shows that, if we allow for 6 per cent deviation caused by the pseudo-viscous part of the current, the distribution of the convection current corresponds to the 5th order spherical harmonic of the sectorial type.

In Section VII we shall see that the earth's topography shows an important term of that type and so it supports the view that the development of that topography has been strongly affected by mantle convection currents. Another point in favour of this hypothesis is that the pattern of geosynclines with their characteristic topography is linear and continues over long parts of the earth's surface. This checks with what we found for the rotating cells in the mantle for the sectorial spherical harmonic distribution.

It is probable that the earth's rotation affects the mantle currents through the coriolis term. This would tend to bring the axes of the rotating convection cells of the equatorial belt of the spherical harmonic system, and thereby also the axis of this system itself, in line with the rotation axis of the earth. This would lead to a north–south preferred direction of geosynclines. Two causes may be given for a more complicated pattern. In the first place the distribution of rotating convection cells may be expected to be more irregular than here surmised, and secondly the crust as a whole must be affected by the drag exerted by the mantle currents and thus is rotated; the effect must be a polar shift and, therefore, also a shift of the above-mentioned geosynclinal orientation.

VII. Spherical Harmonic Development up to the 31st Order of the Earth's Topography

A grant of the Netherlands Organization for Pure Research made possible the spherical harmonic development up to the 31st order of the topographic elevation above mean sea-level of the earth's surface. It was carried out by the Mathematical Centre at Amsterdam, where Dr Ir. D. J. Hofsommer and Mr M. L. Potters did the scientific research and supervised the computations. Professor Ir. G. J. Bruins of the Geodetic Laboratory of the Polytechnical University at Delft with his collaborators provided the 40680 elevation figures, about one per square degree, on which the development was based.

The development was a repetition and extension of a similar undertaking carried out in 1919–22 by Professor Dr A. Prey of the University at Prague; he pursued it up to the 16th order. The 289 coefficients for all the sub-terms up to that order seemed entirely irregular; apparently they did not not show any systematic features. The results of this great work have, practically speaking, remained unused for a long time. Finding that for many problems the order of a term played an important part, but that the kind of sub-term did not matter, the writer combined the different sub-terms of each order in one figure representative for that order, and to his great surprise he thus obtained a fairly regular curve from which important conclusions could be drawn. For this representative figure he took the root mean square over the whole earth of the topographic elevation as represented by all the sub-terms of the order concerned, as mentioned by formula (15). This root

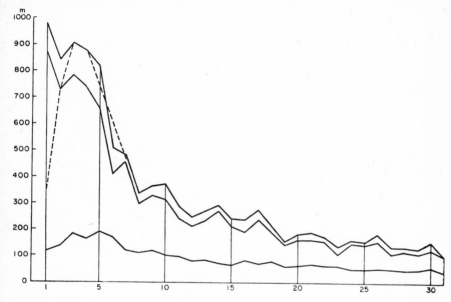

FIG. 6. The earth's topography: mean values of spherical harmonic terms of orders 1 to 31 (upper curve t—total topography, middle curve s—only oceanic topography, lower curve l—only continental topography); broken line—ordinates inversely proportional to Rayleigh number for viscous mantle current, distributed according to the corresponding spherical harmonic.

mean square, which we shall denote as t_n, is the root of the following function of the coefficients a_n; a_{n1}, b_{n1}; ... a_{np}, b_{np}; ... $a_{nn} b_{nn}$ of formula (15) for Y_n:

$$t_n{}^2 = (Y_n)^2 = \frac{1}{2n+1} a_n{}^2 + \frac{1}{2(2n+1)} \frac{(n+1)!}{(n-1)!} (a_{n1}{}^2 + b_{n1}{}^2) + \dots$$

$$+ \frac{1}{2(2n+1)} \frac{(n+p)!}{(n-p)!} (a_{np}{}^2 + b_{np}{}^2) + \dots + \frac{(2n)!}{2(2n+1)} (a_{nn}{}^2 + b_{nn}{}^2) \quad (19)$$

The root of this quantity is the mean value t_n of the topography represented by the order n. Its physical meaning indicates that it is an invariant with regard to a change of co-ordinate system, i.e. it is independent of the axis chosen for the spherical harmonic development.

Having found the regular curve presented by the values t_n derived from Prey's development, and the conclusions which could be drawn from it, there was reason to repeat this development of the topography and to pursue it to a higher order, firstly because since 1922 a great deal more became known of the topography, especially for the ocean floors, where the echo-sounding method had revealed so many new features.

TABLE 1

Table of t, s, l, T, S, L

(*t, s, l* in metres)

n	t	s	l	T	S	L
1	979	869	116	1385	1229	164
2	841	729	135	2060	1786	331
3	905	783	182	3135	2712	631
4	875	738	164	3913	3301	734
5	815	657	190	4464	3599	1041
6	509	409	170	3299	2651	1102
7	481	454	119	3600	3398	890
8	338	300	111	2868	2546	942
9	384	332	120	3643	3150	1138
10	373	316	103	3912	3314	1080
11	289	243	96	3320	2792	1103
12	247	212	80	3085	2648	999
13	271	235	84	3656	3170	1133
14	293	271	73	4246	3926	1058
15	243	212	66	3765	3284	1023
16	239	192	84	3942	3166	1386
17	275	239	71	4810	4181	1242
18	212	192	80	3921	3551	1480
19	156	143	59	3041	2788	1150
20	186	163	63	3812	3340	1291
21	192	163	70	4127	3504	1505
22	175	156	64	3937	3509	1440
23	143	110	65	3360	2584	1528
24	163	150	54	3993	3674	1323
25	156	143	53	3977	3646	1352
26	186	156	56	4928	4133	1483
27	135	110	52	3712	3024	1430
28	135	119	48	3847	3391	1368
29	127	110	50	3746	3245	1475
30	156	127	57	4757	3873	1739
31	101	101	42	3181	3181	1322

In the second place it was important to extend it to a higher order, because the conclusions obtained promised further valuable results if the development could be carried out to greater detail; in this connection it may again be mentioned that the higher orders of the development bring out the smaller details of the topography.

The upper curve of Fig. 6 shows the results for t_n of the new development, which, as mentioned above was taken to the 31st order. This implied the computation of 1024 coefficients for sub-terms. The results for t_n are also given in the second column of Table 1.

Following Prey, a second development of all the topographic elevations of negative sign was carried out besides the main one, the positive topography values being replaced by zero. We shall denote the representative values for each order by s_n. Speaking in general terms, this second development represents only the ocean floor topography. The results for s_n are given by the middle curve of Fig. 6; they are also given in the third column of Table 1. They are, just as t_n, independent of the axis chosen for the spherical harmonic development.

From the two developments mentioned we can also derive the spherical harmonic coefficients of the positive topographic elevations, putting all the negative values zero; each coefficient is the corresponding coefficient of the first development minus that of the second. By means of formula (19) we can derive the representative value for the nth order of this development which we shall denote by l_n; the values of l_n represent the land topography of the earth. They are given by the lower curve of Fig. 6 and by the fourth column of Table 1.

We shall now study the three groups of results up to the 31st order. Up to the 16th order they in general check well with Prey's development, though we find slight deviations. The most striking is a larger value in the oceanic curve for $n = 7$. It is probably caused by the knowledge we now have about the Mid-Atlantic and Mid-Indian Ocean ridges, which in Prey's time were practically unknown.

Examining the curves we see, as we also found in Prey's values, a marked diminishing of the representative values for increasing values of n. Except the first few values, they are, roughly speaking, inversely proportional to n. In the light of the conclusion we shall presently come to, that the main features of the topography are caused by mantle currents exerting a drag on the crust, we can understand this result. The drag must be about proportional to the horizontal size of the current and, therefore, also the height of the topography caused by it. As the horizontal dimensions of this topography must likewise be proportional to the size of the current, we must expect the height of the topography to be proportional to its horizontal dimensions. As,

G

however, these dimensions have a wavelength of a frequency n, they must be expected to be inversely proportional to n.

For studying the details of the curves of Fig. 6 it is helpful to discard this general effect by multiplying the ordinates of our curves by n. For reasons which we shall not discuss here [12, p. 428] we shall slightly modify this procedure by multiplying by $n^{\frac{1}{2}}(n+1)^{\frac{1}{2}}$, which for higher values of n practically gives the same effect as multiplying by $n + \frac{1}{2}$.

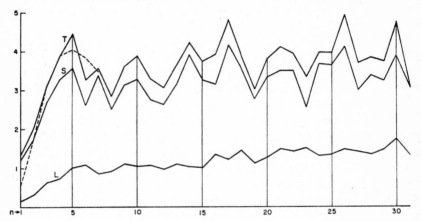

FIG. 7. Ordinates of Fig. 6, multiplied by $\sqrt{n(n+1)}$, curves for T, S and L.

We shall denote the values thus derived from t_n, s_n and l_n by T_n, S_n and L_n. They are listed in columns 5, 6 and 7 of Table 1, and represented by the three curves of Fig. 7. Examining these curves, we see that our purpose has been attained; with the exception of the first two values, the general tendency of the curves becomes horizontal though showing a series of waves, which we shall now study.

The greatest topographic feature of the solid earth's surface is caused by the presence of continents and oceans; it is given by the transition zones between continental shelves and ocean floors. As far as this topography is concerned, we may expect it to be present in the curves for the total topography t and the ocean topography s, as well as in T and S. We see in Figs. 6 and 7 that the curves for t and s as well as those for T and S are very similar, from which it follows that we were right in our surmise that the continent–ocean transition zone is the main part of our topography.

Examining our curves for t and s of Fig. 6 we see a strong first-order term which, after the multiplication, does not show up in the curves for T and S of Fig. 7. The presence of this term in the topography is well known; we are all familiar with the presence of a hemisphere where the land abounds in comparison with the other one. The centre of the land hemisphere, according to this first-order term, is situated in the Black Sea, south of Odessa and east of Constanza. The centre of the sea-hemisphere is antipodic to this point, namely, in the southern Pacific at a great distance east of New Zealand. The origin of this first-order term probably dates from a very early period of the earth's history when the earth was still an undifferentiated fluid sphere of high temperature. If in those conditions the cooling at the outside causes instability, a convection current is likely to assume a first-order distribution, i.e. it passes through the centre and returns in the upper layer over the full circumference of the sphere, subsiding again towards the centre. Such a current system in a sphere, which by its high temperature probably behaved as a Newtonian viscous fluid or very nearly so, must have led to the leaving behind of the heavy metals in the core and the forming at the surface of a layer of light matter, which was pushed together by the current into an urcontinent above the subsiding current. It is likely that it thus assumed an area more or less equal to that of the present continents taken together. The development of the heavy core brought this first-order current to a stop; this distribution was no longer likely in the fluid mantle of dimensions approaching the present ones.

Returning to Fig. 7 we see in the upper two curves a series of waves with peaks for $n = 5, 10, 14, 17, 21, 26$ and 30. In the next section we shall try to interpret these features, but we may here draw attention to the fact that the numbers are in general not multiples of each other. We only find the series 5, 10 and 30 but as 15, 20 and 25 are missing, it does not appear likely that 30 belongs to that series. In the next section we shall find that the peaks are probably produced by mantle convection currents. We thus obtain a further strengthening of our mantle convection hypothesis.

VIII. INTERPRETATION OF THE SPHERICAL HARMONIC DEVELOPMENT OF THE TOPOGRAPHY: CONVECTION SYSTEMS IN THE MANTLE; ORIGIN OF CONTINENTS; RELATIVE DISPLACEMENTS OF CONTINENTS

We shall start by studying the first wave shown by the curves of Fig. 6, in which the ordinates for $n = 3, 4$ and 5 are large. For the explanation of the first two of these ordinates we have again to go back to the first part of the earth's history, when the mantle still had the properties of a viscous Newtonian fluid or was near to it. After the core formed, the convection currents became mantle currents. The equations for such currents and their distribution over the mantle have been dealt with in

Chapter 11 of "The Earth and its Gravity Field"; we shall here only mention that the probability of their distribution according to different orders of spherical harmonics is given by the ordinates of the broken curve of Fig. 6. We see that the orders three and four are by far the most likely. We see, too, a good correlation with the first wave of our main curves for t and s, which confirms our hypothesis.

These currents must have drawn apart the urcontinent, which, as previously described, must have first originated, and transported the parts towards the areas of subsidence, so that we can understand that the actual distribution of the continents still clearly shows a third and fourth order distribution. As explained in the treatment of the phenomenon mentioned above, at that period the urcontinent had already consolidated, while the mantle surface was still fluid and allowed the transportation of these continental floes.

We have already seen that we must assume that during the later history of the earth the mantle crystallized and that the convection currents distributed themselves according to a fifth order spherical harmonic. From the development of the topography in spherical harmonics given by the data of Table 1 and by Fig. 6 we can even derive a strong indication, if not a proof, that in a recent and present period the mantle current has assumed this distribution [see 13, p. 518]; the high value of the ordinate for $n = 5$ in Fig. 6 points to this conclusion. We saw that in this case the convection current takes the character of a rotation, as schematically represented by Fig. 5.

The topography which in Fig. 7 causes the peaks for $n = 26$ and for $n = 30$ must have the horizontal dimensions of the deep basins in the island arc areas, such as the Banda basin in the Indonesian archipelago. As these basins are very deep this topography must at least be a significant part of that which causes these peaks. It is likely that these basins are brought about by mantle convection currents of a small type and so here again there is reason to bring the peaks in connection with mantle convection currents. The question, however, now arises why the smaller type convection currents have preferred sizes corresponding to the different peaks of Fig. 7. We might perhaps think that a solution could be found by the supposition, represented by Fig. 8, that rotation cells leave a space in the corners and that this space is filled by two small cells rotating in contrary direction to the large cells they are tangent to.

The writer investigated this hypothesis and came to a negative conclusion, although no doubt the possibility of such cells being present and affecting the crust is present. Neglecting the pseudo-viscously moving mantle matter between the cells, we find that the small cells must have a radius which is 4·7 times smaller than that of the main cells. This would correspond to a spherical harmonic order which is 4·7 times greater than that of the main cells, of which the order is 5, and this would mean an order of about 24. There is no peak of that order in Figs. 6 and 7, and so it does not seem likely that such cells are indeed dominant. We must realize, however, that the surrounding pseudo-viscously moving matter, which has been ignored, may modify the picture and so it might be possible that the peak in the curves for $n = 26$ is brought about by these cells.

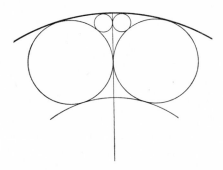

Fig. 8. Schematic picture of small corner cells in the mantle.

It is not easy, however, to find along these lines an explanation for all the other peaks. We can do so in another way, which we shall now investigate. It is simple to see that, if we assume the possibility of rotation convection cells over the full thickness of the mantle, we can also assume the possibility of systems in the mantle of two rotation cells above each other, rotating in opposite directions and together filling the whole height of the mantle. We shall presently see that we can thus explain the peak in the curves for $n = 10$. It is obvious that we can continue in this way and assume in the mantle 3, 4, 5, 6, 7 and more layers of rotation convection cells above each other, and we shall find that in this way all the peaks in the curves become clear. The smaller cells, originating for a number of 6 or 7 layers, are in fact the cells we need for understanding the origin of the deep basins in the island-arc areas.

These views differ considerably from the previous views for explaining deep basin formation by small convection currents as advocated by the writer. These older attempts were based on the assumption of pseudo-viscous mantle currents, for which the laws of hydrodynamics for purely viscous flow were applied. This led to the view that the lower horizontal limb of the small convection cell would be distributed over the whole lower part of the mantle, namely over more than 90 per cent of the mantle, and that the velocities in the lower part of this limb would be very small. The new views assume six or seven rotating cells above each other, consecutive cells rotating in opposite directions. These views explain why the horizontal dimensions of the crust's topography above these cells clearly show preferred dimensions, as demonstrated by the peaks for $n = 26$ and $n = 30$ in the spherical harmonic development. We shall see that they correspond to rotating cells of a vertical dimension fitting to the division of the mantle height into 6 or 7 layers of cells. In the previous picture given for these small convection cells, these preferred dimensions could not be explained.

In assuming a great many rotating convection cells above each other, it is supposed that each of them has the same ratio of vertical to horizontal dimensions, that is appropriate to the character of rotating cells, viz. a ratio approaching unity. It follows that the cross-sections of all the cells in a column have to be conformal. For the different numbers of cells in a column from one to seven this leads to the heights d of the upper cells given by Table 2. For this computation the thickness of the mantle was put at $2,900 - 35$ km $= 2,865$ km.

The upper row of this table gives the values of n for the peaks of Fig. 7. The second row gives the angle $180°/2n$ which is half of the angle which we must expect the mantle convection cell to occupy; we shall

TABLE 2

n	5	10	14	17	21	26	30
$\dfrac{180°}{2n} = \psi$	18°00	9°00	6°43	5°29	4°284	3°461	3°000
$\tfrac{1}{2}d$	1432	823	576	442	359	302	261
$6336 - \tfrac{1}{2}d$ ($=\sin\varphi$)	4904	5513	5760	5894	5977	6034	6075
φ	16°97	8°585	5°740	4°306	3°444	2°874	2°462
ψ/φ	1·06	1·05	1·12	1·23	1·24	1·20	1·22
d	2865	1646	1152	885	718	605	522
		1219	942	761	638	547	479
		2865	771	655	565	494	439
			2865	564	500	448	404
				2865	444	405	370
					2865	366	339
						2865	312
							2865

denote this angle by ψ. The third row provides the values of the ratio $\frac{1}{2}d/6336-\frac{1}{2}d$ in which d is the height of the upper convection cell as supposed by our hypothesis, and 6336 is the radius of the mantle surface at the depth of 35 km, which is the lower boundary of the rigid crust; this ratio equals the sine of the angle φ which is subtended at the earth's centre by the half-diameter of the convection cell of circular cross-section fitting the height of the layer in which we suppose it to rotate. The fourth row contains the angles φ themselves derived from these sines. The fifth row gives the ratio of the values ψ of the second row, divided by the values φ of the fourth row. If the rotation convection cells corresponding to the layers in which the mantle is divided exactly fitted the peaks of our spherical harmonic development of the crust's topography, we should expect these ratios to be unity. They slightly deviate from this value and we shall presently discuss these deviations. The last rows of the table provide the thicknesses of the supposed convection cell layers, of which we denoted the upper one by d. Thus, the sum of these thicknesses in each column equals the thickness of 2,865 km of the mantle.

It may again be emphasized that this picture of rotating rolls is schematic. In reality the central part of the convection cells is no doubt well represented by it, but around these central parts we find pseudo-viscous flow filling the interspaces. As already mentioned, the whole picture concerns a crystalline mantle; it refers to the equator-plane of a sectorial spherical harmonic distribution in an arbitrary orientation in the earth.

Examining the ratios ψ/φ we see that they show a fairly regular behaviour. The first two are practically equal and only slightly larger than the unity. So the cells occupy in the horizontal direction a slightly greater space than vertically but the difference is too small to raise any problems.

The four last values are also nearly equal, namely around 1·22, and so they differ more from the unity. The third value is between those two groups, namely 1·12. The greater deviation from unity seems a systematic feature and so the question arises why these smaller cells are somewhat broader than high. It appears probable that we can attribute this to the presence in the mantle, between the depths of 500 and 900 km, of the transition layer. As we have mentioned in Section II, the density of the mantle matter in this layer shows a transition, partly caused by the change of the orthorhombic phase of olivine to the cubic spinel modification; it changes, if the densities are transferred to surface conditions of temperature and pressure, from a value of 3·3 to 4·0.

Examining the depths of the centres of the upper convection cells, we find that for the cases corresponding to the seven columns of Table 2 these depths, i.e. the values of $\frac{1}{2}d$, are 1,432, 823, 576, 442, 359, 302, and 261 km. So we see that the four latter figures are smaller than the depth of the transition layer and that, therefore, this layer coincides, entirely or at least partly, with the lower limb of the convection cells. For the third figure, this leads only partly to the same conclusion, and for the two first figures this is not the case. If the coincidence mentioned can explain the broadening of the cells by 22 per cent, our problem is solved.

An acceptable explanation can indeed be given. Below the subsiding column of a convection cell the pressure is higher than under the rising column; this difference of pressure accounts in fact for the horizontal flow from the former to the latter. During this flow a decrease of pressure must, therefore, occur and the result must be a corresponding change from the spinel to the olivine modification when this flow takes place in the transition layer. This must, at least partly, occur in the horizontal direction, i.e. in the direction of flow. This increase of velocity must have the effect of changing the rotation type of convection cell into a cell that is broader than high and this would explain our results for the ratio ψ/φ, mentioned in the fifth row of Table 2.

We thus find a satisfactory agreement between the peaks of the curves of Fig. 7 and our hypothesis about rotation convection cells of large and small size in the mantle. The presence of these peaks is a strong support for this supposition. It seems difficult to account for the presence of 7 convection cells, one on top of the other, but the results of old experiments by Griggs [14] appear to allow an understanding of this behaviour of the mantle. He found that Solenhofen limestone under a confining pressure of 10,000 atmospheres could, by applying deviatoric stresses, be made to show pseudo-viscous flow and that the viscosity was high for low deviatoric stresses but low for high deviatoric stresses.

As the mantle in the present period may be supposed to be crystalline, we probably can apply these results and so we can understand that, if we have a small convection cell in the upper part of the mantle, the backward horizontal flow could not take place if spread out over the whole lower part of the mantle, because this would imply small stresses and, therefore, high viscosity. If, however, several rolls form, one on top of the other, their central parts can remain undeformed when making a half-turn, while for the surrounding pseudo-flow the stresses would be high and, therefore, the viscosity relatively low. We thus get a satisfactory explanation for this curious mantle behaviour.

We shall now take up the important problem of whether, after the mantle (including its surface between the continental floes) became crystalline, the continents could still be carried along by the mantle convection currents. There are two indications that the relative position of the continents is still slowly varying.

The first group of indications, obtained by Runcorn and others, is provided by the determination of rock magnetizations. It forms an important part of the subject of this book and so will not be discussed here.

The second indication in favour of relative movements of continents is founded on the data on the Permian glacial period. As is well known we find evidence of Permian glaciation in Southern Brazil, South Africa, the Indian Peninsula and the southern half of Australia. In their present relative positions it is impossible to combine them in a polar cap of the dimensions we may imagine these caps to have had during a glacial period. Only relative movements of the continents can have brought about this divergence. Such movements can easily have taken place in such a way that the arctic basin was originally large enough to explain the absence of Permian glacial evidence in the northern hemisphere. The evidence in favour of relative continental movements thus obtained seems fairly reliable, although we must recognize that the whole phenomenon of glacial periods is still unexplained; the background of our evidence is, therefore, uncertain.

We shall now take up the problem of how these relative movements can have taken place and still occur. We know, of course, that in geosynclines the crust of the earth is subject to horizontal compression caused by the drag exerted by mantle currents. This brings about relative displacement of the crustal blocks on both sides. The question may, therefore, be raised whether this phenomenon can also take place in the oceanic crust and whether perhaps in this case it can involve much greater relative displacements than in the continents.

In the first place, we may remark that the fact that the oceanic crust consists nearly entirely of olivine and, therefore, has nearly the same mean density as the mantle makes it possible that in each oceanic geosyncline the down-buckling crust penetrates deeper into the mantle than is the case for the continental geosyncline where the mean density of the crust is so much less than that of the mantle. The crustal shortening in an oceanic geosyncline may, therefore, be considerably more than for the continental one, and so this represents a possibility that the oceanic areas, under the effect of mantle currents, deform more than the continental areas. Because of the small density difference of crust and mantle it can remain true that when the compression in the crust vanishes, the thickened crust in the ocean areas rises to much lower

G*

elevation than in the continents, although the crustal thickening in the ocean areas was greater.

The number of geosynclines in the oceans is unknown; it may be larger than we think. In the period of rest, following on the mantle convection currents which brought about the development of the geosynclines, these belts in the continents rise to high mountain ranges but in the oceans to low submarine ridges which may easily escape attention and especially so if the area is subject to strong sedimentation.

Finally, we may remark that it is questionable whether for our present problem we can, in the oceans, treat the rigid crust as a separate unit from the mantle in which the currents occur. Below a layer of less than ten kilometres the oceanic crust consists of the same crystalline olivine that forms the upper mantle layer. No doubt the decrease of temperature towards the surface increases the yield stress below which no flow is possible. Still it would be possible that currents in the crystalline mantle are better able to carry along the ocean crust which forms a whole with it, than the continental crust which is chemically different. This likewise would lead to the ocean crust being more affected by mantle currents than the continental crust.

In summary we may say that several indications point to a certain probability, that mantle currents cause greater deformations in the ocean areas than in the continents, but our present knowledge does not allow us to come to any final conclusions about this important question.

References

1. BERNAL, J. D., *Observatory*, **59**, 268 (1936).
2. BIRCH, F., *Trans. Amer. geophys. Un.* **32**, 533 (1951).
3. BIRCH, F., *J. geophys. Res.* **57**, 227 (1952).
4. KORDES, E., *Z. Kristallogr.* **91**, 193, Table II (1935).
5. KUENEN, PH. H., FALLOT, FAURE-MURET, LANTEAUME, *Bull. Soc. géol. Fr.* (1957).
6. MACDONALD, G. J. F., *Amer. J. Sci.* **254**, 713 (1954).
7. RINGWOOD, A. E., *Geochim et cosmoch-Acta*, **13**, 303 (1958).
8. VENING MEINESZ, F. A., "Gravity Expeditions at Sea", Vol. IV, Chapter 2. Publication of the Netherlands Geodetic Commission, Delft (1948).
9. VENING MEINESZ, F. A., *Bull. geol. Soc. Amer.* **65**, 143 (1954).
10. VENING MEINESZ, F. A., *Proc. Acad. Sci. Amst. ser B*, **59**, No. 1 (1956).
11. VENING MEINESZ, F. A., *Proc. Acad. Sci. Amst. ser. B.* **60**, No. 5 (1957); *ibid.* **61**, No. 1 (1958).
12. VENING MEINESZ, F. A., AND HEISKANEN, W. A., "The Earth and its Gravity Field", p. 373 *et seq.* McGraw-Hill (1958).
13. VENING MEINESZ, F. A., *Proc. Acad. Sci. Amst. ser. B.* **64**, No. 4 (1961).
14. GRIGGS, D. T., *Amer. J. Sci.* **237**, 611 (1939).

Chapter 7

The Theory of Convection in Spherical Shells and its Application to the Problem of Thermal Convection in the Earth's Mantle

T. CHAMALAUN AND P. H. ROBERTS

I. The Geophysical Problem 177
II. The Mathematical Stability Problem 181
III. Solution of the Stability Problem 185
References 193

I. The Geophysical Problem

During the last decade, the study of palaeomagnetism has lent impressive support to Wegener's hypothesis of continental drift, and has awakened a renewed interest in the possibility that large-scale convection currents exist in the earth's mantle, and that the crust, floating as a kind of "scum" upon the mantle, is carried horizontally by the convection taking place below it. Moreover, granted the truth of such a concept, it is easily imagined that inhomogeneities in the mantle, such as, for example, a non-uniform distribution of the radioactive heat sources which drive the motion, would allow convection to occur more readily in some parts of the mantle than in others. As a result, convection patterns would be set up which would be unsymmetric with respect to the axis of the earth's rotation and, by conservation of angular momentum, the geographic poles would move slowly across the earth's surface (although, of course, in space the axis of rotation would remain close to the earth's angular momentum vector which would not be affected by the drift of the poles). The studies of palaeomagnetism and palaeowinds have provided strong evidence that such polar wandering has occurred during geological times.

The palaeomagnetic data [1, 2, 3, 4] indicate that the mean velocity of the convection currents must be of the order of a few centimetres per year, a magnitude which is comparable with the relative motion across the San Andreas fault [5]. Velocities of this magnitude would be extremely effective in removing the heat generated by radioactivity within the earth. The rate of flow of heat, S, from the earth's surface is about $1 \cdot 5 \times 10^{20}$ cal per year, i.e. about 30 cal per year per cm^2 of the earth's surface. The radioactivity in the crustal rocks is thought to be high, and to account for much of this heat. Let us, nevertheless, assume that this heat is that carried by the convection currents. Taking the specific heat, c, per unit volume of the mantle to be about 1 cal/cm^3 $°C$ and the mean velocity, v, of the convective motions to be about 1 cm/ year, we see that the temperature difference, T, between the rising and falling convection streams (i.e. the temperature difference across the mantle in excess of the adiabatic value) need only be of the order of $S/cv = 30°C$ in order to transport this amount of heat. This is, of course, quite small compared with the temperature difference which actually exists across the mantle, which may well be of the order of $3,000°C$.

The velocities of steady convective motion must be such that the rate of release of potential energy by the hydrodynamic motions is exactly balanced by the rate at which dissipative (e.g. viscous) forces degrade the energy of these motions to heat. Moreover, the structure of the convection cells must be such that, for a given rate of heat transport, the rate of dissipation of energy is a minimum. Thus, for example, in the absence of rotation, the Bénard convection in a layer of fluid takes the form of cells which are roughly "as broad as they are deep", since, if the cells extended horizontal distances which were either large or small compared with their depth, the velocity gradients horizontally or vertically would be greater, and the viscous dissipation correspondingly larger. Similarly, in a spherical shell such as the earth's mantle, we may expect that, in the absence of strong rotational effects, the convection cells would extend horizontally a distance of the order of 2,900 km, since this is the thickness of the mantle. The mean radius of the mantle is 4,920 km, and in the area of $4\pi(4,920 \text{ km})^2$ one could fit approximately $4\pi(4,920)^2/\pi(2,900)^2 \doteq 11$ such convection cells. Thus, were we to make a spherical harmonic analysis of the convection pattern we would expect a predominance of harmonics of order $\sqrt{11}$, i.e. of orders 3 and 4. In fact, the precise analysis of the problem by Chandrasekhar [6], expounded in sections 2 and 3 below, shows that the harmonics most easily excited in convection are $n = 3$, and that harmonics $n = 4$ and $n = 5$ also convect very readily. This is of particular interest when we recall that the harmonics of order 3, 4 and 5 are strongly represented in the spherical harmonic analysis [7] of the earth's topography. The dominant harmonic is, however, $n = 1$. As Runcorn [4, 8] has pointed out, this may well support Urey's suggestion [9] that the core has evolved slowly during geological time through gradual separation of the silicate and iron phases. Early in the earth's history and while the core was still small, the harmonic most easily excited to convection would be $n = 1$. This mode would tend to carry the continents towards the hemisphere of the downward convective motion; the hemisphere of upward motion would tend to be mainly oceanic. As the core grew, other convective modes would be excited and would tend to break up this distribution of land and ocean. On this view, therefore, the predominance of the harmonic $n = 1$ must be regarded as a legacy from the earth's early development, the importance of the harmonics $n = 3, 4, 5$, as a consequence of convection currents in more recent geological times.

Although the arguments described above make it seem reasonable to suppose that convection in the mantle has actually taken (and is taking) place, it has been correctly argued [10] that at the present time there is no fundamentally satisfactory dynamical theory of the process. The most severe obstacle is that of understanding how it is possible that a material can behave as an elastic solid over short-time scales (such as those characterized by earthquake waves), and yet behave as a viscous Newtonian fluid over long-time scales (such as those characterized by continental drift and polar wandering). However, it is not inconceivable that, if a solid is held strained over a long period of time, the associated stresses should relax, thereby converting the strain into a permanent displacement. Although this relaxation time is probably not independent of the magnitude of the applied stress, it may not be a good approximation to assume, as we do below, that the stress is simply proportional to the rate of strain. It seems more likely that the relaxation time governs the speed of convection.

We have already remarked above that, if the mantle is in a steady state of convection, the rate of release of gravitational energy by buoyancy forces is balanced by the rate of working of the viscous forces. Let g denote the acceleration due to gravity, ρ the mean density of the mantle, α its mean coefficient of volume expansion, ν its mean kinematic viscosity, and d its thickness (2,900 km). The rate of release of gravitational energy per unit area of the earth's surface is approximately $g\rho\alpha\nu Td$. The rate at which viscous forces degrade ordered energy to heat is approximately $\rho\nu v^2/d$, per unit area of the earth's surface. Thus, in a steady state, we have

$$\nu \doteq g\alpha d^2 T/v \tag{1}$$

Further, the rate at which heat diffuses from an element of volume in its passage from the bottom of the mantle to the top must be such as to lower its temperature by an amount of the order of T. Let κ denote the mean thermal diffusivity of the mantle. Then the time scale of the conduction process, in a frame moving with the element, is of the order of d^2/κ. Thus we have $d^2/\kappa \doteq d/v$, since this is the time taken for the element to cross the mantle; hence

$$v \doteq \kappa/d \tag{2}$$

Combining (1) and (2), we find

$$R \equiv g\alpha T d^3/\kappa v \doteq 1 \tag{3}$$

The quantity R defined in (3) is termed the *Rayleigh number*, and a more precise analysis indicates that our rough argument requires some quantitative modification: convection currents cannot set in until the Rayleigh number exceeds a critical value, R_c, of the order of 10^3. It seems that, in place of (2), we should then write

$$v \doteq 10^3 \kappa/d \tag{4}$$

The value of κ for the mantle has been estimated [11, 12] to be of the order of 4×10^{-3} cm²/sec. Thus (4) gives $v \doteq 0 \cdot 4$ cm/year, a figure close to that of 1 cm/year estimated earlier. Moreover, taking α to be of the order of $2 \times 10^{-5}/°$C [13, p. 265], g (which does not vary much in the mantle; see [10, p. 161]) to be 10^3 cm/sec², and T to be 1°C, (1) gives $v \doteq 5 \times 10^{22}$ cm²/sec, a figure not far from that given by the analysis of the Fennoscandian uplift. The value of v in the mantle may well be less than this as, indeed, is suggested by the analysis of the variation in latitude [14], and it must be remembered in this connection that the temperature of much of the mantle may not be far below its melting point. If the viscosity is, indeed, much less than 5×10^{22} cm²/sec, the convection that will occur will be far from the marginal state (i.e. from the critical state $R = R_c$ in which convective perturbations of the conduction solution for the heat transport neither decay nor increase in amplitude (see Section II below). In this case many convection modes will be excited and, in particular, modes for $m = 1$ may appear, and these will produce a polar wandering. Nevertheless, in what follows we study the marginal state only, since otherwise some non-linearities introduced into the analysis would be analytically troublesome. In Section II we set up the basic mathematical apparatus and in Section III we present a variational principle which follows from it. Although the Coriolis force, as measured by the *Taylor number*

$$T_a = \lambda^2 = (2\Omega a^2/v)^2 \tag{5}$$

is likely to be small, we include rotational effects in the analysis. (In (5), Ω denotes the angular velocity of the earth, and a the outer radius of the earth. Even for $\nu = 10^{16}$ cm^2/sec, for example, λ is only 6×10^{-3}.) If we set λ zero, we recover the results of the earlier analysis [6] by Chandrasekhar. Some other results are of interest. It is shown that, for small but non-zero λ and any one particular harmonic number, the axially symmetric mode is convectionally excited more readily than the unsymmetrical modes. The unsymmetrical modes when marginally excited are overstable, although the period of the overstability is extremely large if λ is small. The manner in which the instability of the symmetric modes is affected by the rotation is calculated for small values of λ.

II. THE MATHEMATICAL STABILITY PROBLEM

In view of the discussion of Section I, we shall select the following theoretical model: we shall represent the earth's core by a homogeneous inviscid fluid sphere of radius $\eta a (\eta < 1)$; the earth's mantle by a spherical shell of homogeneous viscous fluid of outer radius a and inner radius ηa. We shall suppose* that there is a uniform distribution of heat sources throughout, which, in the absence of conduction, would cause the temperature, Θ, at each point within the earth to rise at the rate ϵ. Initially we imagine that the whole system is in equilibrium; mechanically under its own gravitation, thermally by the conduction of heat from its interior to its surface (which is thought of as maintained at a constant temperature by the radiation into space of the heat conducted from within). We examine the stability of this conduction solution, i.e. we suppose that the equilibrium is disturbed in some way and that, as a result, the mantle moves with velocity $\boldsymbol{u}$, and that the pressure p, density ρ, and temperature Θ assume values which are slightly different from the values p_0, ρ_0 and Θ_0 appropriate to the conduction solution. We exclude all discussion of the state of the core, and simply assume that the temperature at the core–mantle interface is always maintained at the value appropriate to the conduction solution. It is, in any case, clear that since no significant stress acts across the core-mantle interface, the mechanical state of the core does not influence that of the mantle. If the amplitude of the disturbance we have superimposed on the conduction solution decreases with time, we may presume that conduction is an adequate mechanism for removing the heat from the interior of the earth, and that convection will not occur. If, however, the disturbance increases with time, convection will occur.

---

* Footnote added in proof: since writing this article, further studies of thermal instabilities in a spherical shell have been published by Chandrasekhar [22; see particularly §60]. These deal elegantly with more general thermal excitations than the case ε = constant considered herein.

In actual fact, of course, the amplitude will only increase until such time as the non-linear terms become sufficiently potent to bring the convection into a steady state. In the marginal state, which separates these two possibilities, the amplitude of the disturbance neither increases nor decreases in time. However, there are still two possibilities. First, the principle of exchange of stabilities may hold, i.e. not only may the amplitude of the disturbance remain constant in the marginal state, but also the disturbance itself may remain constant, e.g. $\partial u/\partial t = 0$. Second, the principle of exchange of stabilities may be invalid, but instead overstability may occur, i.e. the disturbance may vary periodically with time, e.g. $u = \mathcal{R}(u_1 e^{ipt})$, where u_1 is independent of time. We will find that, in the absence of rotational effects, the principle of exchange of stabilities will hold, but that, if Coriolis forces are included, overstability can occur.

The equations governing our theoretical model are:

the equation of heat conduction in a form suitable for material in motion

$$\left[\frac{d}{dt} - \kappa\nabla^2\right]\Theta = \epsilon \tag{6}$$

the Navier-Stokes equation

$$\left[\frac{d}{dt} - \nu\nabla^2\right]u = -\frac{1}{\rho} \, grad \, p + grad \, V \tag{7}$$

the equation of continuity

$$div \, u = -\frac{1}{\rho}\frac{d\rho}{dt} \tag{8}$$

and a linear expansion of the equation of state

$$\rho = \rho_c(1 - \alpha\Theta + \kappa p) \tag{9}$$

which is valid provided $\alpha\Theta \ll 1$. In these equations, ρ denotes the density of the mantle at temperature Θ; ρ_c is the density at $\Theta = 0$ which, for convenience, we will take to be at the top of the mantle; α is the coefficient of volume expansion; κ is the thermal diffusivity of the mantle; ν is the viscosity of the mantle and V is the gravitational potential (and is a function of position alone, the variations in V due to the convection itself being, of course, negligible). d/dt denotes differentiation with respect to time following the motion. The pressure p includes small viscous contributions of order $\nu\rho \, div \, u$.

The conduction solution to equations (6) to (9) is

$$\Theta_0 = \epsilon(a^2 - r^2)/6\kappa \tag{10}$$

where

$$0 = -grad\ p_0 + \rho_0\ grad\ V \tag{11}$$

and

$$\rho_0 = \rho_c(1 - \alpha\Theta + \kappa p)_0 \tag{12}$$

According to (10), the temperature difference across the mantle in excess of the adiabatic value is approximately

$$T = \epsilon a^2(1 - \eta^2)/6\kappa \tag{13}$$

Since we have assumed the mantle is uniform in composition, the gravitational field therein is

$$\partial V/\partial x_i = -gx_i/a \tag{14}$$

where g is the acceleration due to gravity at the earth's surface, and x_i is the radius vector from the geocentre.

In examining the stability of the conduction solution to infinitesimal perturbations, we adopt the usual perturbation procedure of writing

$$p = p_0 + p_1, \quad \Theta = \Theta_0 + \Theta_1, \quad \rho = \rho_0 + \rho_1 \tag{15}$$

and neglecting squares and products of u, p_1, Θ_1, ρ_1. Adopting Rayleigh's approximation [15], which can be justified in the manner described by Jeffreys [16],* the following linear equations obtain:

$$\left(\omega\frac{\partial}{\partial t} - \nabla^2\right)F = Rx_iu_i \tag{16}$$

$$\left(\frac{\partial}{\partial t} - \nabla^2\right)u + 2\lambda 1_z \times u = -\ grad\ \varpi + Fx \tag{17}$$

$$div\ u = 0 \tag{18}$$

Here 1_z is a unit vector drawn parallel to the axis of rotation, i.e. the geographical axis; $\varpi = p/\rho_c$; $\omega = \nu/\kappa$ is the Prandtl number; $\lambda = 2\Omega a^2/\nu$ is the square root of the Taylor number; R is the Rayleigh number given by

$$R = g\alpha\epsilon a^5/3\kappa^2\nu = 2g\alpha Ta^3/\kappa\nu(1 - \eta^2) \tag{19}$$

and

$$F = g\alpha a^3\nu^{-2}\Theta_1 \tag{20}$$

* Jeffreys shows that, provided compressibility effects are properly allowed for in the conduction solution, the effect of changes in pressure upon the perturbation in density may be omitted in the equation of state (9), and elsewhere. However, the perturbations in Θ and p must then, of course, be measured from the adiabatic values appropriate to the depth considered.

In deriving the equations (16) to (18), non-dimensional units of length and time (based on a and a^2/ν, respectively), have been adopted. The outer and inner radii of the mantle are, in these units, 1 and η, respectively.

According to (18), we may express $\boldsymbol{u}$ in the form

$$\boldsymbol{u} = curl\ Z\boldsymbol{x} + curl^2\ W\boldsymbol{x} \tag{21}$$

where $curl\ Z\boldsymbol{x}$ and $curl^2\ W\boldsymbol{x}$ are called, respectively, the toroidal and poloidal components of $\boldsymbol{u}$. On adopting spherical polar co-ordinates $(r,\ \theta,\ \varphi)$ with $\boldsymbol{1}_z$ as axis, we find [17] that equations (16) and (17) imply

$$\left(\nabla^2 - \omega\frac{\partial}{\partial t}\right)F = -\mathrm{R}L^2W \tag{22}$$

$$\nabla^2\left(\nabla^2L - \frac{\partial}{\partial t}L^2 + \lambda\frac{\partial}{\partial\varphi}\right)W + \lambda\Phi^3Z = L^2F \tag{23}$$

$$\left(\nabla^2L^2 - \frac{\partial}{\partial t}L^2 + \lambda\frac{\partial}{\partial\varphi}\right)Z - \lambda\Phi^3W = 0 \tag{24}$$

where L^2 and Φ^3 are operators which commute with ∇^2 (but not with each other), and are defined by

$$L^2 = -\left[\frac{1}{\sin\theta}\frac{\partial}{\partial\theta}\left(\sin\theta\frac{\partial}{\partial\theta}\right) + \frac{1}{\sin^2\theta}\frac{\partial^2}{\partial\varphi^2}\right] \tag{25}$$

$$\Phi^3 = \frac{\partial}{\partial z} - \frac{1}{2}\left(L^2\frac{\partial}{\partial z} + \frac{\partial}{\partial z}L^2\right) \tag{26}$$

We examine solutions of (22) to (24) of the form

$$F,\ Z,\ W \propto exp(im\varphi + ipt) \tag{27}$$

Here p is the frequency of overstability, and may be set equal to zero when the principle of exchange of stabilities is valid; m may be set to zero when we examine modes of convection which are symmetric about the axis of rotation. On assuming (27), (22) to (24) give

$$(\nabla^2 - ip\omega)F = -\mathrm{R}L^2W \tag{28}$$

$$\nabla^2[\nabla^2L^2 + i(m\lambda - pL^2)]W + \lambda\Phi^3Z = L^2F \tag{29}$$

$$[\nabla^2L^2 + i(m\lambda - pL^2)]Z - \lambda\Phi^3W = 0 \tag{30}$$

These are the basic equations of our study. The solutions we obtain must also satisfy the boundary conditions that the temperature at the top and bottom of the mantle are the same as for the conduction solution (i.e. $\Theta = \Theta_0$ thereat), and that no mechanical stress acts across these two surfaces. These conditions require that

$$F = 0, \quad W = 0, \quad \partial^2 W/\partial r^2 = 0, \quad \partial(Z/r)/\partial r = 0 \tag{31}$$

$$\text{at } r = 1 \text{ and } r = \eta.$$

III. Solution of the Stability Problem

There are several ways in which equations (28) to (30) may be solved formally. The method we will adopt is based on a variational principle which itself stems from the equality in the rates at which, in the marginal state, buoyancy forces do work and at which viscosity degrades ordered energy to heat:

"Let W be determined from F and Z by means of equation (29) and the boundary conditions $W = \partial^2 W/\partial r^2 = 0$ at $r = 1, \eta$. Let R be determined from these values of W, F and Z by

$$\frac{1}{R} \int \left\{ [grad \ F]^2 + ip\omega F^2 \right\} d\tau = \int \left\{ (\nabla^2 W) L^2 (\nabla^2 W) \right.$$

$$+ (grad \ Z) \cdot (grad \ L^2 Z) + i[grad \ W \cdot grad \ i(pL^2 - m\lambda)W]$$

$$+ Zi(pL^2 - m\lambda)Z \right\} d\tau - \int \left[\frac{\partial W}{\partial r} L^2 \frac{\partial W}{\partial r} + ZL^2 Z \right] \frac{dS}{r} \tag{32}$$

where the integration $d\tau$ is over the volume of the mantle, and the integration dS is over the upper and lower surfaces of the mantle (dS taken positive for the upper surface $r = 1$ and negative for the lower surface $r = \eta$). Then, if F and Z are zero at each bounding surface and are such that δR is zero for all independent first-order variations δF and δZ in F and Z, then equations (28) and (30) are satisfied."

We shall not enter into the proof, which is fairly straightforward (see [6], [18], for example).

We shall first discuss the case $\eta = 0$, i.e. convection in a sphere. Any function F which vanishes at $r = 1$ can be expanded in the form

$$F = \sum_{n=m}^{\infty} \sum_{i=1}^{\infty} f_{ni} r^{-1/2} J_{n+1/2}(\alpha_{ni} r) P_n^m(\cos \theta) \tag{33}$$

where $\alpha_{n1}, \alpha_{n2}, \alpha_{n3}, \dots$ are the (positive) roots of

$$J_{n+1/2}(\alpha_{ni}) = 0 \tag{34}$$

In the non-rotating case, the problem is completely separable among the different Legendre polynomials P_n^m (and, of course, the final result is independent of m). Also, in this case a good approximation for R can, as Chandrasekhar [18] has shown, be obtained by including in F the first term of the series (33) only. In the rotating case, the work of Bisshopp [19] indicates that here also, provided λ is of order 10^2 or less, the first term of the series is an adequate approximation to F. We assume, therefore, that λ is so small that we need only work to order λ^2 and that we may take

$$F = r^{-1/2}J_{n+1/2}(\alpha_n r)P_n^m(\cos\theta) \tag{35}$$

as a trial function for F in the variational principle. (For simplicity we here, and henceforth, omit the suffix 1 from α_{n1}.)

In a like manner, we assume for a trial function for Z the form

$$Z = Cr^{-1/2}[\alpha_{n-1}rJ'_{n-1/2}(\alpha_{n-1}r) + 3J_{n-1/2}(\alpha_{n-1}r)/2]P_{n-1}^m(\cos\theta)$$

$$+ Dr^{-1/2}[\alpha_{n+1}rJ'_{n+3/2}(\alpha_{n+1}r) + 3J_{n+3/2}(\alpha_{n+1}r)/2]P_{n+1}^m(\cos\theta) \tag{36}$$

(and adopt the convention $P_{m-1}^m = 0$). By (35), the choice (36) automatically satisfies the requirement that $\partial Z/\partial r = Z/r$, at $r = 1$. We find that $L^2P_n^m = n(n+1)P_n^m$, and that

$$\Phi^3 Z = \left[\frac{(n-1)n(n-m)\alpha_{n-1}C}{(2n-1)r^{1/2}}\left\{\alpha_{n-1}rJ'_{n+1/2}(\alpha_{n-1}r) + \frac{5}{2}J_{n+1/2}(\alpha_{n-1}r)\right\}\right.$$

$$- \frac{n(n+1)(n+m+2)\alpha_{n+1}D}{(2n+3)r^{1/2}}\left\{\alpha_{n+1}rJ'_{n+1/2}(\alpha_{n+1}r)\right.$$

$$\left.\left. + \frac{5}{2}J_{n+1/2}(\alpha_{n+1}r)\right\}\right]P_n^m(\cos\theta) \tag{37}$$

$$+\left(\begin{array}{l}\text{terms in } P_{n+2}^m \text{ and } P_{n-2}^m \text{ which make no contribution to the order}\\ \text{to which we are working.}\end{array}\right)$$

Solving (29), we find

$$W = \left[B_1 r^n + B_2 r^{-1/2}J_{n+1/2}(\xi_n r) + \frac{1}{\alpha_n^2(\alpha_n^2 - \xi_n^2)}J_{n+1/2}(\alpha_n r)\right.$$

$$- \frac{(n-1)\lambda C}{(2n-1)\alpha_{n-1}^3 r^{1/2}}\left\{\alpha_{n-1}rJ'_{n+1/2}(\alpha_{n-1}r) - \frac{3}{2}J_{n+1/2}(\alpha_{n-1}r)\right\}$$

$$\left. + \frac{(n+2)\lambda D}{(2n+3)\alpha_{n+1}^3 r^{1/2}}\left\{\alpha_{n+1}rJ'_{n+1/2}(\alpha_{n+1}r) - \frac{3}{2}J_{n+1/2}(\alpha_{n+1}r)\right\}\right]P_n^m(\cos\theta) \tag{38}$$

where

$$\xi_n^2 = -i[p - m\lambda/n(n+1)] \tag{39}$$

and B_1 and B_2 are determined by the requirement that W and $\partial^2 W/\partial r^2$ must vanish on $r = 1$.

If we work to zero order in λ, we quickly recover from (32) Chandrasekhar's first approximation for R [18]:

$$\frac{1}{R_n} = \frac{n(n+1)}{\alpha_n^6}\left(1 + \frac{4(2n+3)}{\alpha_n(2n+1)}\right) \tag{40}$$

This result remains true when we work to first order in λ, but the condition that R_n is real, namely

$$\left[p(\omega+1) - \frac{m\lambda}{n(n+1)}\right]\left[1 + \frac{(2n+1)\alpha_n^2}{4(2n+3)}\right]$$

$$= \left[p - \frac{m\lambda}{n(n+1)}\right]\left[1 + \frac{2\alpha_n^2}{(2n+1)(2n+3)(2n+5)}\right] \tag{41}$$

determines p to first order in λ, and, since ω is indubitably very large for the mantle, it gives

$$p\omega = \frac{m\lambda}{n(n+1)}\left[1 - \frac{8}{(2n+1)^2(2n+5)}\right]\Big/\left[1 + \frac{4(2n+3)}{\alpha_n^2(2n+1)}\right] \tag{42}$$

When we work to second order in λ^2 we need to determine C and D, both of which are of first order in λ.

The best values of C and D are those for which the value of R given by (32) assumes an extreme value with respect to independent variations of C and D; i.e. for which $\partial R/\partial C$ and $\partial R/\partial D$ vanish. It transpires that these values of C and D are independent of m to first order in λ:

$$\frac{\alpha_{n-1}J'_{n-1/2}(\alpha_{n-1})}{\alpha_n J'_{n+1/2}(\alpha_n)}\cdot\frac{C}{\lambda} = -\frac{6(n+1)}{(2n+1)}\left[\frac{n}{\alpha_{n-1}^2(\alpha_n^2-\alpha_{n-1}^2)^2} - \frac{(n+2)}{\alpha_n^2(\alpha_n^2-\alpha_{n-1}^2)^2}\right.$$

$$\left. - \frac{(n+2)(2n+3)}{(2n+1)\alpha_n^4\alpha_{n-1}^2} + \frac{2(n+2)(2n+3)}{\alpha_n^4\alpha_{n-1}^4}\right]$$

$$\times [\alpha_{n-1}^2 - n^2 + n + 3/2]^{-1} \tag{43}$$

$$\frac{\alpha_{n+1}J'_{n+3/2}(\alpha_{n+1})}{\alpha_n J'_{n+1/2}(\alpha_n)}\cdot\frac{D}{\lambda} = \frac{6n}{(2n+1)}\left[\frac{(n+1)}{\alpha_{n+1}^2(\alpha_{n+1}^2-\alpha_n^2)^2}\right.$$

$$\left. - \frac{(n-1)}{\alpha_n^2(\alpha_{n+1}^2-\alpha_n^2)^2} - \frac{(n-1)(2n+3)}{(2n+1)\alpha_n^4\alpha_{n+1}^2}\right]$$

$$\times [\alpha_{n+1}^2 - n^2 - 3n - 1/2]^{-1} \tag{44}$$

On substituting these values for C and D in (32) we find that p is given to order λ^2 by (41), and that (for large ω)

$$\frac{1}{R_{nm}} = \frac{n(n+1)}{\alpha_n^6}\left(1 + \frac{4(2n+3)}{\alpha_n^2(2n+1)}\right) - \frac{m^2\lambda^2}{n(n+1)\alpha_n^{10}}\left[1 + \frac{16}{(2n+1)^2(2n+5)}\right.$$

$$\left. + \frac{12(2n+3)}{\alpha_n^2(2n+1)} + \frac{32(n+2)\alpha_n^2}{(2n+1)^3(2n+5)^2(2n+7)}\right]$$

$$- \frac{n(n-1)(2n+1)}{3(2n-1)}\left[\alpha_{n-1}^2 - n^2 + n + \frac{3}{2}\right]\left[\frac{\alpha_{n-1}J'_{n-1/2}(\alpha_{n-1})}{\alpha_n J'_{n+1/2}(\alpha_n)}\right]^2 C^2$$

$$- \frac{(n+1)(n+2)(2n+1)}{3(2n+3)}\left[\alpha_{n+1}^2 - n^2 - 3n - \frac{1}{2}\right]$$

$$\left[\frac{\alpha_{n+1}J'_{n+3/2}(\alpha_{n+1})}{\alpha_n J'_{n+1/2}(\alpha_n)}\right]^2 D^2 \qquad (45)$$

where C and D are given by (43) and (44).

Two conclusions may be drawn immediately from (45): first, this expression for R_{nm} proves that, at least for small angular velocities, rotation tends to inhibit the onset of convection. Further, it is evident that, for given n, the modes least affected by Coriolis forces are those of zero m, i.e. convection patterns which are axisymmetric about the geographical axis. For zero λ, the value of R_{nm} is, of course, independent of m, or, in the language of quantum theory, the n level has a $(2n+1)$ fold degeneracy. Rotation has the effect of splitting this degeneracy into $(n+1)$ distinct levels, one of which is a singlet and the remainder of which are doublet levels. In Fig. 1, the values* of R_{nm} as a function of $T_a = \lambda^2$ are shown for small values of λ^2, and for $n = 1$ to $n = 5$.

We continue our discussion with the case $\eta \neq 0$, i.e. we no longer consider the earth's early history when the radius of the core may have been small, but return to the question of convection in the mantle in

---

* It may be noticed that the values obtained for $m = 0$ do not agree very closely with those obtained by Bisshopp [19]. In view of this, the present authors have rederived (45) by another method, and have also made the analogous calculation for a sphere with a "rigid" boundary (i.e. on which $F = W = \partial W/\partial r = Z = 0$). Here the agreement with Bisshopp's calculations is good. The present authors feel that, if the calculation presented here is inaccurate, it must in some way be due to the selection of (36) as trial function for Z. S. K. Trehan has informed us that he has been engaged in some calculations for the case $p = 0$, $m = 0$, $\eta \neq 0$. He has expanded W in a series each of whose terms automatically satisfies the four boundary conditions. He then solves equations (28) and (30) exactly for F and Z, and substitutes the results into equation (29), thereby determining the coefficients in the expansion for W and also the value of R as a function of T_a. His calculations, when completed, should throw light on the discrepancy between our results and those of Bisshopp, for the case $\eta = 0$.

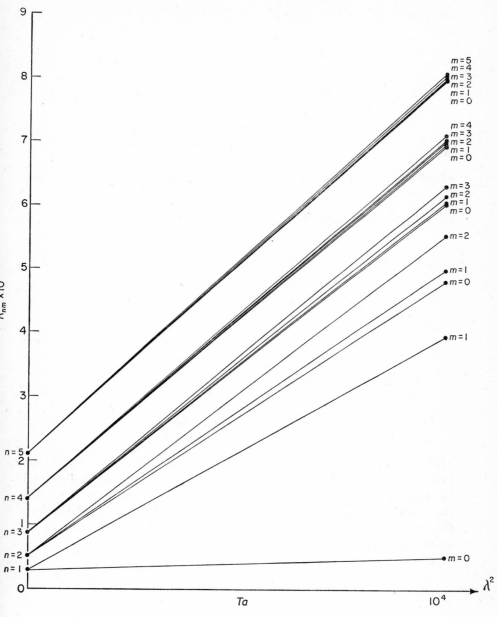

Fig. 1.

more recent times. We replace the trial functions (35) and (36) by

$$F = r^{-1/2}\mathscr{C}_{n+1/2}(\alpha_n r)P_n^m(\cos\theta) \tag{46}$$

$$\mathbf{Z} = \mathbf{C}r^{-1/2}[\alpha_{n-1}r\mathscr{C}'_{n-1/2}(\alpha_{n-1}r) + 3\mathscr{C}_{n-1/2}(\alpha_{n-1}r)/2]P_{n-1}^m(\cos\theta)$$

$$+ \mathbf{D}r^{-1/2}[\alpha_{n+1}r\mathscr{C}'_{n+3/2}(\alpha_{n+1}r) + 3\mathscr{C}_{n+3/2}(\alpha_{n+1}r)/2]P_{n+1}^m(\cos\theta) \tag{47}$$

where $\mathscr{C}_{n+1/2}(\alpha_n r)$ is a cylinder function which vanishes at $r = 1$ and

$r = \eta$ (and has no zeros for $\eta < r < 1$). We take

$$\mathscr{C}_{n+1/2}(\alpha_n r) = J_{-n-1/2}(\alpha_n\eta)J_{n+1/2}(\alpha_n r) - J_{n+1/2}(\alpha_n\eta)J_{-n-1/2}(\alpha_n r) \tag{48}$$

where α_n is the smallest positive root of

$$0 = J_{-n-1/2}(\alpha_n\eta)J_{n+1/2}(\alpha_n) - J_{n+1/2}(\alpha_n\eta)J_{-n-1/2}(\alpha_n) \tag{49}$$

[cf. 6 and 20]. For brevity, we define q_n by

$$q_n = J_{n+1/2}(\alpha_n\eta)/J_{n+1/2}(\alpha_n) = J_{-n-1/2}(\alpha_n\eta)/J_{-n-1/2}(\alpha_n) \tag{50}$$

The analysis is much as before, although the expression corresponding to (38) now involves four constants B_1, B_2, B_3, B_4, which are determined by the four conditions W must satisfy at $r = \eta$ and $r = 1$. Again the modes for which $m \neq 0$ are less easily excited in convection than the axisymmetric modes $m = 0$. If we work to zero order in λ, we quickly recover Chandrasekhar's result [6]:

$$\frac{1}{R_n} = \frac{n(n+1)}{\alpha_n^6(q_n^2 - 1)}\left[(q_n^2 - 1) + \frac{4(2n+3)(q_n - \eta^{n+1/2})^2}{\alpha_n^2(2n+1)(1 - \eta^{2n+3})}\right.$$

$$\left. - \frac{4(2n-1)}{\alpha_n^2(2n+1)}\frac{(q_n - \eta^{-n-1/2})^2}{(\eta^{-2n+1} - 1)}\right] \tag{51}$$

For $m = 0$, we find, on working to second order in λ

$$\frac{1}{R_n} = \frac{n(n+1)}{\alpha_n^6(q_n^2-1)}\left[(q_n^2-1) + \frac{4(2n+3)(q_n-\eta^{n+1/2})^2}{\alpha_n^2(2n+1)(1-\eta^{2n+3})}\right.$$

$$\left. -\frac{4(2n-1)}{\alpha_n^2(2n+1)}\frac{(q_n-\eta^{-n-1/2})^2}{(\eta^{-2n+1}-1)}\right] - \frac{n(n-1)(2n+1)}{3(2n-1)(q_n^2-1)}$$

$$\left[\alpha_{n-1}^2(q_{n-1}^2-\eta^2) - \left(n^2-n-\frac{3}{2}\right)(q_{n-1}^2-1)\right]C^2$$

$$-\frac{(n+1)(n+2)(2n+1)}{3(2n+3)(q_n^2-1)}\left[\alpha_{n+1}^2(q_{n+1}^2-\eta^2)\right.$$

$$\left. - \left(n^2+3n+\frac{1}{2}\right)(q_{n+1}^2-1)\right]D^2 \tag{52}$$

where

$$\frac{C}{\lambda}\left[\alpha_{n-1}^2(q_{n-1}^2-\eta^2) - \left(n^2-n-\frac{3}{2}\right)(q_{n-1}^2-1)\right]$$

$$= \frac{6(n+1)}{(2n+1)}\left[\left\{\frac{n}{\alpha_{n-1}^2(\alpha_n^2-\alpha_{n-1}^2)^2} - \frac{(n+2)}{\alpha_n^2(\alpha_n^2-\alpha_{n-1}^2)^2}\right\}(q_nq_{n-1}-\eta^{-1})\right.$$

$$-\frac{(n+2)}{(2n+1)\alpha_n^4\alpha_{n-1}^2}\left\{(2n+3)\frac{(q_n-\eta^{n+1/2})(q_{n-1}-\eta^{n+3/2})}{(1-\eta^{2n+3})}\right.$$

$$\left. - (2n-1)\frac{(q_n-\eta^{-n-1/2})(q_{n-1}-\eta^{-n+1/2})}{(\eta^{-2n+1}-1)}\right\}$$

$$\left. + \frac{2(n+2)(2n+3)}{\alpha_n^4\alpha_{n-1}^4}\frac{(q_n-\eta^{n+1/2})(q_{n-1}-\eta^{n-1/2})}{(1-\eta^{2n+3})}\right] \tag{53}$$

and

$$\frac{D}{\lambda}\left[\alpha_{n+1}^2(q_{n+1}^2-\eta^2) - \left(n^2+3n+\frac{1}{2}\right)(q_{n+1}^2-1)\right]$$

$$= -\frac{6n}{(2n+1)}\left[\left\{\frac{(n+1)}{\alpha_{n+1}^2(\alpha_{n+1}^2-\alpha_n^2)^2} - \frac{(n-1)}{\alpha_n^2(\alpha_{n+1}^2-\alpha_n^2)^2}\right\}(q_nq_{n+1}-\eta^{-1})\right.$$

$$-\frac{(n-1)}{(2n+1)\alpha_n^4\alpha_{n+1}^2}\left\{(2n+3)\frac{(q_n-\eta^{n+1/2})(q_{n+1}-\eta^{n+3/2})}{(1-\eta^{2n+3})}\right.$$

$$- (2n - 1) \left. \frac{(q_n - \eta^{-n-1/2})(q_{n+1} - \eta^{-n+1/2})}{(\eta^{-2n+1} - 1)} \right\}$$

$$+ \frac{2(n - 1)(2n - 1)}{\alpha_n^4 \alpha_{n+1}^4} \left. \frac{(q_n - \eta^{-n-1/2})(q_{n+1} - \eta^{-n-3/2})}{(\eta^{-2n+1} - 1)} \right] \tag{54}$$

We may write (52) in the form

$$R = R_n{}^\circ + T_a(\partial R_n/\partial T_a)^\circ \tag{55}$$

these being the first two terms in a Taylor expansion of R as a function of T_a. In Table 1, $R_n{}^\circ$ and $(\partial R_n/\partial T_a)^\circ$ are tabulated for different values of n and for $\eta = 0\cdot2, 0\cdot3, 0\cdot4, 0\cdot5, 0\cdot6, 0\cdot8$. The entries for $R_n{}^\circ$ are essentially due to Chandrasekhar [6].

TABLE 1

n	$\eta = 0\cdot2$		$\eta = 0\cdot3$		$\eta = 0\cdot4$	
	$R_n{}^\circ$	$(\partial R_n/\partial T_a)^\circ$	$R_n{}^\circ$	$(\partial R_n/\partial T_a)^\circ$	$R_n{}^\circ$	$(\partial R_n/\partial T_a)^\circ$
1	$5.216\ 10^3$	0.522	$8.503\ 10^3$	0.956	$1.682\ 10^4$	1.694
2	$5.708\ 10^3$	1.431	$7.113\ 10^3$	1.584	$1.091\ 10^4$	1.970
3	$8.882\ 10^3$	0.926	$9.552\ 10^3$	0.987	$1.196\ 10^4$	1.169
4	$1.400\ 10^4$	0.657	$1.428\ 10^4$	0.679	$1.585\ 10^4$	0.771
5			$2.131\ 10^4$	0.513	$2.227\ 10^4$	0.557
6					$3.143\ 10^4$	0.433

n	$\eta = 0\cdot5$		$\eta = 0\cdot6$		$\eta = 0\cdot8$	
	$R_n{}^\circ$	$(\partial R_n/\partial T_a)^\circ$	$R_n{}^\circ$	$(\partial R_n/\partial T_a)^\circ$	$R_n{}^\circ$	$(\partial R_n/\partial T_a)^\circ$
1	$4.188\ 10^4$	2.943	$1.403\ 10^5$	5.224	$7.789\ 10^6$	23.938
2	$2.181\ 10^4$	2.746	$6.133\ 10^4$	4.280	$2.753\ 10^6$	17.464
3	$1.924\ 10^4$	1.569	$4.424\ 10^4$	2.384	$1.500\ 10^6$	9.519
4	$2.146\ 10^4$	1.002	$4.076\ 10^4$	1.497	$1.005\ 10^6$	5.902
5	$2.673\ 10^4$	0.699	$4.313\ 10^4$	1.026	$7.656\ 10^5$	3.994
6	$3.492\ 10^4$	0.520	$4.945\ 10^4$	0.748	$6.368\ 10^5$	2.877
7	$4.629\ 10^4$	0.408	$5.933\ 10^4$	0.571	$5.651\ 10^5$	2.172
8	$6.125\ 10^4$	0.335	$7.292\ 10^4$	0.452	$5.270\ 10^5$	1.696
9	$8.027\ 10^4$	0.284	$9.057\ 10^4$	0.369	$5.109\ 10^5$	1.361
10	$1.039\ 10^5$	0.247	$1.128\ 10^5$	0.309	$5.104\ 10^5$	1.115
11	$1.325\ 10^5$	0.220	$1.401\ 10^5$	0.265	$5.223\ 10^5$	0.931
12	$1.669\ 10^5$	0.200	$1.732\ 10^5$	0.231	$5.448\ 10^5$	0.790
13	$2.074\ 10^5$	0.183	$2.126\ 10^5$	0.206	$5.767\ 10^5$	0.679
14	$2.549\ 10^5$	0.170	$2.590\ 10^5$	0.185	$6.178\ 10^5$	0.589

It is evident from the table that, as the thickness of the mantle decreases, the pattern of convection at marginal stability moves progressively to harmonics of higher orders. This is also illustrated in Fig. 2, where the order of the harmonic which is most readily excited in convection is plotted as a function of η. For the present configuration of core and mantle ($\eta \doteqdot 0\cdot55$) it is evident that the harmonics of order 3 are most readily excited, and those of order 4 and 5 at only slightly larger Rayleigh numbers. This is some confirmation of the suggestion [21] of Vening Meinesz that Prey's discovery [7] of the importance of harmonics 3, 4 and 5 in the analysis of the earth's topography may be a consequence of convection in the mantle. (It also confirms the order of magnitude arguments of Section I.)

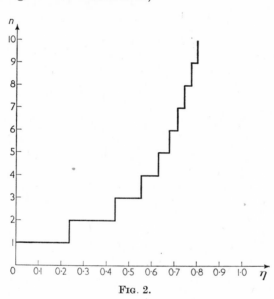

FIG. 2.

This research was supported in part by a special grant awarded by D.S.I.R. We are grateful to F. H. Chamalaun for criticizing an earlier draft of this paper.

References

1. COLLINSON, D. W., AND RUNCORN, S. K., *Bull. geol. Soc. Amer.* **71**, 915 (1960).
2. IRVING, E., AND GREEN, R., *Mon. Not. R. astr. Soc. geophys. Suppl.* **7**, 347 (1957).
3. CLEGG, J. A., DEUTSCH, E. R., AND GRIFFITHS, D. H., *Phil. Mag.* (Ser. 8), **1**, 419 (1956).
4. RUNCORN, S. K., *Quart. J. R. met. Soc.* **87**, 282 (1961).
5. HILL, M. L., AND DIBBLEE, T. W., *Bull. geol. Soc. Amer.* **64**, 443 (1953).
6. CHANDRASEKHAR, S., *Phil. Mag.* (Ser. 7), **44**, 233 and 1129 (1953).

7. PREY, A., *Abh. Ges. Wiss. Math. Phys. Kl.* (Göttingen), **11**, 1 (1922).
8. RUNCORN, S. K., *Nature, Lond.* **193**, 311 (1962).
9. UREY, H. C., "The Planets: their Origin and Development". Yale University Press, New Haven (1952).
10. JEFFREYS, H., "The Earth—its Origin, History and Physical Constitution". Cambridge University Press, London (1922).
11. GUTENBERG, B., *in* "Internal Constitution of the Earth". (B. Gutenberg, ed.) Dover, New York (1951).
12. VERHOOGEN, J., *in* "Physics and Chemistry of the Earth", Vol. 1. (L. H. Ahrens, K. Rankama, S. K. Runcorn, eds.) Pergamon Press, London (1956).
13. BIRCH, F., *J. geophys. Res.* **57**, 227 (1952).
14. MUNK, W. H., AND MACDONALD, G. J. F., "The Rotation of the Earth: a Geophysical Discussion". Cambridge University Press, London (1960).
15. RAYLEIGH, LORD, *Phil. Mag.* (Ser. 6), **32**, 529 (1916).
16. JEFFREYS, H., *Phil. Mag.* (Ser. 7), **2**, 833 (1926); *Proc. Camb. phil. Soc.*, **26**, 170 (1930); see also
    SPIEGEL, E. A., AND VERONIS, G., *Astrophys. J.* **131**, 442 (1960).
17. ROBERTS, P. H., *J. math. Anal. Appl.* **1**, 195 (1960).
18. CHANDRASEKHAR, S., *Phil. Mag.* (Ser. 7), **43**, 1317 (1952).
19. BISSHOPP, F. E., *Phil. Mag.* (Ser. 8), **3**, 1342 (1958).
20. CHANDRASEKHAR, S., AND ELBERT, D., *Proc. Camb. phil. Soc.* **49**, 446 (1953).
21. VENING MEINESZ, F. A., *Kon. Ned. Akad. Wetenschappen* (Amsterdam), (Ser. B), **54**, 212 and 220 (1951).
22. CHANDRASEKHAR, S., "Hydrodynamic and Hydromagnetic Stability". Clarendon Press, Oxford (1961).

Chapter 8

Mountain-Building Hypotheses

P. CHADWICK

I. Introduction 195
II. Facts to be Accounted for by Theories of Crustal Evolution . 198
    A. The Current State of the Earth's Crust . . . 198
    B. The Evolution of the Earth's Surface Features . . 207
III. Diastrophic Forces 212
    A. Rheology of the Earth's Crust and Outer Mantle . . 213
    B. Possible Force Mechanisms 216
IV. Mountain-Building Hypotheses 224
    A. Contraction and Expansion Hypotheses . . . 224
    B. Convection Hypotheses 227
    C. Crustal Displacement Hypotheses 230
    D. General Conclusions 230
    References 232

I. INTRODUCTION

F. D. Adams, writing in 1938 [1, p. 398], concluded a historical survey of the problem of mountain formation with the following remarks. "We cannot indeed but recognize that not only is the problem of the origin of mountain ranges still unsolved, but that toward the final elucidation of this subject geological science has made a less satisfactory advance than in many, if not in most, other directions." Since these words were written, the earth's surface features have been studied more intensively than ever before and much thought has been given to the processes by which they have evolved. But a deeper understanding has brought with it an increased awareness of the extreme difficulty and complexity of the subject, and the possibility of a final solution appears if anything to have receded.

The problem of the origin of mountains is, in a sense, the crux of the wider study of the evolution of the earth's crust, since any pattern of events leading to major changes of crustal structure would almost certainly entail the eventual formation of mountains. The scientific approach to this wider topic proceeds in two stages. Firstly, it is necessary to formulate the problem by collecting observations together and deducing from them the principal facts that have to be accounted for. Secondly, the diastrophic forces which have been responsible for the changing form of the earth's surface must be recognized and their mode of action understood; and it must then be demonstrated how these forces, operating throughout geological time, have led to the creation of the observed surface features. Neither of these complementary aspects of the problem of crustal development can, as yet, claim to be firmly established.

The facts requiring explanation are so numerous and so complex that they must be subjected to drastic simplification and condensed into a reasonably small number of general principles before any theoretical analysis can be attempted. To quote Scheidegger [2, p. 2], ". . . geology traditionally has been a descriptive science whose findings cannot easily be encompassed in numbers." Although the interpretation of observations made in specific parts of the world may be broadly agreed upon, attempts to arrive at conclusions of global validity may lead to "the inadvertent ignoring of unpleasant facts, and to the straining of others to fit preconceived ideas" [2, p. v]. A notable attempt to summarize a vast body of geological data has been made by Bucher [3] in his book "The Deformation of the Earth's Crust", but such a task is being made increasingly difficult by the wide diversity of the evidence bearing on crustal deformations which is constantly being discovered. Important findings are contributed by astronomy, geology, natural history, climatology, geochemistry and geophysics and it is now virtually impossible for one person to be competent to form a balanced assessment of the often contradictory results.

Recent geophysical exploration of the earth's crust has been directed in particular to the regions that are comparatively little known, notably the ocean basins and ridges, the continental margins and the Antarctic continent. These investigations are providing an increasingly detailed picture of the present state of the earth's crust, and further light has been shed on its past history by measurements of the radioactive and magnetic properties of rocks. The employment of radioactive dating methods in a study of the Canadian Shield has led Wilson [4, 5, 6] to elaborate a theory of the development of continents by the successive marginal addition of concentric mountain systems. This theory has brought about the unification of a vast number of previously uncorrelated results. Measurements of the magnetization of rocks suggest that the earth's axis of rotation has been moving relative to the crust at least since Pre-Cambrian times and that continental drift may also have occurred [7]. Such movements have long been indicated by palaeoclimatic studies but, in the apparent absence of forces capable of producing them, geophysicists have continued to doubt their reality. The evidence in favour of polar wandering has meanwhile prompted a re-examination of the assumptions upon which long-established geo-dynamical theories are based.

The root causes of diastrophic forces can, with some confidence, be limited to the heat, gravitational field and rotation of the earth, aided by sub-aerial erosion and by solar radiation, in so far as it affects physical conditions within the atmosphere. In seeking to understand how these enormous sources of energy bring deforming forces to bear on the earth's crust a proper appreciation of the rheological properties of the crust and outer mantle is essential. Until quite recently it was customary to apply the infinitesimal strain theory of elasticity to almost all geophysical problems involving the calculation of stresses and defor-mations. It is now realized that the bulk behaviour of the material forming the solid part of the earth depends upon the time scale of the particular process being studied and that, in particular, the elastic theory is appropriate only when, as in the propagation of seismic waves, the representative time interval is very small. During the last few years several of the simpler theories of idealized mechanical behaviour have found geophysical applications, and most present-day work on crustal dynamics invokes anelastic effects, usually those associated with viscoelasticity and viscoplasticity.

Due to the lack of precise information about the fundamental diastrophic forces, theories of crustal evolution can be constructed from a wide range of more or less plausible assumptions. For this reason theoretical work on the formation of mountains contains an element of speculation which is scarcely avoidable. Mathematical analysis is used in order to check the qualitative consequences of a given hypothesis against the salient facts to be accounted for, and since no theory has yet been found to be entirely satisfactory, as judged by these criteria, theoretical refinements are hardly justified.

The remainder of this chapter is arranged as follows. Section II gives a digest of the facts about the present state and past history of the earth's crust for which an explanation is sought. In Section III a summary of the rheological properties of the crust and outer mantle is followed by a discussion of possible diastrophic force mechanisms. Section IV contains an appraisal of the more promising mountain-building hypotheses at present under consideration. In surveying these alternative theories it should be borne in mind that, for the most part, they are not mutually exclusive. In this connection Eardley [8] has warned against "thinking that one single process or mechanism is operative, and that all the details either fit it or are ramifications of it;

surficial deformation in one place may be a manifestation of a different deep-seated process than in another''.

II. Facts to be Accounted for by Theories of Crustal Evolution

The outstanding properties of diastrophism to be accounted for are the distribution of its effects upon the earth's surface, the way in which these effects have varied in position and intensity during geological time and the characteristics of the major deformations and dislocations by which they are represented. Existing knowledge of these properties imposes conditions with which an adequate theory of crustal evolution must comply.

A. THE CURRENT STATE OF THE EARTH'S CRUST

1. *Structure of the Crust*

The usual geophysical definition of the earth's crust places its upper boundary at the earth's surface and its lower boundary at the *M-discontinuity*, a world-wide interface immediately below which the velocity of P waves has the uniform value 8·1 km/sec. The lower crustal boundary is thus a contact discontinuity, but it is not definitely known whether the observed change of mechanical properties arises from a change of chemical composition or from a phase transition.

Examination of the earth's surface shows that great elevations and depressions do not occur as isolated features but are confined to certain elongated areas of relatively small width which together account for only a small fraction of the total surface area. The broad, comparatively level expanses that cover the bulk of the earth's surface are of two types: continents and ocean basins. The continents represent the upraised portion of the earth's surface, their mean elevation above sealevel being 0·8 km; the average depth of the sea is 3·8 km [9, p. 11].

Seismic refraction and dispersion measurements and gravity surveys show that this hypsometric difference is associated with essential dissimilarities of crustal structure and composition. In continental areas a thin layer of non-uniformly distributed sediments is underlain by a thick crystalline basement the composition of which, on average, is intermediate between that of granite and basalt, and tends to become more basaltic with increasing depth. In certain areas there appears to be an upper granitic layer and a lower basaltic layer, but the interface between them (the so-called *Conrad discontinuity*) is not a universal feature of the continental crust, the detailed structure being one of considerable complexity [10]. The thickness of the crust in continental areas is variable, an average value being 35 km. The ocean basins consist of a superficial layer of sediments, the thickness of which may be as great as 1 km, resting on a layer of basic rock some 5 km thick and similar in composition to the rocks found near the base of the continental crust. The depth of the M-discontinuity beneath the oceanic

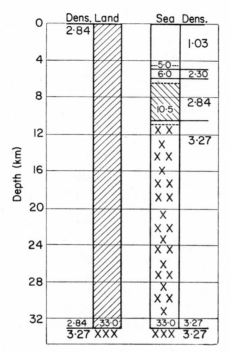

FIG. 1. Standard continental and oceanic crustal sections (after Worzel and Shurbet). Reproduced from [11] by permission of the Geological Society of America.

crust is thus about 10 km. The upper mantle underlying the M-discontinuity is believed to consist of ultrabasic material the composition of which does not differ significantly between continental and oceanic areas. Standard continental and oceanic crustal sections, prepared by Worzel and Shurbet [11], are reproduced in Fig. 1.

The long narrow belts that divide up the continents and ocean basins are broadly of three types: stable continental margins, mountain systems and ocean ridges. A generalized section across a stable continental margin is shown in Fig. 2. Belts of this type, which account for about 5 per cent of the total surface area of the earth, are seen to be characterized by a rapid change of crustal thickness, accompanied by pronounced curvature of the M-discontinuity, together with a considerable thickening of the sedimentary cover in the region where the continental and oceanic crustal segments merge together. These

H

borderlands form a natural depository for clastics eroded from the continental land masses and the accumulated thickness of sediments may be as great as 10 km. So far as is known these deposits are undeformed.

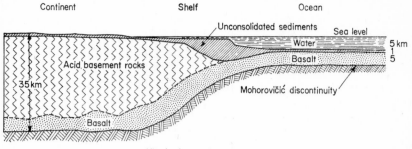

Fig. 2. Generalized section across a continental margin. Reproduced by permission from "The Earth as a Planet", edited by G. P. Kuiper, copyright, 1954, by The University of Chicago Press.

2. *The Active Belts*

The extended mountain formations of most recent age and the volcanic island arcs are observed to constitute a continuous system of narrow belts. As shown in Fig. 3, the pattern of these belts is very simple, consisting of a circum-Pacific ring and, joined on to it through the Philippine Islands and Celebes, a strip with virtually an east–west trend which includes the Himalayas, Caucasus and Alps, and terminates in the Canary Islands. The features situated within these belts exhibit wide variations of composition and structure. The island arcs are mainly volcanic in origin. Some major mountain systems consist predominantly of volcanic and plutonic rocks, while others have been formed by the intense deformation of thick sedimentary deposits. There are also deep offshore trenches following the trends of island arcs and continental mountain systems.

A study of the geographical distribution of earthquakes shows that the epicentres are strongly concentrated towards the circum-Pacific and Eurasian–Melanesian belts which have been seen to contain the great mountain systems and ocean deeps. Figure 4, which represents data obtained during the past 50 years and collected together by Gutenberg and Richter [12], shows that all the deep and intermediate foci and a great many shallow foci are located beneath these belts. Furthermore, the focal depth is seen to increase systematically as the belt is crossed from the oceanic side. From studies of earthquake sequences in a number of profiles across the circum-Pacific belt, Benioff [13] has inferred that the foci define a system of enormous reverse fault planes dipping in the landward direction to the depths (of about 700 km) from which the deepest shocks originate. In some profiles the fault plane dips consistently at an angle of about 60°; in others the angle of dip increases abruptly from about 30° to about 60° at depths of around 300 km. These fault systems are respectively termed *oceanic* and *marginal*,

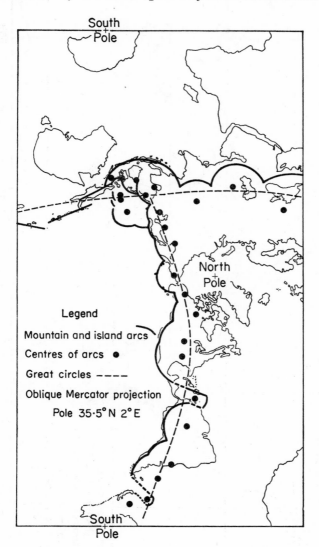

FIG. 3. Geographical distribution of Tertiary active belts. Reproduced by permission from "The Earth as a Planet", edited by G. P. Kuiper, copyright, 1954, by The University of Chicago Press.

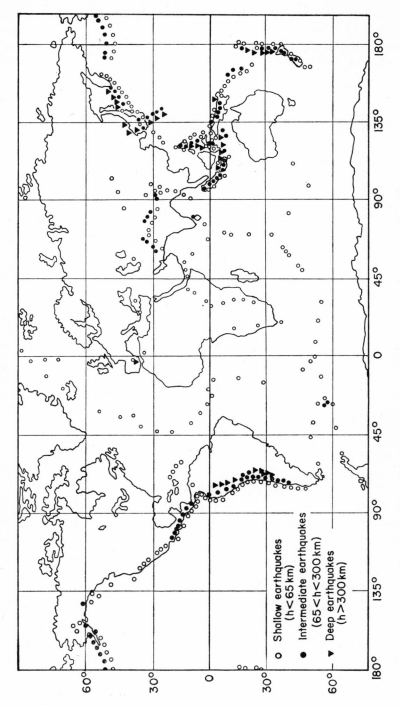

Fig. 4. Geographical distribution of earthquake epicentres. Reproduced from [2] by permission of Springer Verlag.

and generalized crustal sections of each type are shown in Fig. 5. Benioff's results show that, if the structure of the earth's mantle is based, not on the distribution of seismic wave velocities, but on mechanical behaviour under stresses of much longer duration (see III,A,2 below), the lower

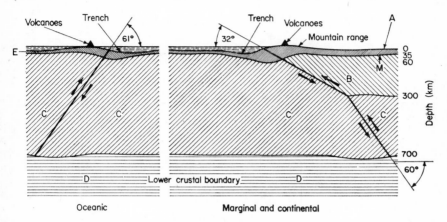

Fig. 5. Generalized oceanic and marginal deep-fault systems (after Benioff). Reproduced by permission from the Bulletin of the Geological Society of America.

boundary of the crust must be placed at a depth of about 700 km, while in continental areas a further major discontinuity occurs at a depth of some 300 km. The arrows in Fig. 5 postulate dip-slip movements on the deep fault planes in accordance with the structural characteristics of the elements which lie at their head. Analysis [2, pp. 41–47; 14] of the first motions produced by some 200 earthquakes shows, however, that the dip-slip component of the relative displacement in the focal region is usually smaller than the strike-slip component. The implications of these preponderantly transcurrent movements have not yet been fully explored.

About two-thirds of the world's active volcanoes are situated in the circum-Pacific belt. They form a line on the continental side of the region of seismic activity which coincides approximately with the epicentral locus of intermediate focus shocks, and the great majority of them emit andesitic lavas. These associations have prompted the suggestion that the fault system indicated by the earthquake foci provides channels for the rise of magmas to the surface, basaltic lavas emerging from the outermost part of the mantle and andesitic lavas from depths exceeding 70 km. From Fig. 6, which shows the geographical distribution of extinct and active volcanoes, it is seen that volcanic activity in the Eurasian-Melanesian belt is much more widely dispersed than in the circum-Pacific ring.

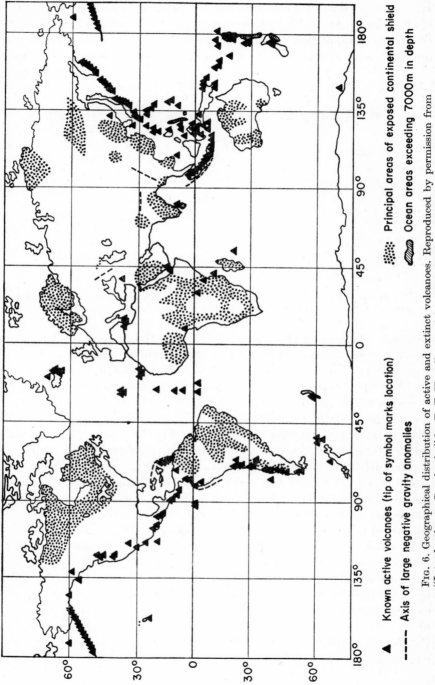

▲   Known active volcanoes (tip of symbol marks location)

---   Axis of large negative gravity anomalies

⦂⦂⦂ Principal areas of exposed continental shield

〰〰 Ocean areas exceeding 7000m in depth

Fig. 6. Geographical distribution of active and extinct volcanoes. Reproduced by permission from "Introduction to Geophysics" by B. F. Howell, copyright, 1959, McGraw-Hill Book Company, Inc.

The discovery that the oceanic ridges connect together to form a continuous world-encircling system is quite a recent one [15]. These belts are known to pass through the Arctic, Atlantic, Indian and Pacific Oceans and to extend landwards into the rift valleys of East Africa and the South Island of New Zealand (Fig. 7). Their total length (60,000 km) is comparable with that of the system of belts containing the island

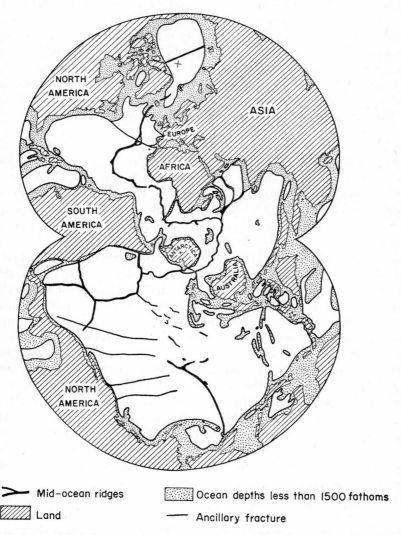

FIG. 7. Geographical distribution of oceanic ridges. Reproduced by permission from "Physics and Geology", by J. A. Jacobs, R. D. Russell and J. T. Wilson, copyright, 1959, McGraw-Hill Book Company, Inc.

arcs, young folded mountains and deep ocean trenches, but the two systems appear to be entirely different in structure. The ocean ridges are several hundred kilometres wide and typically attain heights of 3 km above the ocean floor. The most thoroughly explored segment is the Mid-Atlantic Ridge [16, pp. 83–106], which accurately bisects the basins separating the American and Euro-African land masses. A striking feature of this ridge is a central rift valley, some 25 to 50 km wide, the position of which coincides with a band of shallow focus earthquake epicentres (see Fig. 4). It seems likely that this median rift and associated shallow focus seismic activity are general features of the ocean ridges. The composition of islands of the system and of rocks dredged from the Mid-Atlantic Ridge, together with the absence of intermediate and deep earthquake foci, suggest that the ridges may have been formed by the extrusion of basaltic magma from the outer mantle.

3. *Equilibrium of the Crust*

The simplified picture of the earth's crust presented above suggests that the features which are symptomatic of change and unrest are confined to the two systems of active belts, while the great continental and oceanic blocks which make up the bulk of the crust are essentially in equilibrium. This conclusion must be qualified somewhat in the light of gravity measurements that have been made in various parts of the world. The basis for the interpretation of these results is furnished by the principle of isostasy which may be stated as follows [17, p. 237]: "All large land masses on the earth's surface tend to sink or rise so that, given time for adjustment to occur, their masses are hydrostatically supported from below, except where local stresses are acting to upset equilibrium". The extent of departures from isostatic equilibrium accordingly provides a measure of the stresses acting in the crust. Extensive negative gravity anomalies are found in Fennoscandia and in India. In Fennoscandia the land is rising, apparently due to isostatic recovery from the loading imposed by the Pleistocene ice-cap. It has been pointed out by Jeffreys [18, pp. 345–6; see also 19], however, that the observed rates of uplift cannot be completely accounted for by this explanation. In India no systematic vertical movements have been detected. It appears, therefore, that stresses in the crust can interfere with the process of isostatic adjustment and also result in the long-term persistence of large-scale departures from isostasy. There is nevertheless abundant evidence of rapid isostatic accommodation to changing loads. Enormous volumes of recent sediments have accumulated at the mouths of major rivers, the most notable being the Mississippi delta, while erosion has reduced the height of Palaeozoic mountain systems such as the Appalachians by several kilometres. Yet these regions are found to be largely compensated, indicating that isostatic equilibrium has been maintained by subsidence and uplift. These crustal adjustments must be accompanied by mass transfers at the level of compensation.

Passing from the continents to the active belts, the young mountain systems appear to be quite well compensated [20, pp. 238–240], and measurements in the Atlantic [21] suggest that a similar situation prevails over the ocean ridges. The principal value of gravity traverses of continental mountain systems therefore lies in the additional evidence which they provide on the underlying crustal structure. The results show that, while ranges such as the Sierra Nevada and Alps possess roots of light rocks which produce a thickening of the crust [22, 23], there are elevated features, notably the Colorado Plateau [24], beneath which the M-discontinuity is not depressed. These findings suggest that in certain areas the level of compensation is situated not at the base of the continental crust (as indicated by the standard sections shown in Fig. 1), but at some higher level, possibly the Conrad discontinuity. An alternative hypothesis is that the observed surface structures are compensated at a depth of several hundred kilometres. Small horizontal variations of density must then occur over distances of the order of a few thousand kilometres throughout the upper mantle.

The strongest gravity anomalies encountered within the active belts are associated with the deep ocean trenches (see Fig. 6). According to Vening Meinesz [25, 26], the deficiencies of mass implied by these strips of large negative anomaly are due to a downbuckling of the lighter crustal rocks into the denser material of the outer mantle. This downfold (or *tectogene*) is supposed to extend to a depth of some 40 to 50 km. An alternative explanation has been advanced by Worzel and Shurbet [11] on the basis of seismic refraction and gravity measurements carried out over the Puerto Rico Trench. These profiles do not reveal the crustal thickening predicted by the tectogene hypothesis, but suggest that the trench has been formed by a thinning of the crust caused by tensile stresses.

From this brief survey it may be concluded that the current mechanical state of the earth's crust has been determined by the action of orogenic forces affecting the active belts and gentler epeirogenic movements affecting the continents and ocean basins superimposed upon a general trend towards isostatic equilibrium.

B. THE EVOLUTION OF THE EARTH'S SURFACE FEATURES

1. *Time Distribution of Orogenesis*

The folded mountains contained in the system of active belts described in II,A,2 have, for the most part, originated in a series of orogenic

H*

movements, collectively called the Alpine revolution, which have
occurred since late Jurassic times, especially during the Tertiary
period. Ranges such as the Appalachians and Urals and the Scottish
and Norwegian mountains, which lie away from these belts, are older
features, and three main periods of particularly intense and widespread
orogenesis are known to have occurred since Pre-Cambrian times. The
Pre-Cambrian era occupies perhaps 70 per cent of the whole of geological
time, but the absence of fossils severely handicaps the establishment of a
coherent sequence of Pre-Cambrian tectonic activity. There is no evidence, however, of a significant change of diastrophic mechanism at the
close of the Pre-Cambrian era, and it may therefore be reasonably con-
jectured that the total number of orogenic revolutions which have
occurred is of order ten. The view that mountain building is a periodic
process characterized by the contemporaneous occurrence of crustal
movements throughout the system of belts currently active has been
largely discredited [27, 28, 29]. While the alternation of periods of
orogenesis with inactive intervals, usually of longer duration, has been
confirmed on a regional scale, only in a very general sense can orogenesis
in widely separated areas be correlated in time. "While part of the earth
was in tectonic rest, elsewhere tectonic activity was found. The quiet
regions may have already been folded during an earlier date, or they will
be folded at a later date, or they may remain ultimately undisturbed.
Differences in time of folding may be found not only in different continents, but also along one and the same orogenic belt." [28, p. 1769]

2. *Mode of Formation of Mountains*

The structure of folded mountains provides a clear indication of the
action of severe compressive forces in the earth's crust and invites the
conclusion that the crust has been shortened across an orogenic belt by
an amount which is directly related to the measured degree of folding
within the belt. As the detailed structure of the prominent folded ranges
has been unravelled, however, a degree of foreshortening of individual
strata has been revealed which, if extrapolated through about ten
major orogenies, each affecting a series of world-encircling belts, would
imply either an unacceptably large reduction of the earth's radius over
geological time or the existence of tensional features which could hardly
have escaped notice. Furthermore, Jeffreys [18, pp. 324–327] has
pointed out that crustal shortening of the magnitude indicated by
measurements of folding would entail thickening of the crust to a degree
quite incompatible with the state of approximate isostatic equilibrium
which is observed to prevail over the principal folded ranges. From these
considerations it is evident that the observed folding within the active

belts is not to be regarded as a direct measure of crustal shortening. The belief that gravitational slumping of tilted beds may contribute substantially to the observed contortions is widely held [18, pp. 323–335; 30], although Billings [31] has emphasized the subsidiary nature of this process. In addition, Bucher [32] has shown how the upward elongation of crustal columns during compression may grossly exaggerate the apparent shortening, while Jeffreys [18, p. 334; see also 33] has suggested that folding may be a manifestation of some kind of plastic instability. Thus, although the existence of large compressive forces in the crust is hardly in question, the extent to which they have produced shortening across mountain belts cannot at present be assessed with confidence. Considerable uncertainty likewise attaches to current understanding of the way in which the active belts have developed. In the past, wide credence has been given to the *geosynclinal theory* according to which folded mountain ranges originated in the heavy deposition of shallow marine sediments in long narrow troughs formed in the crust at an earlier date and undergoing gradual subsidence. The enormously thick deposits laid down in this way were subsequently flexed and folded by the vice-like closing together of the edges of the geosyncline. They were then uplifted and this process, which may have taken place in several phases, was accompanied by the axial growth of extensive batholiths. Latterly the ranges have been cooled and modified by isostatic response to denudation. A particular version of this theory, proposed by Vening Meinesz [25], assumes the primary geosyncline to be the surface expression of a tectogene. Since the root is depressed into a region of high temperature and, moreover, is rich in radioactive heat sources by virtue of its granitic composition, the formation of batholiths and their subsequent encroachment into the sedimentary cover are then readily accounted for. As mentioned in II,A,3, however, serious objections to the tectogene hypothesis have been raised by recent seismic investigations and, since such a downfolding of the crust would imply a shortening of order 80 km, the difficulties mentioned above arise once more. There can be little doubt that many of the great folded ranges have developed from thick lenses of sediments deposited in geosynclines, but there appears to be little justification for supposing the deep ocean trenches to be present-day specimens of primary geosynclines or for regarding the formation of folded mountains as the controlling influence in the evolution of the active belts.

3. *Spatial Distribution of Orogenesis*

The belts which have been the seat of orogenic activity since Pre-Cambrian times have been investigated in considerable detail [34]. They

are found to occupy roughly concentric positions relative to a number
of ancient shield areas (see Fig. 6) which consist of highly deformed metamorphic rocks. The arrangement of belts around these shields is not
symmetrical, mountains having been formed first on one side of a continent then on another, but in each case the outward progression is broadly
one of decreasing age. Studies of Pre-Cambrian orogenesis, supplemented
by radioactive age determinations, provide results which are generally
consistent with these trends. It appears, therefore, that the continents
have grown by the accretion of peripheral mountain systems [9, p. 402].
This concept of the development of continents has recently been taken
up and considerably extended by Wilson [4, 5, 6].

4. *The Ocean Ridges*

The past history of the oceanic ridge system is as yet largely a
matter of surmise, but the absence of geosynclinal development indicates that the ridges are very ancient features which have gradually
evolved as a result of volcanic action. The median rifts are generally
regarded as evidence that the underlying crust is in a state of tension
and, from a structural comparison of the Mid-Atlantic Ridge and the
East African Rift valleys, Heezen and Ewing [16, p. 103] have concluded
that each is largely the result of normal faulting. Although there is some
difficulty in ascribing the formation of the East African Rifts to crustal
tension [35], the abnormally high values of the surface heat flow which
have been measured over the Mid-Atlantic and Mid-Pacific ridges [36]
do point to stretching and constriction of the crust in those regions.

5. *Transcurrent Faulting*

In addition to the horizontal displacements of the crust associated
with compressive and tensile stresses, large transcurrent movements
have taken place. The sides of the San Andreas fault in California have
been displaced relative to one another by several hundred kilometres
since Jurassic times [37], and recent magnetic measurements [38]
indicate that large transcurrent displacements have occurred across a
series of major fracture zones in the North East Pacific described by
Menard [39]. Interest in transcurrent faults has been stimulated by the
discovery, referred to in II,A,2, that earthquakes usually originate in
strike-slip displacements. Moody and Hill [40] have asserted that
transcurrent faulting is much more prevalent than is ordinarily
supposed and has far-reaching diastrophic implications. This view has
been challenged by Billings [31].

6. *Epeirogenesis*

Vertical displacements of the earth's surface, although less spectacular in their effects than the horizontal movements described above, are nevertheless a universal characteristic of the crust. Most of the present continental areas have, from time to time, been submerged beneath the sea and it is evident that these transgressions and regressions have been caused by regional upwarping and downwarping of the crust as well as by eustatic changes. Notable examples of such movements, which produce only minor faulting and folding, are the uplift of the Colorado plateau and the depression of the south-eastern coastal plain of the United States since middle and late Mesozoic times, while the formation of the shallow, gradually subsiding geosynclines referred to in II,B,2, may also be regarded as a consequence of epeirogenesis. Holmes [9, p. 414] has remarked that, in respect of vertical movements, "the crust behaves somewhat like a flagged or badly cracked pavement on a shifting foundation". The distribution of epeirogenesis through geological time is difficult to determine, but from an analysis of the available evidence King [41, pp. 737–738] has concluded that "the major orogenic and epeirogenic structures have not been created during relatively short periods of movement, but were built up by movements extending over a long period. It appears unlikely that these movements were continuous; more probably they were episodic, and separated by periods of crustal quiescence . . . There is a strong presumption that orogenic movements in one part of the continent are nearly simultaneous with epeirogenic movements and growth of tensional fracture belts elsewhere, as though all were manifestations of the same ultimate forces".

7. *Polar Wandering and Continental Drift*

The remaining types of crustal movement to be considered are those associated with polar wandering, which involves displacement of the whole crust relative to the earth's axis of rotation, and continental drift, in which portions of the crust are translated, and possibly rotated, relative to one another. Evidence bearing on the likelihood of such movements comes from a variety of sources, results obtained from palaeoclimatic and palaeomagnetic studies being of particular importance. Although present-day movements observed in the San Andreas fracture system are sufficient to account for the various continental displacements which have been postulated, no clear evidence of such drifting is discernible in the pattern of major transcurrent faults. Furthermore, there appears to be no way of accounting for forces capable of causing substantial movements of light continental crustal segments over the ultrabasic substratum [18, pp. 364–371]. The apparent absence of expected surface effects and of an adequate driving force constitute powerful objections to the hypothesis of continental drift. Neither of these lines of argument bears upon the possibility of polar wandering, however. Analysis of the palaeoclimatic data suggests that the North Pole has followed a coherent path from a position in the Mid-Pacific to its present location since Carboniferous times [2, pp. 4–6]. An exhaustive survey of palaeomagnetic measurements [42] also provides a strong indication that polar wandering has occurred. This interpretation rests on the assumption that the geomagnetic field has always approximated closely to that of a dipole oriented along the axis of rotation, and makes no distinction between the North and South Poles. The reconstructed path of wandering extends back to Pre-Cambrian times [43], but the post-Carboniferous segment lies well to the west of the path deduced from palaeoclimatic data.

III. DIASTROPHIC FORCES

The development of a theory describing the response of a deformable body to applied loading and heating normally proceeds in two stages. Firstly, it is necessary to represent the rheological properties of the material by means of suitable equations of state. These so-called *constitutive equations* are relationships between sets of variables (and their time derivatives) which define the thermal state and the states of stress and deformation of a typical material element at a given instant. Mathematically they are, in general, non-linear differential or integral equations: physically they describe such effects as hysteresis, creep, stress relaxation and plasticity. The second stage involves the prediction of bulk behaviour under specified initial conditions, boundary conditions, body forces and sources of heat. In this analysis the constitutive equations, in conjunction with equations expressing the conservation of mass, energy and momentum, must be solved to determine the distributions of stress, strain and temperature in the body.

In principle this theoretical framework embraces a complete account of the mechanical and thermal histories of the earth's crust and mantle, but in practice severe difficulties arise, firstly in setting up appropriate constitutive equations, and secondly in formulating conditions under which the field equations are to be solved. In this section, evidence bearing on the rheological properties of the earth's crust and mantle is first summarized under a classification proposed by Scheidegger [2, pp. 102–115]. The nature of the mechanical and thermal constraints which may act on the outer layers of the earth is then discussed.

A. RHEOLOGY OF THE EARTH'S CRUST AND OUTER MANTLE

The types of deformation that affect the crust and mantle of the earth are many and varied, typical characteristic times ranging from 1 sec in the case of bodily elastic waves to 10^8 yr for major tectonic processes. Scheidegger's view is that a single set of constitutive equations can hardly be expected to cover this vast diversity of effects and he has accordingly divided the time scale into three ranges centred on characteristic times of 3 sec, 3 yr and 10^8 yr. These values, which ascend by factors of approximately 3×10^7, typify stresses of short, intermediate and long duration respectively.

1. *Stresses of Short Duration*

The characteristic times of processes which fall under this heading have an upper limit of about 4 hr. Bodily and surface elastic waves, free oscillations of the earth and experimental studies of the mechanical behaviour of rock specimens are therefore of direct relevance.

At the low stress levels which characterize vibrations of the earth and the propagation of elastic waves under laboratory conditions the generalized Hooke's law of classical elasticity is found to give an accurate representation of the mechanical behaviour. The rheological properties of a material element are then specified by the local values of the density, bulk modulus and rigidity. Travel-time data for P and S waves in the mantle permit a reliable determination of the variation of these quantities with depth [18, p. 161], and the application of plausible theoretical concepts to the results provided by seismology and by laboratory measurements yields further information on the structure and composition of the mantle [44, 45]. Additional data on the distribution of elastic constants in the crust and outer mantle are supplied by surface wave studies. The striking structural differences between continental and oceanic parts of the crust revealed by these methods have been mentioned in II,A1. Recent work on the dispersion of long-period surface waves [46] supports a suggestion of Gutenberg's that there exists in the outer mantle (at depths of about 200 km) a layer within which the rigidity decreases with depth. Differences of structure between sub-continental and sub-oceanic parts of the outer mantle are also indicated, but the delineation of such details is beset by difficulties of interpretation.

At high stress levels it is found experimentally that rocks undergo brittle fracture under compression at principal stress differences of 10^9 to 10^{10} dynes/cm^2, but as the relationship between experimental determinations of the compressive strength of rock specimens and the elastic limit in situ is somewhat conjectural, the variation with depth of this quantity is uncertain.

To a first approximation, therefore, the materials of the earth's crust and mantle respond to stresses of short duration like perfectly elastic solids possessing a definite elastic limit at which failure by brittle fracture occurs. It should be added that the observed damping of seismic waves [47, pp. 189–192] and creep tests on rocks [48] provide evidence of short-term anelastic behaviour, but no satisfactory explanation of these effects has yet been given.

2. *Stresses of Intermediate Duration*

The deformations included in this class have characteristic times varying between rough limits of 4 hr and 15,000 yr. Thus, whereas rheological behaviour under stresses of short duration is of little direct significance in the study of diastrophism, characteristic times at the upper end of the intermediate range are comparable with the duration of regional tectonic processes.

Low stress levels of intermediate duration are set up in the earth's crust and mantle by the 14-monthly Eulerian nutation (or *Chandler wobble*), by earth tides and by changes in the loading exerted on the earth's surface by the atmosphere. The Chandler wobble is excited by random forces, the origin of which is still unknown [49], and is subject to an attenuation which reduces its amplitude by a factor of $1/e$ in about 15 yr, the precise value of the relaxation time being highly uncertain [50, pp. 149–150]. The most satisfactory explanations of this damping so far proposed assume some form of linear viscoelasticity in the crust and mantle. Adopting the constitutive equation appropriate to a Kelvin-Voigt solid in shear, and assuming for the rigidity of the mantle the value 2×10^{12} dynes/cm^2 which follows from a discussion of the bodily tides [18, p. 222], Scheidegger [2, pp. 107–108] has shown that the relaxation time of the Chandler wobble implies a Kelvin-Voigt viscosity of about 3×10^{17} gm/cm. sec for the mantle as a whole. Jeffreys [18, pp. 10–11, 263; 51] has based an alternative treatment of the damping of the Chandler wobble upon a modification of a viscoelastic constitutive relation found by Lomnitz [52] to fit the results of creep tests of several days' duration on rock specimens in shear. As this equation contains three independent constants (as compared with two in the deviatoric Kelvin-Voigt equation), the relaxation time of the Chandler wobble and a knowledge of the shear modulus are not sufficient to determine the overall rheological behaviour. Jeffreys therefore considers the distortion of a rectangular S-pulse at an epicentral distance of 80°, but finds that the values of the constants are not sensitive to this datum. Jeffreys has also employed the modified Lomnitz relation in a study of the long-term stress changes involved in the relaxation of surface loads, but his results do not provide an explanation of isostatic adjustments of the crust. Results obtained by applying the Lomnitz creep function to the study of anelastic effects having characteristic times outside the intermediate range should therefore be treated as highly tentative. A recent re-examination by Hales [53] of observations on the non-tidal tilting of the earth's crust points to the presence in the outer mantle of a layer of low rigidity which may be associated with Gutenberg's low velocity layer. The extent of this layer and its rheological properties are, however, unknown.

In most of the regions of high seismicity, relatively large earthquakes are experienced at intervals of from 10 to 100 yr. This suggests that the material within the outer 700 km of the mantle fails by brittle fracture under stresses of intermediate duration, but, as yet, neither the value of the critical stress nor the actual criterion for failure is known. The release of strain energy in aftershock sequences over periods of several months has been studied by Benioff [54]. On the assumption that this energy arises from the relaxation of residual stresses following the occurrence of the original earthquake, information about local rheological behaviour can be obtained. If E_i is the energy released by the ith aftershock, the quantity $S = \sum \sqrt{E_i}$ is a measure of the cumulative strain release. The variation of S with time t (the so-called *strain–rebound characteristic*) has been plotted by Benioff for a number of aftershock sequences. In some of these curves S is of the form $a + b \ln t$ throughout the sequence, a and b being constants: in others the logarithmic variation holds for an initial interval of time after which S is of the form $A - B \exp(-C\sqrt{t})$, in which A, B, C are constants. The logarithmic strain–rebound charactistic resembles Lomnitz's creep relation, but it must be remembered that the latter refers to creep at constant load in states of pure shear. Following a sudden reduction of the loading on a Kelvin-Voigt solid in shear, the strain–time variation is of the form $\alpha \exp(-\beta t)$. Using the values 2×10^{12} dynes/cm^2 and 3×10^{17} gm/cm. sec suggested above for the Kelvin-Voigt rigidity and viscosity to evaluate α and β, the shape of this strain–time curve is found to agree reasonably well with those of exponential segments of strain–rebound curves. Thus, while the types of rheological behaviour needed to account for anelastic effects of intermediate duration at low stress levels are broadly consistent with the aftershock data, no very clear under standing of the observed strain–rebound characteristics has yet been achieved.

3. *Stresses of Long Duration*

The lower limit for the duration of long-term stresses is taken to be about 15,000 yr. Thus the results of experiments on rock specimens provide no guide to rheological behaviour within this time range.

The irregular form of the earth's surface implies that the crust and mantle are subject to stress differences which, in view of the known age of major topographical features such as the Alpine mountain systems, must have persisted at roughly their present level of intensity for periods of order 10^8 yr. Jeffreys [18, p. 210] believes that stress differences of at least $1\cdot5 \times 10^9$ dynes/cm^2 exist within the outermost 50 km of the earth and may reach 3×10^8 dynes/cm^2 at depths between 50 and 600 km. These values evidently set lower limits to the strength of the material of the crust and outer mantle under stresses of long duration. If, as Jeffreys suggests [18, p. 347], no appreciable anelastic effects occur at stress levels which the material can sustain without failing, the long-term rheological behaviour is essentially that of a plastic solid. In the absence of a definite criterion of failure the concept of a yield stress is imperfectly defined, but from Jeffreys' discussion it would appear that the stress level at yield decreases with depth.

Assuming that isostatic adjustments in the earth's crust involve flow of the substratum, evidence of rheological behaviour at stress levels in excess of the failure limit is afforded by the study of regions in which changes of level are presently occurring. The best-known instances are parts of Fennoscandia (see II,A,3), and the Great Lakes–Hudson Bay region where post-glacial uplift has been taking place for times of order 10^4 yr and is currently proceeding at rates of up to 1 m/century. Theoretical discussions of these movements in terms of the flow of a Newtonian liquid lead to estimates of the Newtonian coefficient of viscosity of 10^{22} to 10^{23} gm/cm.sec [47, pp. 193–200].

These findings suggest that the long-term rheological behaviour of the crust and outer mantle in shear can be idealized as that of a material which possesses a stress threshold, below which it is perfectly rigid, and above which flow takes place, the stress in excess of the yield value then being proportional to the rate of strain. The viscoplastic material characterized by these properties is known as a *Bingham solid*.

B. POSSIBLE FORCE MECHANISMS

The diastrophic force mechanisms considered in this sub-section arise from postulated modes of physical or physico-chemical behaviour of the earth's crust and outer mantle. For the most part they have little or no direct observational basis and have been formulated only in a qualitative way. They are classified here according to the source from which their energy is derived.

1. *The Earth's Heat*

Three types of thermal process leading to differential stressing of the crust and outer mantle have been suggested: volume changes, convection, and what may be broadly termed magmatic effects.

Throughout its history the earth has been cooling down by the diffusion of its original heat content and has simultaneously been heated up by its radioactive constituents. These temperature changes are responsible for the generation of thermal stresses in the solid crust and

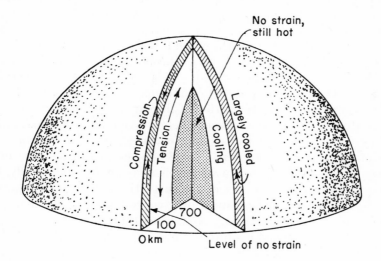

Fig. 8. Thermal stresses in the earth according to the thermal contraction hypothesis. Reproduced by permission from "The Earth as a Planet", edited by G. P. Kuiper, copyright, 1954, by The University of Chicago Press.

mantle. The *thermal contraction hypothesis* embodies the assumption that the earth was very hot at an early stage in its history and that its total heat content has since decreased steadily. The following sequence of events is then predicted. At first the surface regions cool and contract and, since no appreciable temperature changes have yet occurred at deeper levels, this outer layer is put into a state of tension. The level at which the rate of cooling is greatest subsequently moves inwards and the resulting contraction sets up a tensile hoop stress in the surrounding material. In adjusting itself to the underlying zone of shrinkage the crust is then compressed and there results the situation illustrated in

Fig. 8 in which approximate dimensions referring to the present time are indicated. The surface separating the region of tension surrounding the radius of maximum rate of cooling from the compressed shell adjoining the surface is known as the *level of no strain*. The extent to which thermal stresses may have influenced the development of the earth's surface features is discussed in IV,A below, further comment at this stage being restricted to the assumptions which underlie the thermal contraction hypothesis. The initial temperature in the earth is closely connected with the process by which planets are formed. On the view, now widely held, that the planets originated in the accretion of scattered solid material at low temperature, the earth's original heat was acquired during, and in direct consequence of, its formation. The conversion of gravitational potential energy to thermal energy, together with adiabatic self-compression and radioactive decay, particularly of short-lived isotopes, are likely to have been the major factors in raising the temperature of the growing planet. None of these effects can be calculated with any precision, but reasonable estimates [55] suggest that the accretion process continued for about 10^8 yr and may well have resulted in extensive melting and differentiation of the earth. The thermal history of an initially molten earth has been widely studied [56] on the assumption that no convective heat transfer has occurred, but the variation with time of the total heat content is still subject to considerable uncertainty. Thus, although temperature changes have undoubtedly been taking place in the solid part of the earth throughout geological time and must have been accompanied by a varying state of thermal stress, it cannot be asserted with any confidence that the pattern of events required by the thermal contraction hypothesis has been realized.

Stressing of the earth's crust and mantle is an inevitable consequence of volume changes, irrespective of their origin. In recent years polymorphic transitions, in which a change of density occurs and latent heat is either absorbed or released, have been extensively invoked in efforts to understand the structure of the earth's mantle, and an increasing number of geologically important materials have been shown experimentally to undergo changes of phase at elevated temperatures and pressures. It has been pointed out by Adams [57] that, in a region of varying temperature, phase transformations would be expected to take place progressively, the direction of motion of an inter-phase boundary depending upon the relative gradients of the equilibrium curve of the transition and the environmental temperature–pressure curve. For this process to cause a significant secular volume change in the mantle, the temperature–pressure variation in the earth would evidently have to lie in close proximity to the equilibrium curves of the principal phase transitions over long periods of time. Since such agreement would be rather fortuitous it appears unlikely that polymorphism in the mantle could be the source of a major diastrophic force.

In a layer of static Newtonian liquid of total depth h, having kinematic viscosity ν, thermal diffusivity κ and coefficient of volume expansion α, in which the rate of increase of temperature with depth is β, a state of marginal stability is set up when the Rayleigh number $h^4 g \alpha \beta / \nu \kappa$ reaches a critical value which depends somewhat upon conditions at the plane boundaries. It is then possible for steady cellular convection to take place. Convective flow can also be maintained by horizontal temperature differences, there being in this case no threshold gradient. By analogy with these results the existence of large-scale convection currents in the earth's mantle has been envisaged. Perhaps the most cogent evidence in favour of this hypothesis is the observed approximate equality of surface heat flows in continental and oceanic areas, attempts to explain this uniformity on the basis of heat conduction and radiative transfer in the mantle requiring either an improbable lack of correlation between rock type and radioactive content or a temperature distribution which would be incompatible with the known high rigidity of the mantle. Simple order of magnitude calculations [2, p. 147] show that a toroidal convection current, some 1,000 km in radius, capable of maintaining the observed surface heat flux would have a circulation time of order 10^8 yr and involve particle velocities of a few mm/yr. The rheological behaviour adduced from long-term deformations is therefore relevant. If the mantle is regarded as a Bingham solid, the radial temperature gradient must be sufficient to overcome the yield stress of the material as well as the inhibiting effects of viscosity and heat conduction for thermal instability to occur. Brooks [58] has stated that pre-existing horizontal temperature differences great enough to cause yielding would then be needed for the actual initiation of convection. Theoretical studies of thermal instability in anelastic solids corresponding to the well-known analysis of cellular convection in Newtonian liquids have not yet been undertaken and it is by no means clear what types of convective flow are admissible. Jeffreys, for instance [59], has shown that steady convection cannot occur in a solid which in shear satisfies his proposed modification of Lomnitz's creep relation, while Scheidegger [2, pp. 91-92] has suggested that, in a viscoplastic material with a high yield stress, thermal instability may give rise to turbulent flow. It follows that the stresses which would be exerted on the crust by convective movements in the mantle can be estimated only very roughly, but the suggested order of magnitude, 10^8 to 10^9 dynes/cm^2, is a sufficient indication that this mechanism is potentially of major diastrophic importance. Two points which raise difficulties for the convection hypothesis should be mentioned. Firstly, there is strong evidence [44] that the part of the mantle between depths of about 300 and 800 km (the so-called *transition layer*) is inhomogeneous. If this feature marks a change of chemical composition, the critical temperature gradient would be increased to a value which would effectively exclude the possibility of convection at these levels [60]. If, however, the transition layer is accounted for mainly by phase modifications, it could conceivably be spanned by convection currents. Secondly, a system of *steady* convection currents in the mantle would imply a pattern of crustal stress quite different from that indicated by the observational data presented in Section II. If, on the other hand, as appears likely, heat-flow from the core is insufficient to maintain steady convection in the mantle, an initial instability would eventually be corrected and flow damped out. It is difficult to see how a further state of instability affecting more than a small part of the mantle could then be brought about by heat conduction alone, but intermittent convection could possibly occur in the deep crust and outer mantle where radioactive heating would assist the restoration of relatively large temperature gradients, accompanied perhaps by differences of temperature between sub-continental and sub-oceanic regions. The idea of a recurring thermal instability suppressed by convective overturn and re-established by radioactive heating derives from Joly's concept of thermal cycles [61, pp. 89–106].

The widespread occurrence of igneous activity in the earth's active belts is a clear indication of the importance of magmatic effects in orogenesis, but it is not known whether such effects are directly geared to the operation of a major diastrophic force or appear as by-products. Wilson [6, pp. 311–312] and Rubey [62] have suggested that the whole of the earth's crust, as well as the oceans and the atmosphere, have been formed from materials extruded from the mantle. Setting aside doubts as to whether the current rate of lava production by the world's volcanoes is sufficient to support this hypothesis, the gradual removal of some 6×10^9 km³ of matter from the mantle would evidently induce a contraction of the original surface, now the M-discontinuity. Since magmas have apparently been extracted from a wide range of levels within the outer mantle (see II,A,2), it is unlikely that the accompanying stress differences could be of major significance but they would, of course, augment forces arising from other condensational mechanisms such as thermal contraction. The hypotheses that associate basic diastrophic forces with magmatic effects appeal to volume changes which are much more localized. In the *bicausal theory* of van Bemmelen [63], density changes arising from a process of magmatic differentiation are assumed to produce primary deformations (the so-called *undations*) of the earth's surface. Rich [64] and Rubey [62] have postulated volume changes due to selective fusion of the crust and outer mantle respectively, while Hess [65] believes that water escaping from the mantle combines with peridotite immediately below the M-discontinuity to form serpentine which is less dense. Of these hypotheses only that of van Bemmelen has been developed quantitatively (see [2, pp. 198–203]). The analysis is, however, purely phenomenological and sheds little light on the inherent plausibility of the differentiation mechanism.

2. *The Earth's Gravitational Field*

Current knowledge of the structure and composition of the earth's interior suggests that the materials from which the planet originally accumulated have undergone a rigorous sorting process. If, contrary to the view expressed in III,B,1, the newly-formed earth was relatively cool, the observed uniformity of the geological record would require that these rearrangements should have proceeded gradually throughout the earth's history. Such activity would result in the generation of forces in the crust and mantle. In the early planetesimal theory of the origin of the earth, it was supposed that the principal forces affecting the evolution of the crust are associated with contraction caused by the continued rearrangement of material under the influence of the planetary gravitational field [66]. Urey [67, pp. 182–183] has further suggested that instabilities arising during gravitational differentiation would promote convective flows exerting viscous drag on their material surroundings. The assumption that secular reorganization of matter in the earth's interior would necessarily be accompanied by contraction has recently been questioned. By constructing plausible models of the primitive earth in which the radius is smaller than its present value but the total gravitational potential energy is greater, Beck [68] has shown that material rearrangements (or some other mechanism) could have led to an increase of the earth's radius during geological time amounting perhaps to 100 km. A steady expansion of the earth would also be a consequence of a cosmological hypothesis advanced by Dirac [69] which entails a decrease with time of the gravitational interaction constant G. Some of the implications of this trend have been considered by Dicke [70]. No estimates have yet been made of the forces which might be made available for diastrophism by these dilatational processes.

Any proposed diastrophic force mechanism must operate in the earth's gravitational field and, in particular, any postulated mode of rheological behaviour must be examined in relation to the distribution of pressure induced by gravity. A hypothesis of continental growth recently suggested by Evison [71] is based upon the assumption that, in continental parts of the crust, the basement rocks to depths of 2 to 3 km yield plastically under long-term stress differences of order 10^6 dynes/ cm^2. The proposed mechanism is thus one of plastic subsidence under gravity but, surprisingly, knowledge of the physical properties of rocks at these shallow levels is still inadequate to provide a rigorous test of the hypothesis.

3. *The Rotation of the Earth*

Effects connected with the earth's rotation which produce stress differences in the crust and mantle can be described under two headings: polar wandering, and crustal displacement hypotheses.

The possibility that the configuration of the earth as a whole might vary relative to its axis of rotation was first investigated by Darwin in 1877 and has recently been re-examined [50, pp. 250–285]. It is found that if the material forming the earth yields by flow under stress differences of arbitrarily small magnitude, then polar wandering will occur in response to any exciting force, however small. If the material has a non-zero yield stress, polar wandering will take place only when the excitation stress is sufficient to exceed the threshold. As seen in III,A,3, the outer mantle of the earth appears to have a long-term strength of order 10^8 dynes/cm^2 [see also 50, pp. 279–282]. The major contribution to the torque tending to produce polar wandering arises from the distribution of continents and oceans, and the effect of wandering would be to align the continents as closely as possible to the equator. The present arrangement does not have this property, however, and no corrective movement of the poles is apparent. Thus theoretical studies can hardly be said to strengthen the case for polar wandering made out in II,B,7, and they have not yet reached the stage of enabling realistic estimates to be made of the stresses which such movements would produce.

The crustal displacement mechanism which has been most extensively discussed is the hypothesis of continental drift according to which the relative positions of the continents are variable. It has been suggested that tidal effects, Coriolis forces and the Eötvös force (or pohlfluchtkraft) are factors contributing to continental drift, but analyses by Jeffreys [18, p. 352; see also 2, pp. 132–133] show that, since none of these forces could exert shear stresses of more than about 4,000 dynes/ cm^2 at the base of a continent, they are most unlikely to be of diastrophic significance. A further possibility is that of the entire crust being able to slide over the substratum. Munk and MacDonald [50, pp. 281–282] have considered such displacements as a form of polar wandering and conclude that the stress differences generated at the base of the crust would be too small to cause failure. A much more extended investigation has been undertaken by Hapgood [72] who, noticing that the centre of gravity of the Antarctic ice-cap is some 500 km from the South Pole and that almost any orientation of the axis of rotation relative to the present arrangement of continents would place one pole on or near land, suggests that displacements of the entire crust could result from the centrifugal action of eccentric, non-isostatically compensated ice-caps. The deformation of the crust entailed by its passage over the equatorial bulge would then produce stresses, estimated to be of order 10^8 dynes/cm², and the motion would be damped out by the melting of the ice-cap on entering warmer latitudes, the characteristic time of the process being of order 10^4 yr. A number of objections can be raised to these interesting ideas. Firstly, recent gravity and seismic measurements made in Antarctica suggest that the ice-cap is, if anything, over-compensated [71, p. 167; 73]. Secondly, without a proper understanding of the mechanical properties of the crust and substratum it is impossible to state whether a tangential force would in fact displace the whole crust or merely produce localized deformation. Some model experiments carried out by Griggs [74] point to the latter alternative. Finally, the displacement mechanism suggested by Hapgood requires for its continuance the repeated formation of eccentric polar ice-caps, but, according to Holmes [9, p. 250], "polar ice caps are exceptional features of the earth's history, and a region does not automatically receive a shroud of ice merely because it happens to lie over or near one of the poles."

4. Secondary Processes

All the primary diastrophic force mechanisms which have been described in this sub-section lead to non-elastic deformation of the earth's surface, and the resulting inequalities are at once subject to the modifying influences of gravity and erosion. Gravitational sliding of thin plates of rock produces, typically, folding and over-thrusting. Erosion tends to eradicate surface inequalities and alters the distribution of loading on the earth's crust, notably by the accumulation of thick sedimentary deposits in deltas and geosynclines. Gravity and erosion are therefore directly responsible for many of the characteristic features of the active belts and are universal components of theories of orogenesis, but their basic importance is essentially subsidiary to that of the mechanisms which produce the primary deformations.

The above discussion of diastrophic forces is intended not as a catalogue of possibilities but as a classification of those hypotheses which appear to be most worthy of further investigation. Critical reviews of speculations on the evolution of the earth's surface features, written from differing standpoints, are to be found in references 2, 6, 8, 9, 17, 18, 31, 47, 75, the last-mentioned of which (p. 186) aptly summarizes the situation as follows: ". . . a hypothesis that starts with the forces and explains the observations would be much more trustworthy. However, no unimpeachable force has yet been found, and it seems very likely that several larger sources of stress differences as well as a large number of smaller ones cooperate in creating the changes that we observe."

IV. MOUNTAIN-BUILDING HYPOTHESES

Attention has been drawn in Section II to the existence of two world-encircling systems of active belts. The continental belts are associated with deep, intermediate and shallow focus earthquakes, and appear to have migrated outwards from a number of primitive nuclei. They are made up of arcuate elements, and the quasi-periodic deformations which they undergo arise from predominantly compressive forces. The oceanic system is probably subject to tensile stresses. Its location is essentially fixed and the associated seismic activity is confined to shallow levels. The spatial relationships of the two systems suggest that they have developed in unison, while examination of the continental belts indicates that individual elements have evolved according to a common pattern.

It appears from these facts that the basic character of orogenesis is determined by a single force mechanism, or by a small number of inter-linked mechanisms, and it is with the mode of action of such "master forces" that this final section is concerned. Only a few of the processes discussed in III,B, could produce global deformations having the profound connections within the outer mantle exhibited by the continental fracture system. Thus the following review is selective and, in view of the detailed treatments of this topic already available, only the salient advantages and shortcomings of the various hypotheses are discussed.

A. CONTRACTION AND EXPANSION HYPOTHESES

The sequence of events predicted by the thermal contraction hypothesis (see III,B,1) implies that the rate of increase of strain energy will be greatest near the level of maximum rate of cooling. Hales [76] has based detailed calculations of the state of thermal stress in a cooling earth upon a temperature distribution given by Jeffreys [18, pp. 302–311]. His results indicate that the greatest principal stress difference is currently increasing at a maximum rate of about 3 dynes/ cm² yr, and that failure is likely to occur at depths of 250 to 600 km. The suggested mode of failure involves the creation of a region of reduced stress which spreads away from the point of initial failure and, on reaching the earth's surface, pulls down the crust to form a trough, the present-day expression of which is a deep ocean trench (see II,A,3; also [77, pp. 244–251]). The cross-sectional areas of a number of Melanesian and circum-Pacific trenches suggest that periods of failure recur at intervals of about 5×10^7 yr. The overall rate of seismic energy release, as computed by Gutenberg and Richter [12] for the period 1904–1945, has a very pronounced minimum at a depth of 70 km. Hales cites this anomaly as evidence for the existence of a level of no strain, and shows that his calculations are broadly consistent with such an interpretation.

The above results refer to a version of the thermal contraction hypothesis which was originated by Davison and Darwin in 1887 and has since been extensively developed by Jeffreys. It has two serious shortcomings. Firstly, no explanation is given of the position of the active belts relative to the continents and ocean basins; and secondly, it is supposed that the primary trough or geosyncline is the controlling factor in orogenesis. This is contrary to the view of Wilson [4], Hess [65] and other geologists that the volcanic island arcs are the basic elements in the evolution of the continental active belts, folded mountain systems being secondary features.

A formulation of the thermal contraction hypothesis which is free from these deficiencies has been proposed by Scheidegger [2, pp. 162–179] and further developed by Wilson [4, 5 and 6, pp. 353–361]. Heavy deposits of sediments accumulate at continental margins, notably in river deltas, and impose additional loading on the crust. Superimposing the resulting state of stress upon the stress distribution predicted by the contraction hypothesis, and adopting a criterion of fracture applied by Anderson [78] to regional fault systems, Scheidegger predicts that failure will occur along conical faults, the axes of which intersect the surface at points where the loading is most intense. The supposed relationship of these conical fractures to the formation of island arcs is illustrated in Fig. 9.

This version of the thermal contraction hypothesis has been developed alongside Wilson's theory of the concentric growth of continents and has been followed into considerable detail at several points. Beyond the doubts expressed in III,B,1 as to the validity of the assumption

P. CHADWICK

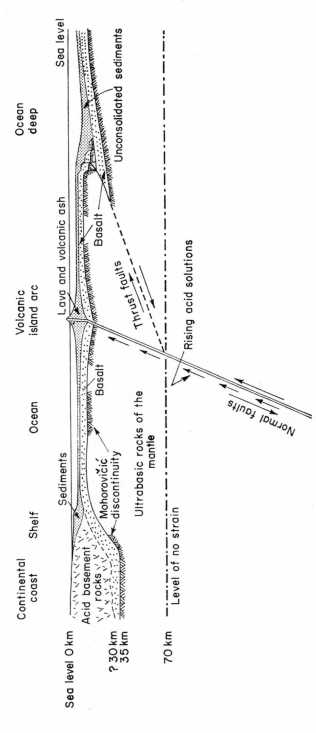

FIG. 9. Generalized section across an active island arc (after Wilson). Reproduced by permission from "The Earth as a Planet", edited by G. P. Kuiper, copyright, 1954, by The University of Chicago Press.

that the earth has undergone secular cooling, two principal objections can be raised to all forms of the thermal contraction hypothesis. Firstly, no explanation is given of the oceanic system of active belts. Secondly, the predominance of transcurrent movements near earthquake foci, revealed by fault plane studies (see II,A,2), is inconsistent with the primarily normal and reverse fault movements which would be expected to occur within a contracting earth (see Figs. 5, 9). Attempts to remove this contradiction [2, pp. 178–179; 6, pp. 356–357] are unconvincing. In addition to these basic shortcomings, further difficulties are encountered in attempts to develop a detailed account of orogenesis from the contraction hypothesis. Thus on a contracting earth a gradual deepening of the oceans would be expected, particularly if the extrusion of magmas from the outer mantle is responsible for a steady increase in the total volume of water. Furthermore, in the Scheidegger-Wilson hypothesis no adequate account has been given of the transformation of a volcanic island arc (such as the Kuril Islands) into a primary mountain arc (such as the Central Andes), and it has not been explained why the conical fractures should form a single scalloped pattern at the surface (see Fig. 3) in preference to one of the various alternative arrangements of intersecting circular arcs.

Wilson [79] has recently examined his theory of crustal evolution in relation to the hypothesis of an expanding earth. Expansion is assumed to produce widening of the mid-ocean ridges with simultaneous buckling of continental margins, so that the main advantages of the contraction hypothesis are retained. It is also suggested that widening of oceanic ridges having an east–west trend could result in transcurrent movements along ridges striking north–south. This hypothesis is therefore, in principle, free from the two main defects pointed out above and accounts in a natural way for the very high values of the surface heat flow measured in the mid-ocean ridges (see II,B,4). It evidently requires, however, that oceanic segments of the earth's crust should be able to transmit high stresses over distances of several thousand kilometres, while the sweeping statement that Scheidegger's formulation of the contraction hypothesis applies equally well to an expanding earth deserves a more careful analysis.

B. CONVECTION HYPOTHESES

Mountain-building hypotheses based upon sub-crustal convection currents have not been developed in very great detail and, in contrast to the orogenic processes discussed in IV,A, they do not stand in any clear relationship to a theory of continental evolution. Due to the essentially episodic nature of orogenesis, any explanation of mountain formation in terms of convection currents must assume the existence of unsteady flows which are responsible for the application of shear stresses to the underside of the crust. The principal feature of the resulting deformation

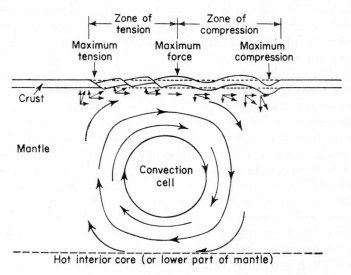

FIG. 10. Forces exerted on the crust by a convection cell. Reproduced by permission from "Introduction to Geophysics", by B. F. Howell, copyright, 1959, McGraw-Hill Book Company, Inc.

(illustrated in Fig. 10) is a shallow downfold or geosyncline which continues to subside under the combined effects of sedimentary deposition and continued compression arising from the convection current. The subsequent development of the downfold is characterized by the gradual heating of its root, as described in II,B,2, and isostatic uplift in response to diminution of the downward drag as the current decays [74].

This hypothesis again over-simplifies the mountain-building process by assigning major importance to the primary geosyncline, and is difficult to reconcile with the observed concentration of earthquake foci towards inclined faults of the types illustrated in Fig. 5. Vening Meinesz [80, pp. 439–440] has pointed out that, since the viscous shear stresses are greatest at the "corners" of a convection cell, an apparent clustering of earthquake foci about the diagonal through the downfold might be expected. This expedient does not account for the prevalence of transcurrent displacements near earthquake foci; nor is it clear why the other two "corners" of the convection cell should be seismically quiescent.

More elaborate mountain-building mechanisms involving the action of two or more convection cells have been discussed by Griggs, Hess, Vening Meinesz and others. These hypotheses again aim at explaining the deformations observed within a generalized cross-section of an active continental belt, but give no account of the longitudinal structure. Scheidegger [2, p. 146] has emphasized that the axis of a convection cell must be closed. Since heat is being transported outwards, it follows that the contours of the resulting pattern of surface deformation must be roughly circular. No combination of such patterns has yet been found which could reproduce the deformations contained within the two systems of active belts, and in which the directions of flow are at once compatible with determinations of the surface heat flux and the suspected distribution of compressive and tensile stresses in the crust. Even if an appropriate arrangement of convective flows could be constructed, it would still, of course, be necessary to show that thermal conditions within the crust and mantle could actually bring it into being and produce the continuing modifications required to explain the migration of the continental active belts.

Finally, mention should be made of an interesting attempt by Vening Meinesz [80, pp. 397–441] to explain the development of the continents in terms of convection currents in the mantle. The starting point of this work is a comparison between the properties of steady convective flow in a spherical shell of Newtonian liquid and a harmonic analysis of the earth's surface topography carried out by Prey. The dominant first-order harmonic is taken as evidence of the existence at an early stage of the earth's history of a first-order spherical harmonic convection current which was responsible for the formation of the nickel-iron core and a primitive continent made of granitic material which positioned itself over the confluence of descending currents. Subsequent phases of convection, now confined to the mantle, are assumed to have produced the higher order components of the topography. In particular, the second phase resulted in the disruption of the ur continent and the dispersion of the fragments to sites determined by the distribution of sinking currents, and was followed by a period of rest during which the mantle solidified and the ocean basins were formed. This account of the origin of the earth's major surface features does not appear to have been satisfactorily integrated with the orogenic hypotheses outlined above. It is, of course, incompatible with the view that the continents have grown outwards from a number of primitive nuclei by the systematic incorporation of marginal mountain arcs.

C. CRUSTAL DISPLACEMENT HYPOTHESES

The continental drift hypothesis regards the continents as light granitic plates floating in a denser basaltic substratum. Initially the continents were connected together in a single block (or perhaps in two blocks) which were supposedly sub-divided in late Palaeozoic times. The fragments have since drifted about, and crumpling at their leading edges is assumed to have resulted in the formation of mountains. This hypothesis has been strongly criticized, especially by Jeffreys [18, pp. 364–371], who holds that the lack of an adequate driving force and the considerable strength of the oceanic crust preclude both continental drifting and the postulated mode of mountain formation. Further difficulties are encountered in relating the supposed displacements of the continents to the creation of the two systems of active belts and in seeking an association between an essentially crustal orogenic mechanism and deep focus earthquakes. On the other hand, the occurrence of transcurrent displacements is not particularly difficult to understand on the basis of continental drift which, in this respect, has a distinct advantage over the hypotheses considered in IV,A and B. Scheidegger [2, pp. 183–185] has shown that the root mean square velocity of continental drifting indicated by palaeomagnetic data (about 5 cm/yr) could arise from the action of a randomly directed drag force having an auto-correlation time of 1.5×10^8 yr. The nature of this random force is unspecified, but convective movements in the mantle seem to represent the only likely source.

Palaeoclimatic and palaeomagnetic indications of polar wandering and the dynamical theory of this effect have been considered in II,B,7 and III,B,3, and the balance of evidence at present appears to favour displacements of the whole crust over the substratum rather than polar wandering of the entire earth. Vening Meinesz [26] has suggested that displacements of this type might be produced by large-scale convection currents in the mantle. It is usually supposed (see, for instance, [6, p. 349]) that the orogenic significance of polar wandering is slight, but the possible effects of the equatorial bulge on movements of the whole crust [72, pp. 79–131] would appear to merit further investigation.

D. GENERAL CONCLUSIONS

The most complete and coherent account of the development of the earth's crust currently available is that given by Wilson and his collaborators who have attempted, on the one hand, to recognize from field studies and laboratory measurements the mode of evolution of the major structural elements of the crust and, on the other, to explain the indicated sequence of events on the basis of the thermal contraction (or, latterly, an expansion) hypothesis. These two aspects of their work should be carefully distinguished, the uncertainties and inadequacies of the assumed diastrophic force mechanism (discussed in III,B,1 and IV,A) being without prejudice to the validity of the reconstructed evolutionary pattern.

The basic physical ideas upon which convection hypotheses rest are more complex than those which underlie contraction and expansion hypotheses, and the superstructure which has been erected, notably by Vening Meinesz, is correspondingly more speculative. Theoretical model studies of convection in the mantle similar to those which have for some time been employed in the investigation of the thermal state and history of the earth [see, for instance, 55] would provide some welcome guidance to the realities of a process which is potentially of very considerable importance. With the aid of fast computers such calculations may be already feasible.

The dynamic principles of crustal movements are likewise highly conjectural, and until displacements of the land masses relative to the earth's axis of rotation, indicated in particular by palaeomagnetic measurements, can be interpreted with some degree of certainty it seems that mountain-building hypotheses of this type will lack a definite starting point.

In the hypotheses described in this section the association of the continental active belts with deep-seated seismic disturbances is a persistent source of difficulty, aggravated in most cases by the discovery that the majority of first movements in earthquakes are directed transcurrently to the focal fault plane. Scheidegger [2, p. 183] has observed that seismic activity is connected with the release of strain energy accumulated over intervals of time which, according to the definitions of III,A, are of intermediate duration, while orogenesis is a long-term process, but the implications of this difference of time scale remain to be explored.

Of the many mountain-building mechanisms that have not been discussed in detail, none seems likely to be of dominating importance, but they should not be ignored on that account. Certain of the deformations arising from magmatic effects in particular have probably contributed in some way to the development of the major crustal features.

Recent reviews of work on the formation of mountains agree unanimously that none of the hypotheses so far proposed is free from serious drawbacks. This conclusion also emerges from the present survey alongside the view that the subject is likely to remain in its

I

present unsatisfactory state until the nature and mode of action of the basic diastrophic forces are much more clearly understood.

References

1. ADAMS, F. D., "Birth and Development of the Geological Sciences". Williams and Wilkins, Baltimore (1938).
2. SCHEIDEGGER, A. E., "Principles of Geodynamics". Springer-Verlag, Berlin, Göttingen and Heidelberg (1958).
3. BUCHER, W. H., "The Deformation of the Earth's Crust". Princeton University Press, Princeton (1933).
4. WILSON, J. T., in "The Earth as a Planet", pp. 138–214. (G. P. Kuiper, ed.) University of Chicago Press, Chicago (1954).
5. WILSON, J. T., Amer. Scient. 47, 1 (1959).
6. JACOBS, J. A., RUSSELL, R. D., AND WILSON, J. T., "Physics and Geology". McGraw-Hill, New York, Toronto and London (1959).
7. RUNCORN, S. K., in "Handbuch der Physik", Vol. XLVII, pp. 470–497. (J. Bartels, ed.) Springer-Verlag, Berlin, Göttingen and Heidelberg (1956).
8. EARDLEY, A. J., Amer. Scient. 45, 189 (1957).
9. HOLMES, A., "Principles of Physical Geology". Nelson, London, Edinburgh, Paris, Melbourne, Toronto and New York (1944).
10. EWING, W. M., AND PRESS, F., in "Handbuch der Physik", Vol. XLVII, pp. 246–257. (J. Bartels, ed.) Springer-Verlag, Berlin, Göttingen and Heidelberg (1956).
11. WORZEL, J. L., AND SHURBET, G. L., in "Crust of the Earth", pp. 87–100. (A. Poldervaart, ed.) Geological Society of America Special Paper 62 (1955).
12. GUTENBERG, B., AND RICHTER, C. F., "Seismicity of the Earth and Associated Phenomena", 2nd edition. Princeton University Press, Princeton (1954).
13. BENIOFF, H., in "Crust of the Earth", pp. 61–74. (A. Poldervaart, ed.) Geological Society of America Special Paper 62 (1955).
14. HODGSON, J. H., Bull. geol. Soc. Amer. 68, 611 (1957).
15. EWING, W. M., AND HEEZEN, B. C., in "Antarctica and the I.G.Y.", pp. 75–81. (A. P. Crary, ed.) American Geophysical Union, Geophysical Monograph No. 1 (1956).
16. HEEZEN, B. C., THARP, M., AND EWING, W. M., "The Floors of the Oceans: I. The North Atlantic". Geological Society of America Special Paper 65 (1959).
17. HOWELL, B. F., "Introduction to Geophysics". McGraw-Hill, New York, Toronto and London (1959).
18. JEFFREYS, H., "The Earth", 4th edition. Cambridge University Press, London (1959).
19. STILLE, H., in "Crust of the Earth", pp. 171–192. (A. Poldervaart, ed.) Geological Society of America Special Paper 62 (1955).
20. GARLAND, G. D., in "Handbuch der Physik", Vol. XLVII, pp. 202–245. (J. Bartels, ed.) Springer-Verlag, Berlin, Göttingen and Heidelberg (1956).
21. EWING, J. I., AND EWING, W. M., Bull. geol. Soc. Amer. 70, 291 (1959).
22. GUTENBERG, B., Bull. geol. Soc. Amer. 54, 473 (1943).
23. PRESS, F., Bull. geol. Soc. Amer. 67, 1647 (1956).
24. TATEL, H. E., AND TUVE, M. A., in "Crust of the Earth", pp. 35–50. (A. Poldervaart, ed.) Geological Society of America Special Paper 62 (1955).

25. VENING MEINESZ, F. A., *Proc. Acad. Sci. Amst.* **33**, 570 (1930).
26. VENING MEINESZ, F. A., "Gravity Expeditions at Sea, 1923–1938", Vol. 4. Netherlands Geodetic Commission, Delft (1948).
27. GILLULY, J., *Bull. geol. Soc. Amer.* **60**, 561 (1949).
28. RUTTEN, L. M. R., *Bull. geol. Soc. Amer.* **60**, 1755 (1949).
29. HAWKES, L., *Quart. J. geol. Soc. Lond.* **113**, 309 (1957).
30. BUCHER, W. H., *Bull. geol. Soc. Amer.* **67**, 1295 (1956).
31. BILLINGS, M. P., *Bull. geol. Soc. Amer.* **71**, 363 (1960).
32. BUCHER, W. H., *in* "Crust of the Earth", pp. 343–368. (A. Poldervaart, ed.) Geological Society of America Special Paper 62 (1955).
33. COOK, A. H., *Geophys. J. R. astr. Soc.* **1**, 356 (1958).
34. UMBGROVE, J. H. F., "The Pulse of the Earth". Nijhoff, The Hague (1947).
35. BULLARD, E. C., *Phil. Trans.* **235A**, 445 (1936).
36. BULLARD, E. C., MAXWELL, A. E., AND REVELLE, R., *in* "Advances in Geophysics", Vol. 3, pp. 153–181. (H. E. Landsberg, ed.) Academic Press, New York (1956).
37. HILL, M. L., AND DIBLEE, T. W., *Bull. geol. Soc. Amer.* **64**, 443 (1953).
38. MASON, R. G., *Geophys. J. R. astr. Soc.* **1**, 320 (1958).
39. MENARD, H. W., *Bull. geol. Soc. Amer.* **66**, 1149 (1955).
40. MOODY, J. D., AND HILL, M. J., *Bull. geol. Soc. Amer.* **67**, 1207 (1956).
41. KING, P. B., *in* "Crust of the Earth", pp. 723–740. (A. Poldervaart, ed.) Geological Society of America Special Paper 62 (1955).
42. COX, A., AND DOELL, R. R., *Bull. geol. Soc. Amer.* **71**, 645 (1960).
43. RUNCORN, S. K., *Bull. geol. Soc. Amer.* **67**, 301 (1956).
44. BIRCH, F., *J. geophys. Res.* **57**, 227 (1952).
45. BIRCH, F., *in* "The Earth Today", pp. 295–311. (A. H. Cook, T. F. Gaskell, eds.) Royal Astronomical Society (1961).
46. DORMAN, J., EWING, W. M., AND OLIVER, J., *Bull. seismol. Soc. Amer.* **50**, 87 (1960).
47. GUTENBERG, B., "Physics of the Earth's Interior". Academic Press, New York and London (1959).
48. HUGHES, D. S., *in* "Techniques in Geophysics", Vol. 1, pp. 308–324. (S. K. Runcorn, ed.) Interscience Publishers, New York and London (1960).
49. MUNK, W. H., AND HASSAN, E. S. M., *in* "The Earth Today", pp. 339–358. (A. H. Cook, T. F. Gaskell, eds.) Royal Astronomical Society (1961).
50. MUNK, W., AND MACDONALD, G. J. F., "The Rotation of the Earth". Cambridge University Press, London (1960).
51. JEFFREYS, H., AND CRAMPIN, S., *Mon. Not. R. astr. Soc.* **121**, 571 (1960).
52. LOMNITZ, C., *J. Geol.* **64**, 473 (1956).
53. HALES, A. L., *in* "The Earth Today", pp. 312–319. (A. H. Cook, T. F. Gaskell, eds.) Royal Astronomical Society (1961).
54. BENIOFF, H., *Bull. seismol. Soc. Amer.* **41**, 31 (1951).
55. MACDONALD, G. J. F., *J. geophys. Res.* **64**, 1967 (1959).
56. VERHOOGEN, J., *in* "Physics and Chemistry of the Earth", Vol. 1, pp. 17–43. (L. H. Ahrens, K. Rankama, S. K. Runcorn, eds.) Pergamon Press, London (1956).
57. ADAMS, L. H., *Trans. Amer. geophys. Un.* **28**, 673 (1947).
58. BROOKS, H., *Trans. Amer. geophys. Un.* **35**, 92 (1954).
59. JEFFREYS, H., *Geophys. J. R. astr. Soc.* **1**, 162 (1958).
60. VERHOOGEN, J., *Trans. Amer. geophys. Un.* **35**, 85 (1954).

61. JOLY, J., "The Surface History of the Earth". Clarendon Press, Oxford (1925).
62. RUBEY, W. W., *Trans. Amer. geophys. Un.* **34**, 350 (1953).
63. VAN BEMMELEN, R. W., "Mountain Building". Nijhoff, The Hague (1954).
64. RICH, J. L., *Bull. geol. Soc. Amer.* **62**, 1179 (1951).
65. HESS, H. H., *in* "Crust of the Earth", pp. 391–408. (A. Poldervaart, ed.) Geological Society of America Special Paper 62 (1955).
66. CHAMBERLIN, R. T., *in* "Theory of Continental Drift. A Symposium", pp. 83–87. American Association of Petroleum Geologists, Tulsa (1928).
67. UREY, H. C., "The Planets, Their Origin and Development". Oxford University Press, London (1952).
68. BECK, A. E., *J. geophys. Res.* **66**, 1485 (1961).
69. DIRAC, P. A. M., *Proc. roy. Soc.* **165A**, 199 (1938).
70. DICKE, R. H., *Rev. mod. Phys.* **29**, 355 (1957).
71. EVISON, F. F., *Geophys. J. R. astr. Soc.* **3**, 155 (1960).
72. HAPGOOD, C. H., "Earth's Shifting Crust". Museum Press, London (1959).
73. GASKELL, T. F., *Nature, Lond.* **183**, 1575 (1959).
74. GRIGGS, D. T., *Amer. J. Sci.* **237**, 611 (1939).
75. GUTENBERG, B., *in* "Internal Constitution of the Earth", pp. 177–217. (B. Gutenberg, ed.) McGraw-Hill, New York and London (1939).
76. HALES, A. L., *Mon. Not. R. astr. Soc., Geophys. Suppl.* **6**, 458, 486 (1953).
77. COULOMB, J., "La Constitution physique de la Terre". Albin Michel, Paris (1952).
78. ANDERSON, E. M., "The Dynamics of Faulting", 2nd edition. Oliver and Boyd, Edinburgh (1951).
79. WILSON, J. T., *Nature, Lond.* **185**, 880 (1960).
80. HEISKANEN, W. A., AND VENING MEINESZ, F. A., "The Earth and its Gravity Field". McGraw-Hill, New York, Toronto and London (1958).

Chapter 9

The Deep-Sea Floor*

BRUCE C. HEEZEN

I. Introduction 235
II. The Ocean Floor 236
    A. Continental Margin 236
    B. Ocean-Basin Floor 244
    C. Mid-Oceanic Ridge 255
III. Seismological Evidence for a Difference between the Continental
      and Oceanic Mantle 263
IV. Petrography of the Oceans 268
V. Age of Ocean Basins 269
VI. Discussion of the Hypotheses of Continental Drift . . 276
    References 286

I. Introduction

When Wegener and Taylor published their first papers on continental drift the ocean floor was virtually unknown. In the subsequent half-century many new techniques have been developed and employed in the exploration of oceanic areas. The echo sounder has permitted the mapping of deep-sea physiography [1]. Rock dredging and core sampling have provided data on the petrography of the ocean floor [2]. Seismic-refraction and seismic-reflection studies have provided important data on crustal layering under the oceans [3, 4, 5]. Gravity measurements interpreted in conjunction with the seismic-refraction results have led to more sophisticated structural interpretations [6]. Total field magnetic measurements have given information relative to the composition of the oceanic crust, as well as important data of horizontal displacement along sea-floor fault systems [7]. Measurements of the heat flow through the sea floor have delineated significant patterns [8]. The study of earthquake surface waves has shed light on the structure of the upper mantle and the probable contrast between the oceanic and continental mantle [9]. Sufficient earthquake epicentres have been located to delineate the seismic zones of recent tectonic activity [10].

Almost all of these investigations bear in an important way on

* Lamont Geological Observatory (Columbia University) Contribution 530.

continental drift. If the continents have drifted through the ocean floor, an indelible mark must have been left which should be observed in the morphology, structure, history, and petrography of the sea floor. The sub-oceanic lithosphere must be assigned very special characteristics if it is to be imagined that the continents have drifted through, or glided over the oceanic crust.

In the present chapter, the results of pertinent investigations of the deep-sea floor are in the first part briefly summarized; and in the latter part, these results are discussed in relation to various hypotheses of continental displacement.

II. THE OCEAN FLOOR

A knowledge of the physiography of the deep-sea floor is a basic prerequisite to any consideration of the geology or structure of the oceans. The earth's surface is divided into two first-order features; the

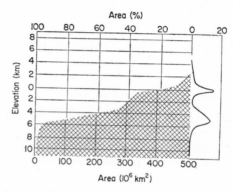

FIG. 1. The two first-order features of the earth's topography. Hypsographic curve showing the area of the earth's solid surface above any given level of elevation or depth. Curve on the right shows the frequency distribution of elevations and depths for 2 km intervals.

continents and the oceans (Fig. 1). The oceans, in turn, are divided into three major morphologic divisions; continental margin, ocean-basin floor, and mid-oceanic ridge (Figs. 2, 3).

In the Atlantic, Indian, and South Pacific Oceans, each of these divisions accounts for about one-third of the total area. However, the ocean-basin floor accounts for the major part of the North Pacific.

A. CONTINENTAL MARGIN

The continental margin includes those physiographic provinces of the continents and of the oceans which are associated with the boundary between the two first-order morphologic features of the earth. Three

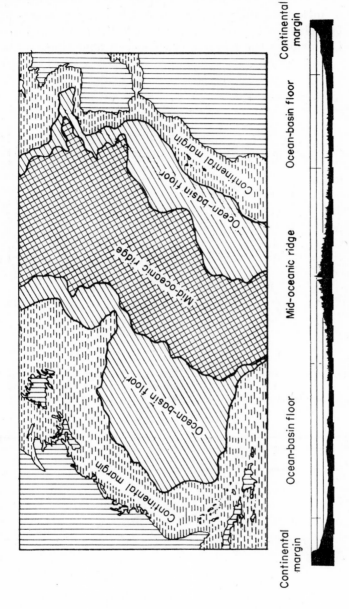

FIG. 2. The three major morphological divisions of the ocean, illustrated by a trans-Atlantic profile from New England to the Spanish Sahara.

categories of continental-margin provinces can be distinguished:
Category I includes submerged portions of the continental block;
Category II includes the steep, seaward edge of the continental block;
Category III includes the margins of the ocean floor (Fig. 4). At first

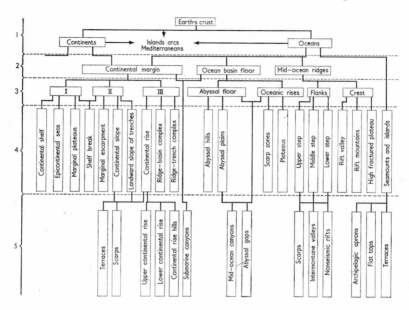

FIG. 3. Outline of submarine topography. 1, first-order features of the crust; 2, major
topographic features of the ocean; 3, categories of provinces and super-provinces;
4, provinces; 5, sub-provinces and other important features. (After Heezen [1]).

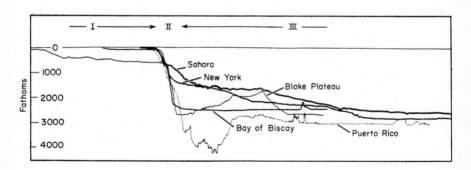

FIG. 4. Three categories of continental margin provinces. Representative profiles taken
from various parts of the North Atlantic. Note the great similarity in form of the
Category I provinces, and the great diversity in expression in the Category III provinces,
particularly in that portion of Category III closest to the boundary of the Category II
provinces.

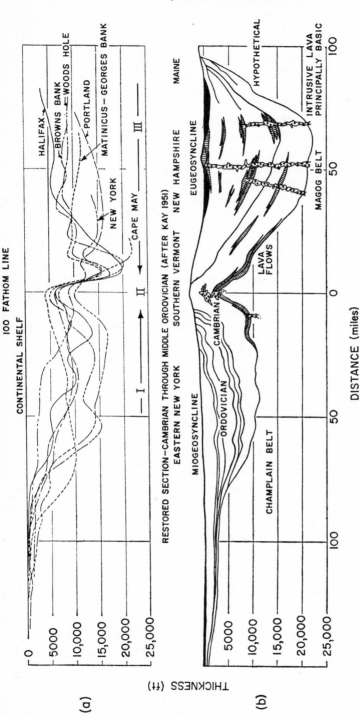

Fig. 5. Continental margin profiles.

(a) Isopachous sections off the east coast of North America. (After Drake [11]).

(b) Restored geosynclinal section off east coast of North America. (After Kay [15]).

Three categories of physiographic provinces are indicated in the top profile. Note that the inner, or miogeosynclinal thickness of sediment occurs within the Category I provinces; that the basement ridge between the two troughs correlates with Category II provinces, and that the eugeosynclinal thickness correlates well with the deep trough on the landward margin of the Category III provinces. The typical orthogeosyncline seems to be duplicated in the sediment-filled troughs of the continental margin off eastern North America. Similar patterns have been found elsewhere in the continental margins of the world.

view the continental margin seems to have a great diversity of morphologic expression. On this basis it has been generally inferred that
radically different tectonic processes have been exerted from place to
place along the continental margin. However, when comparing continental-margin profiles, it is found that this great diversity in morphological form is largely limited to the Category III provinces (Fig. 4).
This complexity largely disappears when the seismic-refraction results
[1, 11] for the Category III provinces are examined in more detail.

In each of the profiles of Fig. 5(a) very similar basement topography is
observed. The small differences in surface expression in these areas are
thus the result of differing amounts of sediment fill. Of course, it is
certainly true that the filled trench off New England is much older than
a seismically active, nearly unfilled trench such as the Puerto Rico or
Peru-Chile Trench. There are differences in crustal layering and
probably, when a more detailed picture emerges, significant differences
in structural development will become apparent. Nevertheless, the
similarities between continental-margin profiles are more striking than
are the differences. The conclusion that a marginal trench is characteristic of all continental margins seems to be a safe extrapolation—
although many workers would take exception to this statement. In the
seismically quiet, more mature margins of the Atlantic and Indian
Oceans, the trenches have been filled in a large part by turbidity-
current transported sediment; while in the younger, seismically active
margins of the Pacific, the trenches exist as rugged topographic features
of the sea floor, only partially filled with sediment.

Extensive studies have been made of the Puerto Rico Trench
(Fig. 6), employing gravity and seismic-refraction techniques [6]. As a
result of this work, the hypothesis of a great compressional downbuckle
(tectogene), originally proposed by Vening Meinesz [12] and eloquently
championed by Hess [13] had to be abandoned, since in recent detailed
studies no crustal downbuckle was found. Ewing and Heezen [14]
pointed out that the gravity and seismic data could be better explained
in terms of the extension of the crust than in the previously advocated
compression. If we grant that the interpretation of the Puerto Rico
Trench in terms of tension is correct, and if we grant that the Puerto
Rico Trench or the Peru-Chile Trench represent an early stage in the
evolution of a typical continental margin, we might conjecture that
normal continental margins are dominated by extensional deformation.

In the case of the filled trenches, this deformation has ceased and
allowed processes of sedimentation to fill these quiescent troughs. But
it has been pointed out [1, 11] that the present filled trenches of north-
eastern United States greatly resemble the reconstructed Paleozoic

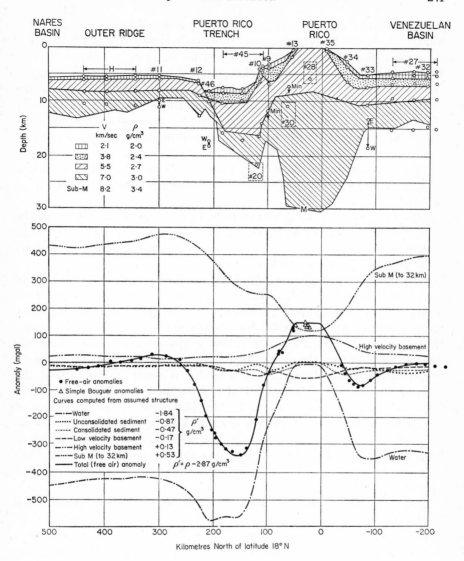

FIG. 6. Structure of the Puerto Rico Trench.

(a). Computed crustal section. Crustal layering is from seismic data; M-discontinuity is from gravity data; points are seismic interfaces.

(b). Computed attraction of layers to 32 km depth, using reduced densities ρ'. Solid curve is total attraction (computed free-air anomalies) which is compared with observed anomalies. (After Talwani [6]).

Earlier interpretation of negative gravity anomaly of the Puerto Rico Trench was a huge downbuckle in the earth's crust reaching depths of 80 to 100 km. No such downbuckle is seen. The steep northern scarp of the Puerto Rico Trench, close to the position of Station 46 on upper profile, has long been thought to be a fault scarp along which outcrops should be found. Recent exploration by Hersey revealed outcrops of ultrabasic rock on this scarp, and it has been claimed that the samples represent the third layer of the earth's crust. This claim is based on a slightly different interpretation of the seismic data in which the third layer turns up, rather than down, between km 200 and km 210.

Appalachian geosyncline [15]. An analogy is drawn between the ortho-quartzites of the Paleozoic miogeosyncline and the lens of similar sedi-ments that lies beneath the modern continental shelf. A further analogy is drawn between the graywacke suite [16] of the Paleozoic eugeo-syncline and the second, thicker lens of sediments that lies beneath the modern continental rise at the base of the continental slope. The inference is, of course, that the Appalachian geosyncline represents a continental margin which before deformation was nearly identical to the present continental margin of eastern North America. However, to complete the sequence from filled continental margin trench to folded mountain range, a yet unspecified mechanism of crustal thickening is required.

Although we have no evidence of compressional deformation in the continental margin provinces, through the geosyncline analogy we have reason to expect compression at some future time, brought about by some process of crustal thickening.

The continental slope has often been compared to the fore-set beds of a classical textbook delta. However, recent studies of cores, rock dredgings, and topographic profiles [1] have shown that there are many areas where nearly horizontal formations are truncated by the conti-nental slope (Fig. 7). Although it seems apparent from the structure sections (Fig. 5) that the continental slope owes its location and primary origin to deep-seated fundamental faults, it seems unlikely that the faulting truncated late Tertiary beds. Thus, the outcrop pattern on the upper continental slope seems to be controlled by an interplay of depositional processes on the continental shelf and erosional processes on the continental slope. However, the original scarps, now partially buried, must have been fault scarps. The present continental slope thus seems to be a relic related to normal faulting which occurred at some earlier time.

Distension and normal faulting along the borders of the Atlantic and Indian Oceans is completely in agreement with the continental drift hypothesis. However, according to both Taylor's [17] and Wegener's [18] hypotheses, the trenches of the Pacific margin should be under compression since the continents should be over-riding the ocean along the great circum-Pacific belt. We see no compelling reasons to classify Atlantic trenches as extensional and Pacific trenches as compressional; and thus we see here an apparent obstacle to continental drift.

The degree of irregularity of small scale sea-floor relief is the result of the interplay of erosional, depositional and tectonic processes. With the exception of the trenches, marginal escarpments and submarine canyons the continental margins are characterized by relatively gentle

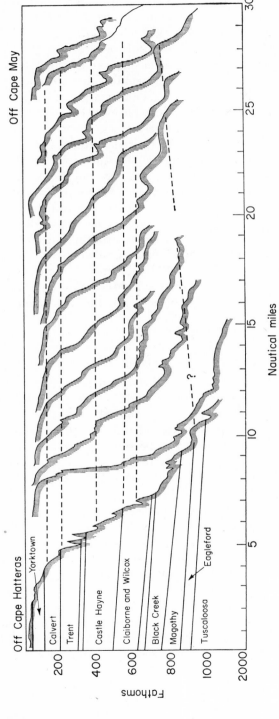

Fig. 7. Correlation of structural benches on the continental slope, Cape Hatteras to Cape May. Soundings by U.S. Coast and Geodetic Survey. Profile on left is based on extrapolations of deep test-borings in the coastal plain. It is believed that turbidity currents, slumps, and bottom currents have removed sediment from the continental slope so as to expose the pattern of outcrops shown in this figure. This does not indicate faulting in late Tertiary time, but simply the inability of sediments to be permanently deposited on a steep slope.

relief (Fig. 8). The submarine canyons, deep-sea fans, levied deep-sea channels and abyssal cones can be adequately explained through the activity of turbidity currents [1, 19]. The smooth topography of the continental rise (Fig. 8) is the combined result of a relatively high rate of sedimentation of both particle-by-particle type and turbidity-current type and the smoothing processes of both turbidity currents and oceanic bottom currents [20]. In the average continental margin only the largest morphotectonic features are observed, since most of the smaller tectonic relief is deeply buried beneath a relatively thick cover of sediments. However, recent detailed studies by the United States Coast and Geodetic Survey and the Scripps Institution of Oceanography off the west coast of North America [21] and investigations by the Research Vessel VEMA off the east coast of Brazil have revealed a parallelism between the minor topographic features of the continental rise and the trend of the continental slope. Apparently, in these areas either the sedimentary blanket is thin, or the balance between sedimentation and tectonics is more favourable to the preservation of tectonic relief than it is off the coast of Morocco and eastern United States. Since the orientation of this relief is dominantly parallel to the trend of the continental margin, it implies deformation essentially normal to the continent–ocean boundary.

B. OCEAN-BASIN FLOOR

The abyssal floor, the oceanic rises, and the seamount groups are the three subdivisions of the ocean-basin floor [1]. The abyssal floor is divided into two types of provinces: (1) the smooth abyssal plains; and (2) the intensely disrupted, finely textured relief of the abyssal hills (Figs. 9, 10). The abyssal floor seems to be structurally one unit, the sharp contrast between the abyssal plains and the abyssal hills being the result of turbidity-current deposition that buried the abyssal hills in the areas now occupied by abyssal plains.

Rising from the abyssal floor are the oceanic rises typified by the Bermuda Rise in the western Atlantic [1] or the Mendocino Rise [22] in the eastern Pacific. The local relief of the rises is moderate, being much smoother than the abyssal hills but more irregular than the continental rise. A unique feature of the oceanic rises is their asymmetry, both in gross form and in detail. The Mendocino Rise of the eastern Pacific is a prime example. Extending over 2,000 miles in an east–west direction, the entire southern side is formed by the Mendocino Escarpment, while the northern side is in the form of a gentle ramp. The Bermuda Rise seems to be more complexly fractured than the Mendocino Rise. In

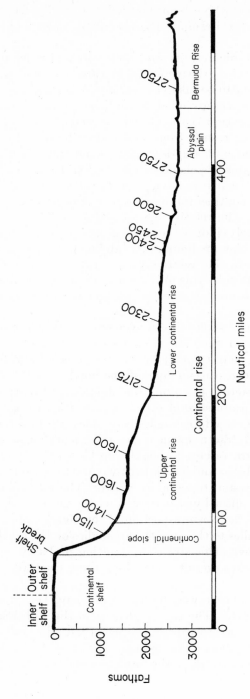

Fɪɢ. 8. Continental margin provinces: type profile off eastern United States. Note the generally subdued relief typical of Atlantic continental margins.

addition to the 600-fathom-high, 600-mile-long scarp which forms the eastern boundary, the Bermuda Rise is cut by a series of other south-east-facing scarps.

Their lack of seismic activity and their subdued relief suggests that oceanic rises must be relatively old features. In mid-oceanic areas smoothness of relief can be taken as evidence of relative age if turbidity-current deposition can be excluded. Turbidity-current deposits are absent from oceanic rises, except in the vicinity of islands. Smoothing in areas of pelagic deposition results from local redistribution of sediments by gravitational movements, and deep-sea bottom currents. Such smoothing is limited by rates of pelagic sedimentation. In contrast, turbidity-current deposition, which involves transportation of huge volumes of sediment from the continental margins, is independent of local rates of pelagic deposition. The relative age of abyssal hills and oceanic rises cannot be accurately judged because of the higher rates of pelagic sedimentation on the predominantly globigerina ooze-covered rises, in comparison with the relatively low rates on the clay-covered abyssal hills [23]. Despite this uncertainty, it still seems likely that the rugged abyssal hills are tectonically younger than the smooth oceanic rises.

Evidence of huge strike-slip movements between crustal blocks comes from studies of magnetic anomalies in the eastern Pacific (Figs. 11 and 12, and Fig. 6 of Chapter 5). A series of east–west fractures are recognized in the ocean-basin floor of the north-east Pacific [24]. The most prominent fracture lies along the Mendocino Escarpment. South of this major scarp are several other parallel fracture zones of lower relief which can be traced for hundreds of miles. Both to the north and to the south of each fracture zone minor relief features, as well as magnetic anomalies, are oriented roughly north–south [7]. The spacing between magnetic highs and lows is irregular and the correlation between magnetic anomalies and topography is poor. The north–south pattern is interrupted and offset by east–west fracture zones. If the pattern of anomalies north of the western portion of the Mendocino fracture zone is translated 650 miles to the east, the anomalies on the north and south sides can be matched. This strike-slip faulting probably occurred long ago, since earthquakes do not occur along these fractures in the deep-sea floor.

Recently a series of east–west fracture zones have been mapped in the equatorial Atlantic [25]. The crest provinces of the Mid-Atlantic Ridge have been displaced westward by a series of left-slip faults for a total distance of nearly 2,000 miles between 2°S and 15°N. It is highly probable that the entire ridge (the flank provinces as well as the crest

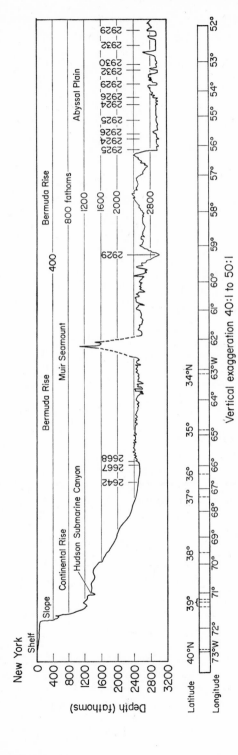

FIG. 9. Ocean-basin floor. Precision Depth Recorder profile between the Mid-Atlantic Ridge and New York; showing abyssal plain, the Bermuda Rise, and continental margin. Note steep, asymmetrical scarps along east side of Bermuda Rise and fine-textured relief in west portions of Bermuda Rise, which sharply contrast with smooth topography of continental margin. Note also extremely flat gradients of the abyssal plain, in eastern part of profile. Depths in fathoms.

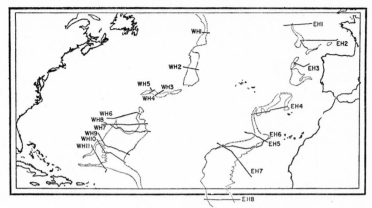

Limits of abyssal hills provinces shown by dotted lines.

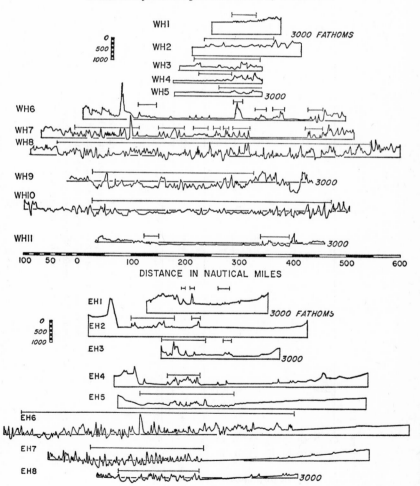

provinces) is displaced, but the extent of the fractures into the eastern
basin has not been adequately surveyed [26].

The strike-slip displacements between oceanic crustal blocks,
amounting to several hundreds of miles, which have been demonstrated
west of California; and the similar displacements between crustal
blocks in the equatorial Atlantic, suggest a crustal rigidity sharply
contradictory to the concept of a viscous sima envisioned by advocates
of continental drift.

Seismic-refraction studies in the abyssal floor generally reveal the

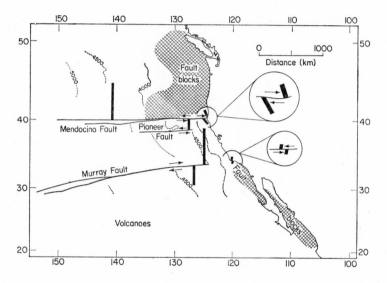

FIG. 11. Displacement along major strike-slip faults off California. (After Menard [44].)
The heavy bars, oriented in a north–south direction, represent characteristic magnetic
anomalies that have been identified. The sense of the displacement is indicated by arrows.
Note that the sense of the movement is reversed near shore on two of the faults. Points
of no movement appear to lie near the crest of the landward prolongation of the mid-
oceanic ridge. If this interpretation is correct, the area north of the Mendocino Fault
must have undergone over 600 miles of distension.

FIG. 10. Abyssal hills and abyssal plains, North Atlantic Ocean. Vertical exaggeration
40:1. The main difference between abyssal hill areas and the abyssal plains of the ocean-
basin floor is the fill of blanketing sediment which has buried the irregular relief in the
abyssal plains. Gravity and magnetic anomalies and sub-bottom reflection records
indicate that the topography of the basement under the abyssal plains is similar to
bottom topography in the abyssal hill areas. Reflection data suggest that many of the
abyssal hills are outcrops of basement topography. Transportation of large quantities of
terrigenous sediments by turbidity currents offers a satisfactory explanation for the
abyssal plains.

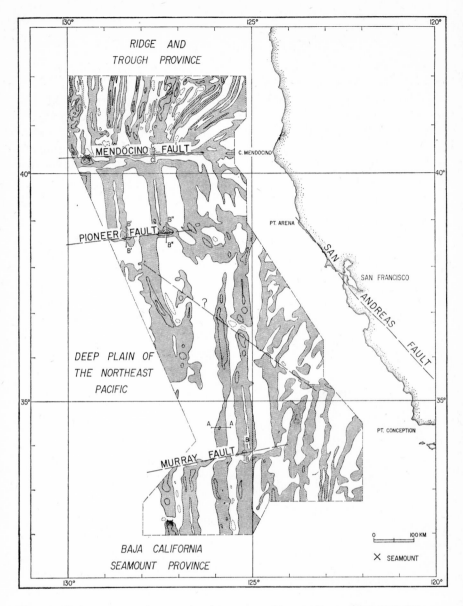

FIG. 12. Skeleton magnetic map showing geomorphic provinces and principal known faults off California. Contour interval 250 gammas. Areas of positive anomaly are stippled. Negative contour lines are broken. (After Vacquier [7]). The strong lineation of the magnetic topography, which roughly parallels the coast and intersects the fracture zones at right angles, is paralleled by a similar pattern in the minor topographic relief. However, the magnetic anomalies do not correlate precisely with the topographic features. Nevertheless, this seems to indicate that the deformation which created the minor topography also created the characteristic magnetic anomalies. If the displacements along the Mendocino Fault, indicated in Fig. 11, are both east and west on the north side of the fault some of the anomalies shown north of 41° must have been created relatively recently and be younger than the anomalies of other areas. Perhaps this topography is characteristic of areas in which horizontal extension in the crust has occurred.

oceanic column shown in Fig. 13 [4, 5]. However, the oceanic rises generally differ in having more layers of lower velocity [27]. The typical oceanic crustal section indicates a 0·25 to 1 km upper, relatively low-velocity (2 km/sec) layer of "sediments". However, measured rates of deep-sea sedimentation and calculations of probable erosion products

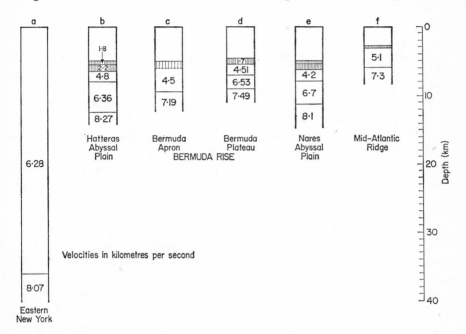

FIG. 13. Crustal thickness measurements in the North Atlantic.

suggest that greater thickness should be observed [28]. In order to explain the inferred lower rates of sedimentation in the past, it was suggested that pelagic foraminifera, which account for much of the calcareous globigerina ooze, only evolved in the Mesozoic. However, a modern globigerina ooze is often nearly half coccoliths, and the coccolithophoradae may have existed in Paleozoic time [29]. It has also been suggested that lower relief on the land during earlier geologic periods vastly decreased the erosion of the continents. Hamilton [30] has suggested that the layer of approximately 4·5 km/sec frequently found underlying the sediments represents lithified sediments. He supports this contention with measurements made on samples of lithified globigerina ooze dredged from various parts of the Pacific.

Extrapolating from present rates of sedimentation the 0·5 to 1 km of sediments in the Atlantic may have been deposited since the Mesozoic. This would agree with conventional ideas of continental drift; for, if the continents on either side of the Atlantic began drifting apart some time in the early Mesozoic [18], sediments of an earlier date would not be expected in the Atlantic basin. The similarity of sediment thickness in the Atlantic and Pacific, and the presence of a second layer of nearly the same velocity and thickness in both oceans, presents a serious problem for conventional ideas of continental drift. If the continents, originally grouped together in one or two ancient proto-continents, drifted apart, forming the Atlantic and Indian Oceans and encroaching on the centre of the North Pacific, the most complete record of sediments should lie in the North Pacific. A significant difference of sediment thickness and unique topographic forms would be expected in the North Pacific. Although the data is still meagre, there seems to be no significant difference in crustal structure between the Pacific Ocean and the Atlantic or Indian Oceans, as would be expected from Wegener- or Taylor-type drift. The oceanic crustal layer is found throughout the ocean-basin floor and varies little in velocity or thickness from place to place except on the oceanic rises.

In the first experimental test of the Mohole drilling apparatus, basalt was encountered beneath about 500 feet of Miocene and post-Miocene sediments [32]. It is suspected by marine geologists that this basalt, possibly related to the volcanic activity of nearby Guadalupe Island, is not indicative of the composition or age of the "second layer". Only subsequent drilling or dredging could confirm or discredit this view. Possibly the nature of the second layer could be determined by dredging from escarpments. Present evidence is scanty, for only a few rock dredge hauls have been made in the deep sea. Rocks recovered that seem *in situ* and not rafted are predominantly basalts and ultra-basic types [2]. However, two dredge hauls in the north-east Atlantic contained trilobites [33] and, although rafting is suspected, it cannot be definitely proved.

A conical seamount over 1,000 fathoms high can be safely assumed to be volcanic in origin. The fact that seamounts virtually all lie in linear patterns [34] suggests that fundamental faults in the earth's crust may have dictated their distribution (Fig. 14). Of the hundreds of seamounts discovered, many have been found to possess flat tops. From the flat surfaces of several 500 to 800 fathom deep mid-Pacific seamounts [35] Cretaceous reef corals were dredged. Thus, either these drowned, ancient islands have subsided or the ocean surface has risen.

The guyots prove that the mid-Pacific was at least 2,000 fathoms deep in mid-Cretaceous time, and that no extensive continental land area

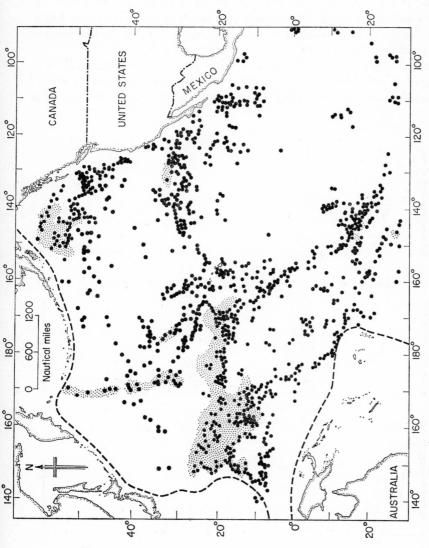

FIG. 14. Volcanic mountains of the Pacific. (After Menard [34]). The chart shows the distribution of mountains rising more than 500 fm above the sea floor. Those mountains within the shaded area are predominantly flat-topped guyots. Note the tendency of the mountains to lie along straight lines, possibly indicating major faults in the earth's crust.

existed there. The guyots are of significance in considerations of continental drift because they prohibit reconstructions that would require continents to drift at a later time through areas occupied by dated guyots. If the seamounts subsided as individual loads on the crust, the ocean could have been deeper than the minimum stated above, but it could not have been shallower than an amount equal to the present heights of the flat tops above the adjacent ocean floor.

Some seamounts are surrounded by a moat [36], which has been interpreted as evidence of the subsidence of the sea floor under the load of the seamount. Surrounding the islands and flat-topped seamounts

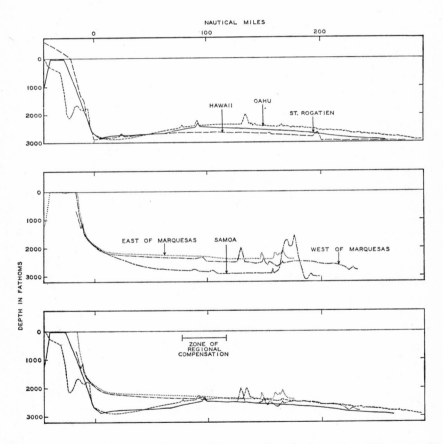

FIG. 15. Archipelagic aprons and associated features. Note the depression which surrounds the Hawaiian Islands. It is believed that similar depressions were either filled by turbidity-current sediments to form the archipelagic aprons or that the depression surrounding the Hawaiian Islands represents an archipelagic apron downbowed by the weight of the islands. (After Menard [36]).

archipelagic aprons are often found which spread out from the base of the pedestal (Fig. 15). Often much of the area of an archipelagic apron has been smoothed by turbidity-current deposition. Menard [36] does not believe that the aprons could have been built by deposits eroded or erupted from the mountains, since the volume of the aprons exceeds by many-fold the volume of the whole remaining pedestal. However, the presence of shallow-water deposits on the smooth surface of the archipelagic plains certainly suggests that the smooth surface was produced by turbidity-current deposition. Shallow-water shells [37] have been cored from the Bermuda archipelagic plain, and the present writer considers this plain to be entirely the result of turbidity-current smoothing.

The existence of flat-topped seamounts in the Pacific, and in the Atlantic as well, which appear to have existed for tens of millions of years, is hard to reconcile with that fundamental assumption of continental drift—that the floor of the ocean is weak right up to the surface. Although we do not know the age of the escarpments and the oceanic rises, they appear to be relatively old and, if so, impossible to reconcile with a concept that would cause one to expect such scarps to have long since flattened out. Crustal extension, strike-slip faulting, normal faulting and subsidence seem to be the dominant tectonic factors in the ocean-basin floor.

C. MID-OCEANIC RIDGE

The centre third of the Atlantic, Indian and South Pacific Oceans is occupied by a continuous, broad, fractured swell known as the mid-oceanic ridge [1, 38]. The Mid-Atlantic Ridge, that portion of the mid-oceanic ridge lying in the Atlantic Ocean, is the best known portion of this 35,000 mile long feature. A profile across the mid-oceanic ridge closely resembles any other (Fig. 16). There is a crest zone of extremely rugged relief and a broader, rugged flank on either side. The physiographic details of the mid-oceanic ridge are extremely difficult to follow because of the strong relief, the scarcity of data, and the lack of precision navigation systems in mid-ocean.

The rift valley, a deep cleft in the crest provinces, lies along the axis of the ridge and coincides with the belt of mid-oceanic epicentres (Fig. 17). The rugged rift mountains parallel the rift valley on either side. The flank provinces descend to the ocean-basin floor on each side of the crest. The pattern of provinces described above and illustrated in Fig. 19 has been traced for 35,000 miles along a world-encircling mid-oceanic belt. All major features of the mid-oceanic ridge system are roughly parallel to the axis of the ridge median rift and to the major trends of the

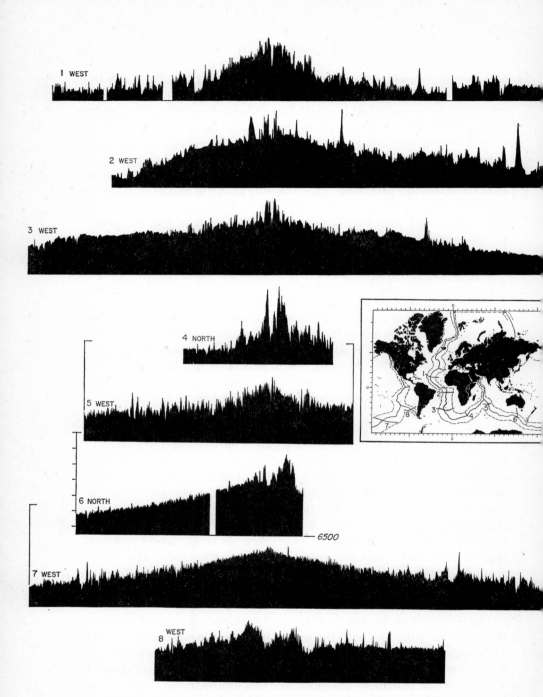

Fɪɢ. 16. Eight profiles of the mid-oceanic ridge. Profiles 1 to 6 all have a well-defined rift valley set in the midst of very rugged relief. However, profile 7 in the South Pacific sharply contrasts with the others, in having its highest relief near the flanks of the ridge rather than near the crest. Base-line is 6,500 m for all profiles. All profiles, except the second, were obtained with Precision Depth Recorder aboard Research Vessel VEMA.

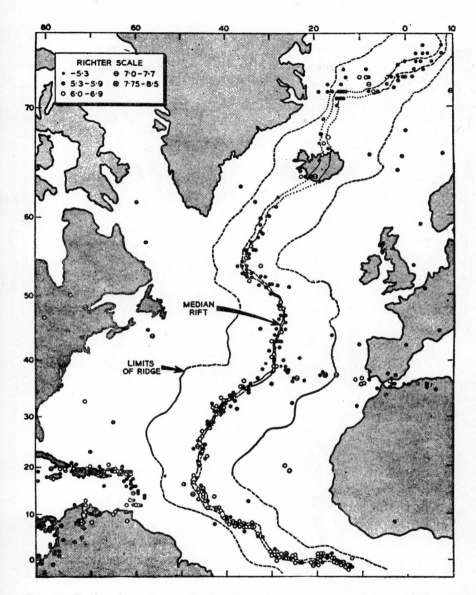

RICHTER SCALE
- • −5·3   ⊖ 7·0−7·7
- • 5·3−5·9 ⊗ 7·75−8·5
- ○ 6·0−6·9

MEDIAN
RIFT

LIMITS
OF RIDGE

FIG. 17. Earthquake epicentres in the North Atlantic. Note that all epicentres are closely clustered near crest of ridge. It seems likely that all earthquakes occur either in or near median rift valley. On the basis of this excellent correlation in the North Atlantic, rift valley and crest provinces of the ridge have been traced throughout 35,000-mile belt encircling the world.

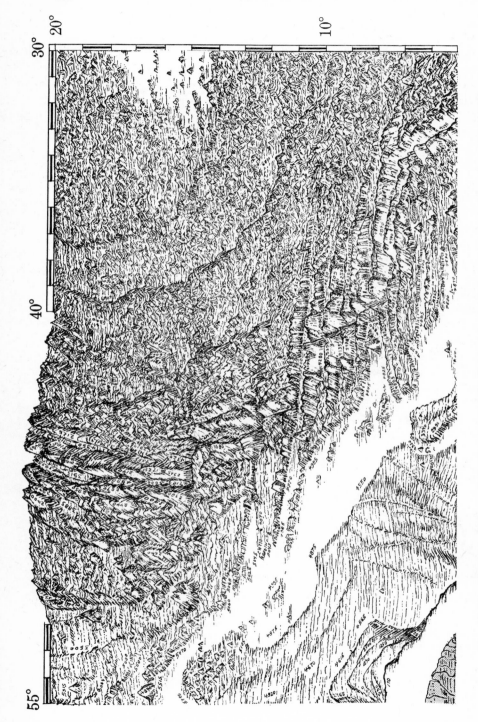

FIG. 18. Physiographic diagram of the equatorial Atlantic, showing several prominent fracture zones which displace the axis of the Mid-Atlantic Ridge. (This is a portion of the Physiographic Diagram of the South Atlantic published by the Geological Society of America. Copyright 1961 by Bruce C. Heezen and Marie Tharp. Reprinted by permission.)

continental margins, as if all were minor splinters and fissures in the floor of one grand crack; the ocean basin.

The rifted mid-oceanic ridge impinges on the continents in several places. It traverses the Gulf of Aden, the median rift merging with the rift valleys of East Africa. The rift valleys in the high plateaux of East Africa are nearly identical in form to the rift in the mid-oceanic ridge (Fig. 20). Since they form parts of a continuous feature, we can infer that both are the result of similar tectonic processes. The geology of East Africa is fairly well known, at least in comparison with the geology of the mid-oceanic ridge. Although attempts have been made to explain the structure of the East African Rifts in terms of compression [39, 40], the dominant view is that the rifts are due to extension of the crust. In short, it is believed that the rift valleys are graben. The mid-oceanic rift valley belt is probably not a continuous, canyon-like feature. The belt is probably composed of a series of semi-continuous, semi-*en echelon* troughs somewhat similar in plan to the pattern of East African rifts.

The Mid-Atlantic Ridge extends through Iceland, and the central graben of Iceland is the extension of the mid-oceanic rift. All Quaternary vulcanism in Iceland is localized in the central graben [41]. The floor of the central graben is cut by numerous active fissures (gjá) which parallel the boundary faults of the graben (Fig. 21). Here again, in the landward extension of the mid-oceanic rift valley, distensional tectonics are characteristic. The rifted mid-oceanic ridge crosses the Arctic Basin [38], impinging on the Siberian continental shelf in the vicinity of the Lena Delta. A landward extension of the line of epicentres associated with the Arctic portion of the mid-oceanic ridge follows the Verkhoyansk Trough and the western flank of the Verkhoyansk Mountains for hundreds of miles into the interior of Siberia [42].

In the east Pacific the Easter Island Ridge runs north-east toward the Gulf of California (Fig. 22). The epicentre belt, which continues along the axis of the Easter Island Ridge, extends into the Gulf of California and appears to connect with the three seismicity belts of western United States. The eastern branch follows a line of great trenches, including the Rocky Mountain Trench. The middle fork extends up the Inyo Valley on the east flank of the Sierra Nevada, and the western flank follows the San Andreas fault of California to a point north of Cape Mendocino, where the epicentre belt again extends out to sea. In the region between Cape Mendocino and the mouth of the Lynn Canal of Alaska, the belt of epicentres follows a system of parallel ridges and troughs [24], which seem similar to the rifted mid-oceanic ridge. The long, linear Lynn Canal is apparently fault-controlled.

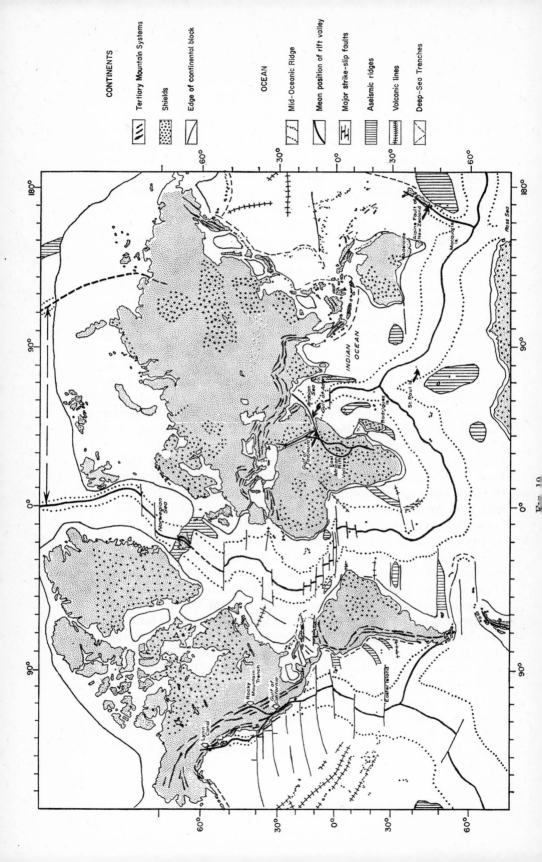

CONTINENTS

⊿ Tertiary Mountain Systems

⊡ Shields

⊿ Edge of continental block

OCEAN

⋯ Mid-Oceanic Ridge

⟋ Mean position of rift valley

⊢⊣ Major strike-slip faults

≡ Aseismic ridges

⊥⊥⊥ Volcanic lines

⊠ Deep-Sea Trenches

Fig. 10

South-east of Easter Island a branch of the mid-oceanic ridge extends toward southern Chile [43], and although this area has not yet been adequately explored, the fault-bounded canals of southern Chile seem to be the landward extension of the mid-oceanic ridge tectonic complex.

Seismic-refraction measurements in the North Atlantic [3] and across the eastern Pacific [4, 44] reveal that the structure of the mid-oceanic ridge strongly contrasts with the typical ocean basins. Instead of the typical column shown in Fig. 13b, the mid-oceanic ridge is underlain at shallow depths by a crustal layer characterized by compressional wave velocities of 7·2 to 7·4 km/sec. Normal 8·2 km/sec velocities have never been found in the crest provinces of the ridge. A schematic structure section of the North Atlantic is shown in Fig. 23. The 7·2 to 7·4 velocity material has been interpreted by the Ewings as a mixture of the 6·4 and 8·1 km/sec material. On the other hand, it might be a distinctive layer, not represented in deep ocean or in continental structure. A further possibility is that the 7·2 to 7·4 km/sec rocks represent the upper mantle, somewhat altered by its shallow depth. Recently the very intriguing suggestion has been made that this layer represents the low-velocity layer of the mantle, which lies about 120 km beneath the continents, but only 50 km beneath the ocean-basin floor, and could possibly come to the surface beneath the mid-oceanic ridge (Fig. 24).

Strongly positive magnetic anomalies were found to be characteristic of most crossings of the rift valley in the North and South Atlantic [45]. However, only a few of the profiles across the rift valley of the Indian Ocean revealed such an anomaly. It is concluded that in most areas of the Atlantic a body of high magnetic susceptibility lies beneath the rift valley, but that this body is not universally present, and is therefore not a completely essential feature of the ridge [45].

Free-air gravity anomalies are much lower over the rift valley than over adjacent rift mountains, but when the effects of topography

---

FIG. 19. Major tectonic features of the earth. The map of the mid-oceanic rift valley is essentially a plot of the mid-oceanic earthquakes. In every area in which the bathymetry is known, the epicentre belt follows the crest of the mid-oceanic ridge. In almost every area where detailed submarine topographic studies have been carried out in the region of the epicentre belt, the median rift valley has been discovered, with the exception of certain areas of the South Pacific. Wherever the rift-valley extends across continental margins, it joins either rift, graben (as in East Africa or Iceland) or great strike-slip faults (as in California or New Zealand). The axis of the mid-oceanic ridge is displaced by fracture zones in the equatorial Atlantic and in the north-east Pacific. The oceans are so poorly surveyed that it cannot be known if additional fracture zones exist. A few fracture zones are highly speculative, particularly those in the South Pacific and the Norwegian Sea. Note that the mid-oceanic ridge is a much longer and more extensive feature than the Tertiary mountain systems of the continents.

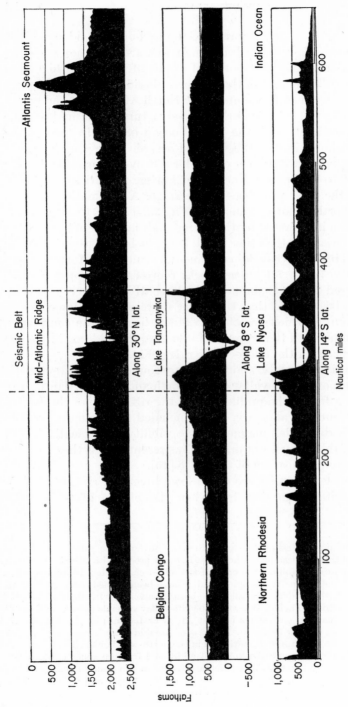

FIG. 20. Profiles of African rift valleys and the Mid-Atlantic Ridge. Note the great similarity in form of the rift valley and the rift mountains on these three profiles. The lower two were taken from topographic maps of Africa, while the top profile was taken from echograms across the crest of the Mid-Atlantic Ridge in the North Atlantic. The rift valley of the Mid-Atlantic Ridge is indeed similar in form and probably in origin to the rift valleys of Africa. All three profiles shown in this figure lie along the same epi-centre belt (as indicated in Fig. 19).

are taken into account the values over the rift are not found to be anomalous [46]. Thus, neither gravity nor magnetics offers definitive evidence of a unique crustal structure beneath the rift valley (Fig. 25).

Measurements of heat-flow indicate that the flow through the mid-oceanic ridge is much higher than that measured in the basins [8]. Measurements of heat-flow in the ocean basins indicate values of about $1 \cdot 2 \times 10^{-6}$ cal/cm^2/sec, roughly equivalent to the average continental values (Fig. 26). A value for the Mid-Atlantic Rift Valley of $7 \cdot 5 \times 10^{-6}$ cal/cm^2/sec has been determined by Bullard [47], and von Herzen [8] has reported several values near $6 \cdot 5 \times 10^{-6}$ cal/cm^2/sec near the crest of the Easter Island Ridge (Fig. 27).

III. Seismological Evidence for a Difference between the Continental and Oceanic Mantle

Advocates of continental drift generally choose the crust–mantle boundary as the interface above which drift occurred. The 35-km thick continental rafts, it might be maintained, ride over the oceanic crust, possibly incorporating the thin oceanic crust along their leading edges. However, this picture is complicated by structure in the upper mantle. Gutenberg long advocated the existence of a low velocity channel in the upper mantle [48]. His last estimates were that this channel lay at approximately 140 km depth. Since he used the earthquake travel-times between hypocentres of intermediate and deep-focus earthquakes and recording stations, his studies really only applied to continental areas. Landisman and Dorman [49] working with Love wave and Rayleigh wave dispersion respectively, showed that the depth of the minimum velocity channel lies at only 50 km under the oceans, versus about 150 km beneath the continents.

Press [50, 51] has developed a model which he feels fits the surface wave data as well as that proposed by Dorman. He suggests that the axis of the low velocity channel is everywhere at the same depth, but that the velocity in the channel is several per cent lower beneath the oceans than beneath the continent.

Both Love wave and Rayleigh wave data indicate a contrast between continental and oceanic mantle. The geological cause of this difference is unknown, but a difference in composition or history is suggested. If continents have drifted, it would seem necessary to assume that the drift occurred below 400 km, the depth at which the differences between continent and ocean mantle seem to disappear. Alternatively, if continental drift occurred at the M-discontinuity, it would seem necessary to devise a mechanism to alter the surface wave transmission characteristics of the mantle at both leading and following edges of the drifting continent.

K

(a)

FIG. 21. Vertical fissures (gjá) in the central graben of Iceland. Photographs taken from the air near Thingvellir. (a), photograph of Alamannagjá; (b), photograph of Hrafnagjá. Geological investigations in Iceland have allowed the conclusion that the central graben

(b).

of Iceland is extending at the rate of 3·5 m/km/1,000 years. The vertical fissures parallel the boundary of the median graben of Iceland, and lie along the active earthquake epicentre belt of central Iceland.

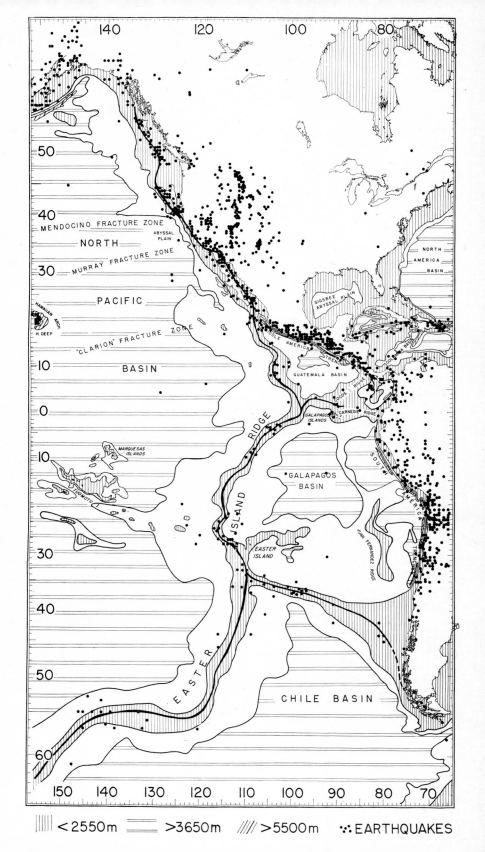

‖‖‖ < 2550m	══ > 3650m	⫽⫽⫽ > 5500m	⁚⁚ EARTHQUAKES

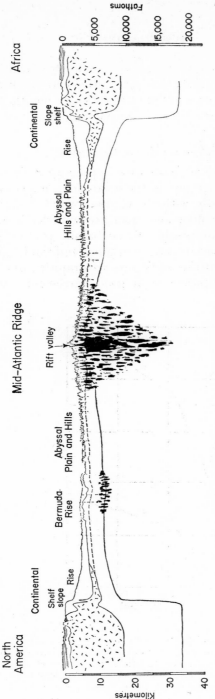

Fig. 23. Crustal section across the North Atlantic. The dark shaded area represents the 7·2 to 7·4 km/sec material which lies beneath the crest of the Mid-Atlantic Ridge. This material may be altered upper mantle or a mixture of mantle and crust. The first layer under the oceans represents sediments; the second, possibly lithified sediments or, more probably, volcanics; and the third is the oceanic crustal layer. Beneath this layer lies the mantle. This illustration is based on the correlation of crustal thickness measurements and physiography throughout the North Atlantic.

Fig. 22. Bathymetry and seismicity of the eastern Pacific. The large scatter in epicentres located in the South Pacific can be attributed to poor determinations far from seismograph stations. The generalized bathymetry shown on the chart is modified from the General Bathymetric Chart of the Oceans.

MacDonald [52], in trying to explain the similarity of continental and oceanic heat-flow has suggested that radioactive material is three times more plentiful in the upper 500 km of the oceanic mantle than in the upper portion of the mantle beneath the continents.

IV. PETROGRAPHY OF THE OCEANS

The continents and oceans are more than hypsographic divisions of the earth's surface. The petrography of the ocean floor, imperfectly known as it is, contrasts markedly with the continents [2, 53, 54]. All rocks collected from the ocean floor and from oceanic islands are basic in composition, consisting of basalt, olivine basalt, gabbro, serpentine, and peridotite. Oceanic basalts are remarkably uniform in composition. The Wegenerian view that the continents are granitic rafts which float in the simatic mantle beneath is in good agreement with existing petrographic data.

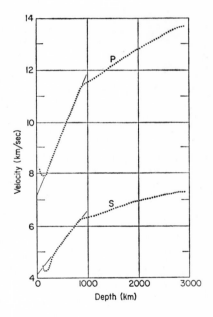

FIG. 24. Compression (P) and shear (S) wave velocities in the earth. (After Gutenberg[48].) Note that, if the slope of the compressional wave velocity curve between 100 and 900 km were extrapolated to the surface, it would intersect the surface at a velocity of about 7·4 km. Such velocities are found at the crest of the mid-oceanic ridge, whereas elsewhere velocities near 8·2 km/sec are found. It has been suggested that mantle material newly emplaced at the surface of the earth might be characterized by lower velocity, and only after some time through the action of unspecified processes would the upper part of the mantle increase in velocity and reach the characteristic 8·2 km/sec value.

V. Age of Ocean Basins

It is obvious that if there were a positive way to determine the age of ocean basins, most of the problems concerning continental displacement would already have been solved. Although we have no positive means of dating basins, there are some interesting arguments based in part on unverifiable assumptions which may be considered.

Of the many thousands of cores and dredge hauls from the ocean floor, an appreciable percentage have revealed ancient sediments. Yet the oldest sediment obtained is Middle Cretaceous or early Upper Cretaceous in age [23]. It is possible that older sediments are too deeply buried or that the thousands of cores we have constitute too small a

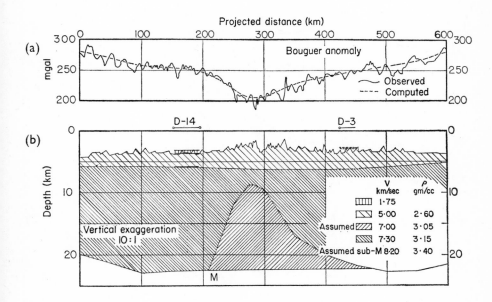

Fig. 25. Gravity anomalies and structure of the Mid-Atlantic Ridge. (a), Bouguer anomaly; kilometre 300 is located at Latitude 32°N, Longitude 40°W. (b), Possible structure of the Mid-Atlantic Ridge. Stations D–14 and D–3 are seismic refraction stations. A hypothetical layer of 7·00 km/sec (3·05 gm/cc) has been introduced below the crest provinces. Alternate interpretations: (i) thickening in the upper crustal layer; (ii) deepening of the M-discontinuity under the crest of the ridge. Interpretation shown is considered better, since it ascribes unique characteristics to the axis of the mid-oceanic ridge along which high heatflow, high seismicity and high relief are observed. The following is a possible interpretation of the magnetic anomalies generally but not always associated with the crest of the ridge; if the 7·0 km/sec velocity body reaches a depth at which temperatures fall below the Curie point, a high magnetic susceptibility might be found in the upper portion of this body, whereas if the top of this body does not reach that depth, the temperatures would always be higher than the Curie point and therefore no magnetic anomaly would occur. (After Talwani [46].)

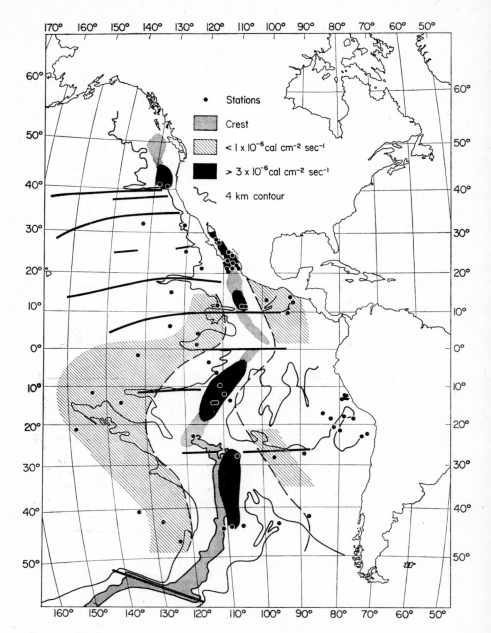

Fig. 26. Slip faults and heat-flow in the mid-oceanic ridge of the east Pacific. The east–west trending black bars indicate the slip faults which cross the crest of the mid-oceanic ridge. The band of high heat-flow associated with the crest of the ridge appears to pass through the western United States. (After Menard [44]). High heat-flow has been observed along the crest of the mid-oceanic ridge in the Pacific, as well as at a few points in the North Atlantic. The slip faults in the south-east Pacific, although probable, are largely hypothetical. Insufficient data has been obtained to indicate whether slip faults have offset the crest of the mid-oceanic ridge in the equatorial or South Pacific.

sample. Nevertheless, it seems apparent that if the oceans are much older than Cretaceous, a serious reorganization in the ocean floor occurred in Cretaceous time.

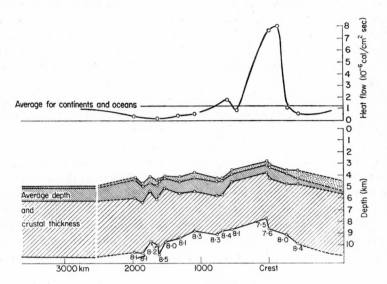

FIG. 27. Crustal section and heat-flow profiles of the mid-oceanic ridge in the eastern Pacific. Velocities below the crust are in km/sec. The region of very high heat-flow and anomalous mantle velocities is associated with the crest of the mid-oceanic ridge. (After Menard [44].) There are several differences between the mid-oceanic ridge in the eastern Pacific and the North Atlantic. (*i*) lower topographic relief is found over the entire ridge in the Pacific; (*ii*) if a rift valley exists it must be small in the eastern Pacific; (*iii*) mantle velocities in the Easter Island Ridge are, in general, normal—except near the exact axis of the ridge; whereas in the Mid-Atlantic Ridge the region of 7·2 to 7·4 km/sec rocks is more extensive. Although only a few measurements are made in the North Atlantic, the localization of high heat-flow along the crest of the ridge seems to be similar in both oceans.

As we have already pointed out, the guyots of the Pacific prove that deep sea existed over much of the mid-Pacific during Upper Cretaceous time; and presumably the area must have been deep sea for a considerable time prior to Upper Cretaceous.

A large number of measurements of thickness of sediments of the ocean basin have been made by the seismic-refraction technique. If an estimate of the average rate of sedimentation during the deposition of this sediment could be made, a rough estimate of the age of the basins would be obtained. Rates of sedimentation are known to vary widely in the late Pleistocene and Recent [55]; and earlier rates may have varied even more. It is still uncertain whether the second layer

(4·5 km/sec) is sediment, effusives, or both. Using average sedimentation rates and correcting for compaction, Hamilton concludes that the major ocean basins are Paleozoic to pre-Paleozoic in age. However, if he were not to consider the 4·5 km/sec layer as sediment, these ages would be radically younger and probably lie somewhere in the Mesozoic.

Potassium argon dates determined by G. Erickson on several basalts dredged from the crest of the Mid-Atlantic Ridge indicate that rocks outcropping in the crest provinces are less than 20,000,000 years old. Rocks from the flank provinces have not been dated, due to the extremely weathered condition of existing samples, but this fact alone suggests that the flank province rocks may be older. There is some suggestion of an increase in age from the crest of the ridge outwards towards the flanks. However, only a few samples have been dated.

An instrument has recently been developed which records sub-bottom seismic reflections in a manner very similar to the conventional echo sounder. Small charges of TNT are exploded at intervals of 1 to 3 minutes. The echoes received from various sub-bottom layers are recorded on a chart similar to the conventional Precision Depth Recorder. The results of the first studies with this instrument, recently reported in a lecture by Maurice Ewing, are of great importance in considerations of continental drift and the age of the ocean basins. Throughout the North and South Atlantic several characteristic features have been found (Fig. 28). There is an extremely smooth interface 0·5 to 3 km below the sea floor. Ewing believes that the surface of interface 1 is in general smoother than the modern ocean-basin floor. Interface 2 is extremely irregular with topography greater than the modern ocean-basin floor. On the ocean-basin floor the thickness of the sediments between interface 1 and interface 2 varies from 0 to 1·5 km.

In profiles run toward the continent from the ocean-basin floor, the thickness of the sediments between interface 1 and interface 2 increases rapidly until interface 2 becomes so deep that no echoes are received. As the Mid-Atlantic Ridge is approached, the thickness of the layer between interface 1 and 2 decreases until only small pockets of sediment corresponding to this layer are found in intramontane basins. On the Mid-Atlantic Ridge both layers are generally absent, and sediments occur only in widely separated intramontane basins.

There seems to be no difficulty in tracing interface 1 from the continental rise, across the abyssal plains and oceanic rises to the flanks of the Mid-Atlantic Ridge. It is extremely persistent and appears to be firmly correlated. However, the possibility of miscorrelation cannot be neglected at this early stage of the investigation.

Extrapolating from ancient rates of sedimentation a date for the event which created interface 1 is extremely difficult. In Fig. 28a, a profile south-east of New York, the thickness of the sediment layer between the ocean floor and interface 1 varies from 3 km on the upper continental rise through less than 0·5 km on the abyssal plain, to about 1 km on the Bermuda Rise. In the lower continental rise, rates of sedimentation close to 4 to 5 cm/1,000 years might be expected. If, after allowance is made for compaction, a rate of sedimentation of 4·5 cm/1,000 years is assumed for the continental rise, interface 1 might date some

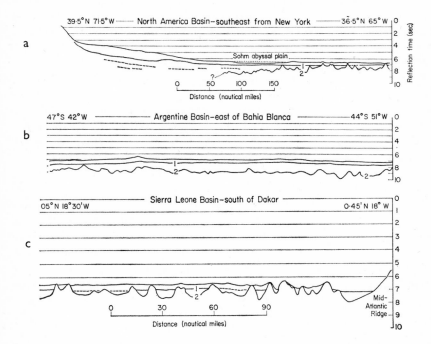

Fig. 28. Seismic reflection profiles of the North and South Atlantic, made with a seismic profiler. Two prominent interfaces are found on all seismic-profiler records in the North and South Atlantic. Interface 1 is, in general, smoother than the modern ocean-basin floor. Interface 2, which lies beneath, is in general rougher than the modern ocean-basin floor. Interface 2 seems to sink deep beneath the continental rise and rise to form the sea bed in the mid-oceanic ridge. It appears that some major event in the sedimentation history of the ocean created interface 1. This event may have been a change from clay to carbonate sedimentation, some vast reorganization of the oceanic circulation, or the deposition of a world-wide layer of volcanic ash or cosmic dust. Estimating from current rates of sedimentation, interface 1 could date from some time in the late Mesozoic. Interface 2 forms the upper surface of 4·5 to 5·0 km/sec layer. Since dredgings from the Mid-Atlantic Ridge have revealed basaltic and ultra-basic rock, it is concluded that the rocks beneath interface 2 are igneous rocks extruded or deformed during the creation of the Atlantic Ocean basin. Interface 1 is absent from the Mid-Atlantic Ridge, and it appears that the entire Mid-Atlantic Ridge has formed subsequent to the creation of interface 1. (After Ewing and Ewing [in press] and Ewing and Talwani [in press].)

75,000,000 years old. The present rate of sedimentation on the northern, lower-lying part of the Bermuda Rise represented in this profile should be expected to be very low, and one would infer from the low carbonate content in the area that the present rate would be measured in millimeters per thousand years. But if interface 1 represents an event some 75,000,000 years ago, a rate of 1·5 cm/1,000 years of compacted sediment would be deduced. This rate, higher than expected, might be explained if we presume that during the Tertiary the bottom waters of the Atlantic were warmer than at present, that the solution of calcareous oozes was on an average much less than at present, and therefore that a sedimentation rate for calcareous ooze should be assumed for the area rather than the rate for modern abyssal clay.

In the section of the flanks of the Mid-Atlantic Ridge in the equatorial Atlantic (Fig. 28c), the thickness between the sea floor and interface 1 is about 1 km. A reasonable guess for the present rate of sedimentation in this area, deduced from the rates measured in cores from the area, is about 2 or 2·5 cm/1,000 years of uncompacted sediment. A rate of 1·5 cm of compacted sediment per thousand years seems reasonable and again gives a date of 75,000,000 years. On the Argentine Rise the present sediment is entirely red clay and the rates of sedimentation would seem to be of the order of 1 or 2 mm/1,000 years. If interface 1 is to be everywhere the same age, we are again forced to appeal to the hypothesis that red clay was not deposited in this area throughout the Tertiary, but is a Pleistocene characteristic of the area and that Tertiary deposits are of deep-sea ooze. Although there are many uncertainties, horizon 1 could have originated approximately 100,000,000 years ago.

The occurrence of middle Tertiary carbonate oozes beneath red clay in the eastern Pacific, as reported by Arrhenius, adds certain support to the hypothesis that the bottom waters of the oceans have radically cooled throughout the Tertiary and that average Tertiary rates of sedimentation in deep basins of the oceans should be higher than the present-day rates of red clay accumulation and closer to the present-day rates of globigerina ooze accumulation (a difference of one order of magnitude).

If some great event caused a radical change in sedimentation, producing interface 1, we could perhaps presume that the material lying between interface 1 and interface 2 represents all previous sedimentation since the origin of oceanic crust in any particular area. Seismic-refraction results indicate that the material directly underlying interface 2 has a seismic velocity of 4 to 4·5 km/sec. Hamilton considers this material lithified sediment. The intense ruggedness of the relief is thought by some investigators to indicate a volcanic origin. It has also been suggested by some that the surface may be analogous to the surface of the moon, and be the primordial surface of the ocean floor. However, it seems possible that the rugged nature of this relief will turn out to have a strong tectonic lineation. Since horizon 2 seems to come to the sea bed and form appreciable parts of the Mid-Atlantic Ridge, it would seem that the buried relief should be similar to the relief of the mid-oceanic ridges. Since basaltic and ultrabasic rocks have been dredged from the crest of the Mid-Atlantic Ridge, it seems likely that the 4·5 km/sec layer is predominantly somewhat altered igneous rock.

To explain the absence of sediments from the Mid-Atlantic Ridge it has been suggested by Ewing that sediments laid on the Ridge were very mobile and flowed or were swept off the ridge. This presumed nature of the sediments seems inconsistent with the present stability of organic oozes cored on the flanks of the Mid-Atlantic Ridge. The observation of ripple marks, scour marks, rock outcrops and winnowed sands along the crest of the Mid-Atlantic Ridge indicates that the crest zone is very strongly influenced by the bottom currents; but that bottom currents, slides and turbidity currents could completely denude a kilometre of sediments from the entire Mid-Atlantic Ridge to depths of 6,000 m does not seem likely. Thus, the present writer concludes that a small thickness of sediment on the flanks of the mid-oceanic ridge could only be explained by a relatively youthful origin of the Mid-Atlantic Ridge. The high relief of the axis of the ridge, the high heat-flow, the characteristic seismic velocities, and the high seismicity all point to a very youthful mountain range. However, the flanks of this mountain range which extend outward for hundreds of miles, have a low heat-flow, low seismicity, more nearly normal crustal velocities and much lower relief. On the evidence of the absence of interfaces 1 and 2 from the ridge, it seems that virtually the entire width of the Mid-Atlantic Ridge must have been formed recently, probably during the Tertiary. If interface 1 dates from the end of the Mesozoic, the ocean-basin floor is considerably older than late Cretaceous, depending on the assumed rate of deposition and specific history of shell-bearing planktonic organisms.

The thickening in the layer between interface 1 and 2 in approaching the continents may, at least in part, be explained as the effect of the greater rate of sedimentation in the environs of a continent. However, the age of interface 2 may be older and older as one proceeds from the axis of the Mid-Atlantic Ridge towards the continents. If, as many have suggested, the Paleozoic was devoid of calcareous, shell-bearing plankton, then one may assume for the sediments lying between interface 1 and interface 2 rates of sedimentation of the order of a millimetre or less per thousand years.

What is the nature of the sharp transition which produced interface 1? Various events could have produced an interface having strong contrast of seismic impedence. One such event could be the change from a low carbonate to a high carbonate sediment, such as a change from red clay to globigerina ooze. Thus, if the sediments prior to horizon 1 represented abyssal clays laid down either in the colder bottom waters of the early Mesozoic or in an ocean devoid of calcareous shell-bearing plankton, one might find a plausible explanation for this sharp horizon. On the other hand, some of the sharpest reflectors found in the upper layers of sediment are beds of volcanic ash.

Considering the evolution of the deep ocean basins in terms of continental displacement, one would expect to find the age of interface 2 to be older and older as continents are approached. In Fig. 28a, the thickness of the sediment between the bottom and interface 1 is identical on the lower continental rise and on the Bermuda Rise; and only on the upper continental rise does the thickness of this upper layer increase radically, whereas the thickness of the sedimentary layer between interface 1 and 2 begins to increase markedly on the Bermuda Rise— nearly 200 miles farther from the continent.

VI. DISCUSSION OF THE HYPOTHESES OF CONTINENTAL DRIFT

According to the hypotheses of continental drift there have always been continents and oceans, but patterns of distribution have varied through time. Such changes have been accomplished by the drift of continents through oceans much in the way icebergs drift through seawater. The block composing the sea floor is assumed to be relatively weak with respect to the more rigid blocks constituting the continents. However, the existence of submarine mountain ranges seems to conflict with the assumption that the crust of the earth beneath the ocean is weak right up to the surface. If, despite this problem, we take the view that continental drift of the sort proposed by Wegener, Taylor, du Toit, and others has indeed occurred, and look for a way to fit the geology of the sea floor into a reasonable pattern within this general framework, we must assume the continuous creation of typical deep-sea topographic forms in the lee of the drifting continents. We must have an *ad hoc* explanation of the effect of a drifting continent upon the sea floor lying immediately in front of a moving continent. Since most advocates of drift believe that the continents have drifted away from the Atlantic, and the Atlantic is indeed a rift ocean, all conventional theories would presumably predict that new oceanic crust would be continually formed somewhere in the Atlantic. For, regardless of how weak the ocean crust is presumed to be, the existence of topographic forms in the oceans suggests that there is an oceanic layer of some thickness which has been deformed to produce the observed submarine topography.

One view might be that the drift of a continent, such as the supposed westward drift of North America, would create a narrow zone in its lee; which would fill up from below by sub-crustal upwelling. The surface of this upwelling mass might be expected to be irregular, for as the chilled surface of the newly formed crust was gradually uplifted, it would be expected to break and deform.

A second view might be that the distension due to the westward drift of America would be distributed across the breadth of the Atlantic Ocean. Under this hypothesis one would expect the topography of the Atlantic to be equally irregular throughout its width; except, of course, for the smoothing by sedimentation in the vicinity of the continental margins.

A third view might be that the new crust which must form due to the westward drift of America may be added in the mid-oceanic ridge. In support of this view is the seismic activity of the mid-oceanic rift valley and the fact that the highest and probably youngest relief in the entire width of the Atlantic is found along the crest of the mid-oceanic ridge [1].

Atlantic margins of North and South America are probably characterized by a continuous filled trench. It might be argued that these trenches are rifts on the back side of the continent—the space left when the continent moved away from the previously formed Atlantic ocean crust. However, these trenches are filled with enormous volumes of sediment, which could not be expected to have been deposited in any less than one or two hundred million years, so it seems unlikely that the filled trenches of the Atlantic can be used in such an explanation. On the Pacific margin of South America and Central America modern marginal trenches exist; and if we were to explain marginal trenches as gaps left behind drifting continents, we would be forced to assume that Central and South America were drifting east rather than west.

The second alternative, that the extension has been distributed throughout the width of the ocean at any one time, does not explain the apparent regional differences in age of the relief in the Atlantic. The youngest relief of the ocean appears to be along the axis of the ocean; the relief becoming progressively older toward adjacent shores.

It seems most likely that the continents on either side of the Atlantic are moving apart by the successive addition of new crustal material along the axis of the ridge in the floor of the median rift valley, and that the continents and a large part of the crust of the Atlantic, Indian, and South Pacific deep-sea floors are moving away as units from the median line. Thus, if we go back to Taylor's original suggestion that the margins of the North Pacific are all encroaching on this ocean—that all parts of the continental crust are moving toward the North Pacific—it is possible that the topography of the sea floor of the Atlantic, Indian, and South Pacific Oceans can be adequately explained. One would, however, expect the topography of the North Pacific to be vastly different in form from all the other oceans. According to this hypothesis, the North Pacific would be undergoing compression while the other oceans would be under extension. Some encouragement can be gained by the unique occurrence of the great island arcs in the North Pacific and by the lack of a median ridge in this ocean. The fracture zones, which apparently represent faults along which hundreds of miles of strike-slip movement have occurred, are not indicative of compression and are not limited to the North Pacific. The topography of the Pacific sea floor is covered in large part by abyssal hills. Seamounts of the Pacific differ little from seamounts of the Atlantic and Indian Oceans, except perhaps in their greater abundance in the Pacific. There seems to be nothing particularly unique about the North Pacific deep-sea floor, with the exception of the pattern of arcuate trenches which surround it.

The pattern of the mid-oceanic ridge when examined on a globe presents a formidable difficulty to conventional continental drift, for the Ridge tends to get in the way of the drifting continents. One might suppose, of course, that the mid-oceanic ridge is of recent origin, and that it only originated in its present mid-oceanic position since the drift of the continents to their present position. However, this view is not a particularly satisfying one since the flanks of the mid-oceanic ridge, many hundreds of miles in width, are no longer seismically active and have the appearance of having been located in mid-ocean for a considerable period of time.

If one takes the view that the Mid-Atlantic Ridge represents a rift line from which the new and old hemispheres drifted apart, the pattern looks favourable until one considers the relationship of the Mid-Indian and Easter Island segments of the ridge in relation to this drift. If Africa has moved east relative to the Mid-Atlantic Ridge, it must be running into the Mid-Indian Ridge. If South America has moved west relative to the Mid-Atlantic Ridge, it must be colliding with the Easter Island Ridge; and if one considers the drift of Antarctica relative to the Mid-Atlantic, Mid-Indian and Easter Island portions of the Ridge, one must only conclude that Antarctica has shrunk, for the pattern of the

Ridge would indicate that Antarctica must have drifted towards its geographical centre.

One of the older explanations of the Mid-Atlantic Ridge offered by proponents of continental drift was that it represented a piece of continental crust left behind when the continents drifted apart. Another view, in fact that of Wegener himself, was that it represented a pile of sediments which collected in the incipient rift before the continents had completely drifted apart.

The recent geophysical work on the mid-oceanic ridge can be used to refute both of these hypotheses. The seismic velocity observed in the ridge of 7·2 to 7·7 km/sec is certainly not that which one could attribute to sediment left in the former filling of the original rift, as proposed by Wegener. Neither does it seem likely that the 7·2 to 7·6 velocity represents continental crust. There is no apparent reason why the axis of a dead remnant of crust, or an abandoned pile of sediment should have high tectonic activity continuant to the present day.

The high heat-flow observed under the mid-oceanic ridges has given great encouragement to convection current theorists. Before the first oceanic heat-flow measurements were made, it was expected that deep-sea values of heat-flow would be at least one order of magnitude below continental values, since basic rocks are much lower in radioactive minerals than granitic rocks. To the great surprise of everyone concerned, heat-flow values measured in the deep ocean basins were approximately equal to those measured on the continents.

Even more perplexing were the five to six times higher values observed in the mid-oceanic ridge. Many scientists were quick to realize that such a high heat-flow could be accounted for by rising convection cells in the earth's mantle. Among those who have expressed such views, either in public lectures or in print, are Maurice Ewing, Sir Edward Bullard, Harry Hess [56], Roger Revelle, Henry W. Menard [44] and Robert Dietz [57].

If one examines the crustal section shown in Fig. 23, one can easily imagine rising convection currents beneath the axis of the ridge which could supply the high heat-flow and, perhaps, through mixing of the crust and mantle, produce the characteristic 7·2 to 7·6 km/sec velocities of the ridge (Fig. 29). These currents as they diverge from the crest of the ridge might flow towards the continents, presumably carrying the ocean floor on either side of the ridge towards the continents. These convection cells would then presumably sink, either below the eastern or the western boundary of the continents, or perhaps beneath the younger mountain ranges.

When such a pattern of convection cells is envisaged in a single

L

cross-section of one ocean, it is relatively easy to reconstruct the
geometry [44, 56]. But when one examines the continuous 35,000-mile-
long mid-oceanic ridge on the surface of the earth, it becomes apparent
that the convection cells must be in the unlikely form of long tubes of

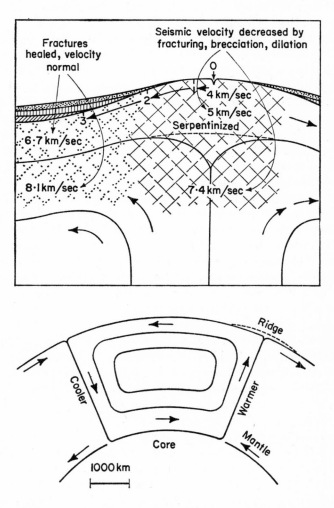

Fig. 29. Origin of the mid-oceanic ridge through convection cells and serpentinization.
The figure illustrates the ideas of Hess [56] for the origin of the mid-oceanic ridge. The
rising convection cell under the crest of the ridge brings mantle rock to the surface. This
rock is serpentinized to form the 4·5 and 4·0 km/sec layers along the crest of the ridge.
These rocks are carried laterally, and by deserpentinization and the healing of fractures
the velocity increases to form the 6·7 km/sec of oceanic crust. On cooling, the 7·4 km/sec
increases in velocity to form the normal high velocity upper surface of the mantle.
(After Hess [56]).

varying diameter which everywhere rise beneath the mid-oceanic ridge and sink somewhere beneath the continent. Although convection cells rising beneath the ridges and sinking somewhere beneath the continents supply a plausible explanation of the origin of any one ocean basin, it becomes very difficult to suggest a pattern which adequately explains the entire mid-oceanic ridge.

Convection cells in the upper mantle have often been proposed as a genetic explanation of mountains, trenches, and geosynclines [12]. Recently Menard [44], Dietz [57] and Hess [56] have each advanced similar hypotheses of mantle convection in an attempt to explain the formation of the mid-oceanic ridge. The evidence of high heat-flow near the crest of the ridge suggests that the ridge generally lies over the rising limbs of a pair of convection cells. More difficult is the question of where the convection cells are sinking. By what criteria do we identify the descending arms of the current? Menard, Dietz and Hess have each suggested that the marginal trench of Central and South America marks a line of compression where the Atlantic and Pacific cells converge and sink. It seems a bit difficult to understand the geometry of these cells, particularly in Mexico and the Caribbean. Still more difficult is the problem of the western descending limb of the east Pacific convection cell. Menard [44] has proposed that a zone of compression exists in the deep-sea floor parallel to the axis of the mid-oceanic ridge (Fig. 30).

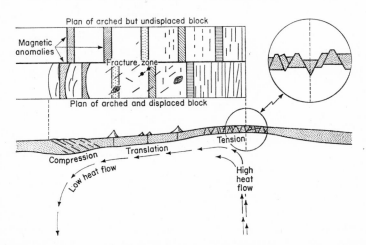

Fig. 30. Diagrammatic presentation of Menard's convection current hypothesis for the origin of the various features associated with the mid-oceanic ridge in the eastern Pacific. (After Menard [44]). A major difficulty with his explanation is the lack of any evidence of the zone of compression shown on the left side of the diagram. This same criticism can also be made of the explanation of Hess shown in Fig. 29. Overall extension of the earth's crust may be necessary to explain this pattern.

However, no physiographic or structural evidence for this zone has been found. Indeed, if a really significant amount of compression occurred in the oceanic crust comparable in magnitude to the extension of the ridge inferred from its physiography, isostatic considerations would demand a topographic ridge marking the zone of crustal thickening. Also, it would seem likely that if the convection cell is rising under the crest of the ridge with sufficient energy to cause the relatively high seismicity of the mid-oceanic ridge, a line of seismic activity should mark the descending limb of the cell as well. No such line of earthquakes has been observed in the deep Pacific.

Bernal [58] in a discussion of Dietz's paper has offered the suggestion that convection cells do not exist in the outer 900 km of the earth, but are restricted to greater depths (Figs. 31 and 32). He proposes that the

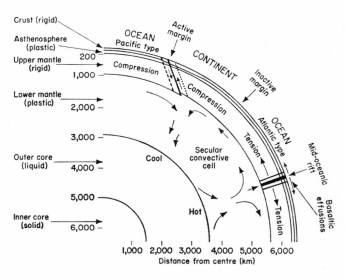

FIG. 31. Convection currents in the upper mantle as an explanation of distension in the mid-oceanic rift and the origin of the inclined fault surfaces of the circum-Pacific belt. (After Bernal [58]).

convection cells which presumably rise under the ridges, drag the ocean floor and western hemisphere continents west, creating the Pacific trenches by over-thrusting along the inclined plane defined by the intermediate and deep focus earthquakes. This concept has an appeal, for it accounts for the inclined plane, but it requires a nearly vertical fracture 900 km deep beneath the axial rift valleys. The fact that all earthquakes in the mid-oceanic belt are of shallow focus does not favour this view.

Despite wide variations in total width, the mid-oceanic ridge occupies approximately the centre third of the Atlantic and Indian Oceans. The feature appears to be genetically related to the basin. If the Atlantic has grown wider, the mid-oceanic ridge must have grown wider too. In Fig. 33, four profiles across the seismicity belt are shown.

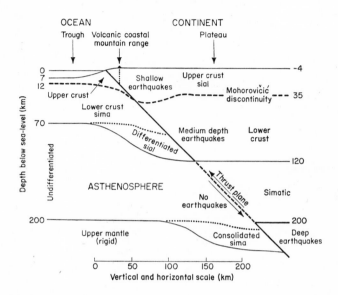

Fig. 32. Bernal's explanation of the inclined fault plane of the circum-Pacific belt. (After Bernal [58]).

If we consider this series a genetic one, we might imagine that the Atlantic and Indian Oceans began as a continental rift similar to those in East Africa; passed through a stage similar to the Red Sea, Gulf of Aden and northern Norwegian Sea, and finally arrived at the present state of development. Crust may have been continually added along the crest of the ridge.

It has been suggested that the displacement of the continents one from another was accomplished by a large internal expansion of the earth [59, 60, 61, 62, 63, 64, 65]. Under this hypothesis, a sialic crust differentiated early in the history of the earth and originally formed an essentially continuous outer shell. After this sialic crust solidified it was broken up by the continued expansion of the interior of the earth. Mantle material, reaching the surface in the cracks between the sialic blocks, formed the simatic ocean floors. As the earth continued to expand, the oceans gradually grew wider, while the sialic continents remained of nearly their original surface area.

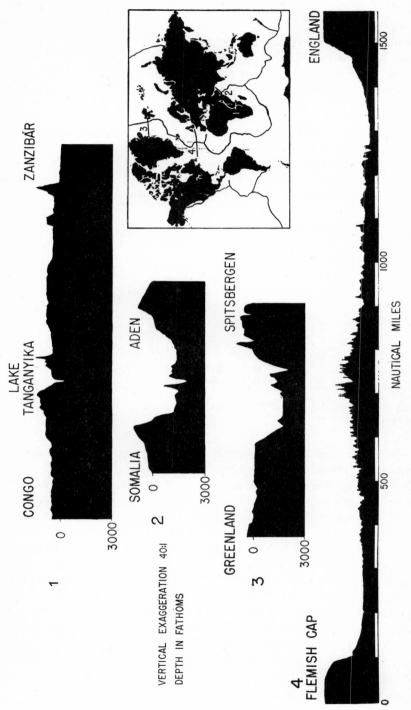

FIG. 33. Four profiles across the mid-oceanic ridge. Note the marked similarity of each profile, despite the large difference in profile lengths. This sequence could represent a genetic series in which the rift valleys of Africa represent an early stage in the development of an ocean, and the Atlantic shown in profile 4 represents a later stage.

The fractures in the ocean basins along which most of the continual extension of the crust occurred are thought to be the mid-oceanic rifts. This explanation would account for the displacement of continents one from another without having to assume that the continents had drifted through oceans. The similarity of the extrapolated zero value for the mantle seismic velocity and that observed at refraction stations on the mid-oceanic ridge would be accounted for by the recent emplacement of mantle material in the mid-oceanic ridge. It might be presumed that this mantle material, on having been near the surface for some time, would cool or somehow age and thus gradually change to the higher velocities observed in the normal oceanic mantle beneath the oceanic crust.

Dicke [61], elaborating on an earlier consideration of the British physicist Dirac, has proposed that the earth has expanded in consequence of a decrease in the force of gravity. Dirac's cosmological arguments led him to propose in 1937 that the gravitational constant is an inverse function of the age of the universe. Dicke suggested in 1956 that geologists and oceanographers may find cracks in the ocean floor which indicate an internal swelling of the earth.

Beck [66] and Cook and Eardley [67] studied the energy requirements of an internal expansion of the earth and concluded that an expansion sufficient, for example, to account for the creation of the Atlantic since the Cretaceous, could not have taken place by purely thermal expansion or phase changes—even assuming the most favourable conditions. However, the possibility of a change in gravity, such as currently advocated by Dicke and Jordan [68] was not considered. It should be pointed out that the amount of expansion indicated by Dicke (neglecting thermal and phase change effects) account for only 2·4 to 10^7 mi^2 increase in surface area, since the origin of the earth, a figure approximately equal to the total area of the mid-oceanic ridge but far too small to account for the paleomagnetic evidence of continental displacements since the Mesozoic. Cox and Doell [69], comparing paleomagnetic results from Europe and Siberia, concluded that the Permian radius of the earth was nearly identical with the present radius. But similar calculations based on data from other parts of Eurasia would clearly give radically different values.

It is just possible that the evidence for continental drift could instead be interpreted as evidence for continental displacement (without drift) due to the internal expansion of the earth accompanied by the growth of simatic oceans through emplacement of mantle material in the floors of the mid-oceanic rifts.

References

1. HEEZEN, B. C., THARP, M., AND EWING, M., "The Floors of the Oceans. I: The North Atlantic". Geological Society of America, New York (1959).
2. SHAND, S. J., *J. Geol.* **57**, 89 (1949).
3. EWING, J., AND EWING, M., *Bull. geol. Soc. Amer.* **70**, 291 (1959).
4. RAITT, R. W., *Bull. geol. Soc. Amer.* **67**, 1623 (1956).
5. HILL, M. N., *in* "Physics and Chemistry of the Earth", Vol. 2, p. 129. (L. H. Ahrens *et al.*, ed.) Pergamon Press, London (1957).
6. TALWANI, M., SUTTON, G. H., AND WORZEL, J. L., *J. geoph. Res.* **64**, 1545 (1959).
7. VACQUIER, V., RAFF, A. D., AND WARREN, R. E., *Bull. geol. Soc. Amer.* **72**, 1251 (1961).
8. VON HERZEN, R., *Nature, Lond.* **183**, 882 (1959).
9. EWING, M., AND LANDISMAN, M., *in* "Oceanography", Pub. 67, p. 3. (M. Sears, ed.) American Association for the Advancement of Science, Washington (1961).
10. GUTENBERG, B., AND RICHTER, C. F., "Seismicity of the Earth". Princeton University Press, Princeton (1954).
11. DRAKE, C. L., EWING, M., AND SUTTON, G. H., *in* "Physics and Chemistry of the Earth", Vol. 3, p. 110. (L. H. Ahrens *et al.*, ed.) Pergamon Press, London (1959).
12. VENING MEINESZ, F. A., *Neth. geodet. Comm.* **2**, 47 (1934).
13. HESS, H. H., *Proc. Amer. phil. Soc.* **79**, 71 (1938).
14. EWING, M., AND HEEZEN, B. C., *in* "Crust of the Earth. Geological Society of America Special Paper 62", p. 255. (A. Poldervaart, ed.) Geological Society of America, New York (1955).
15. KAY, M., "North American Geosynclines. Geological Society of America Memoir 48". Geological Society of America, New York (1951).
16. PETTIJOHN, R. J., *J. Geol.* **58**, 169 (1950).
17. TAYLOR, F. B., *Bull. geol. Soc. Amer.* **21**, 179 (1910).
18. WEGENER, A., "Origin of Continents and Oceans". Dutton, New York (1924).
19. MENARD, H. W., *Bull. Amer. Ass. Petrol. Geol.* **39**, 236 (1955).
20. HEEZEN, B. C., *Roy. astr. Soc. geoph. J.* **2**, 142 (1959).
21. MENARD, H. W., *Bull. geol. Soc. Amer.* **70**, 1491 (1959).
22. MENARD, H. W., AND DIETZ, R. S., *J. Geol.* **60**, 266 (1952).
23. ERICSON, D. B., EWING, M., WOLLIN, G., AND HEEZEN, B. C., *Bull. geol. Soc. Amer.* **72**, 193 (1961).
24. MENARD, H. W., *Bull. geol. Soc. Amer.* **66**, 1149 (1955).
25. HEEZEN, B. C., AND THARP, M., "Physiographic Diagram of the South Atlantic, the Caribbean, the Scotia Sea, and the Eastern Margin of the South Pacific Ocean". Geological Society of America, New York (1961).
26. HEEZEN, B. C., THARP, M., AND GERARD, R. D., Geological Society of America Abstract Volume (1961).
27. KATZ, S., AND EWING, M., *Bull. geol. Soc. Amer.* **67**, 475 (1955).
28. KUENEN, Ph. H., "Marine Geology". Wiley, New York (1950).
29. BRAMLETTE, M. N., *Bull. geol. Soc. Amer.* **69**, 121 (1958).
30. HAMILTON, E. L., *Bull. geol. Soc. Amer.* **70**, 1399 (1959).
31. HAMILTON, E. L., *J. sediment. Petrol.* **30**, 370 (1960).
32. RIEDEL, W. R., LADD, H. S., TRACEY, J. I., Jr., AND BRAMLETTE, M. N., *Bull. Amer. Ass. Petrol. Geol.* **45**, 1793 (1961).

33. Furon, R., *C. R. Acad. Sci. Paris*, **228**, 1509 (1949).
34. Menard, H. W., *Experientia*, **15**, 205 (1959).
35. Hamilton, E. L., "Sunken Islands of the Mid-Pacific Mountains. Geological Society of America Memoir 64". Geological Society of America, New York (1956).
36. Menard, H. W., *Bull. Amer. Ass. Petrol. Geol.* **40**, 2195 (1956).
37. Ericson, D. B., Ewing, M., and Heezen, B. C., *Bull. Amer. Ass. Petrol. Geol.* **36**, 489 (1952).
38. Heezen, B. C., and Ewing, M., in "Geology of the Arctic", Vol. 1, p. 622. (G. O. Raasch, ed.) University of Toronto Press, Toronto (1961).
39. Wayland, E. J., *C. R. 15th Int. geol. Congr.* (South Africa) 2, 223 (1930).
40. Bullard, E. C., *Phil. Trans.* **A235** (1936).
41. Askelsson, J., Bödvarssom, G., Einarsson, T., Kjartansson, G., and Thorarinsson, S., "On the Geology and Geophysics of Iceland: Guide to Excursion No. A 2". (S. Thorarinsson, ed.) International Geological Congress, Reykjavik, 1960.
42. "Tectonic Map of the U.S.S.R." Academy of Sciences, Moscow (1956).
43. Fisher, R. L., "Preliminary Report on Expedition Downwind, University of California, Scripps Institution of Oceanography, I.G.Y. Cruise to the Southeast Pacific". I.G.Y. Gen. Rep. Ser. 2, National Academy of Sciences, Washington (1958).
44. Menard, H. W., *Science*, **132**, 1737 (1960).
45. Ewing, M., Hirshman, J., and Heezen, B. C., in "International Oceanographic Congress Preprints", p. 24. (M. Sears, ed.) American Association for the Advancement of Science, Washington (1959).
46. Talwani, M., Heezen, B. C., and Worzel, J. L., Physiography, gravity and structure of the Mid-Atlantic Ridge. *Trav. sci. Sect. Séism. Un. géod. int.* **22**, 81 (1961).
47. Hill, M. N., *Deep-Sea Res.* **6**, 193 (1960).
48. Gutenberg, B., "Physics of the Earth's Interior". Academic Press, New York (1959).
49. Dorman, J., Ewing, M., and Oliver, J., *Bull. seismol. Soc. Amer.* **50**, 87 (1960).
50. Press, F., *Science*, **133**, 1455 (1961).
51. Aki, K., and Press, F., *Geophys. J. roy. Astr. Soc.* 5, 292 (1961).
52. MacDonald, G. J. F., *J. geophys. Res.* **64**, 1967 (1959).
53. Turner, F. J., and Verhoogen, J., "Igneous and Metamorphic Petrology". McGraw-Hill, New York (1951).
54. Matthews, W. D., *Nature, Lond.* **190**, 158 (1961).
55. Broecker, W. S., Turekian, K. K., and Heezen, B. C., *Amer. J. Sci.* **256**, 503 (1958).
56. Hess, H. H., in "The Sea, Ideas and Observations", in press. (M. N. Hill *et al.*, ed.) Interscience Publishers, New York.
57. Dietz, R. S., *Nature, Lond.* **190**, 854 (1961).
58. Bernal, J. D., *Nature, Lond.* **192**, 123 (1961).
59. Egyed, L., *Geol. Rdsch.* **46**, 101 (1957).
60. Carey, W. S., in "Continental Drift, A Symposium, 1956", p. 177. (S. W. Carey, convener) University of Tasmania, Hobart (1958).
61. Dicke, R. H., *Science*, **129**, 621 (1959).
62. Wilson, J. T., *Nature, Lond.* **185**, 880 (1960).

L*

63. HEEZEN, B. C., *in* "International Oceanographic Congress Preprints", p. 26. (M. Sears, ed.) American Association for the Advancement of Science, Washington (1959).
64. HEEZEN, B. C., *Sci. Amer.* **203**, 98 (1960).
65. HEEZEN, B. C., *in* "Topographie et la Géologie des Profondeur Océaniques". *Colloq. int. Cent. nat. Rech. sci.*, Vol. LXXXIII, p. 295. Paris (1959).
66. BECK, A. E., *J. Geophys. Res.* **66**, 1485 (1961).
67. COOK, M. A., AND EARDLEY, A. J., *J. Geophys. Res.* **66**, 3907 (1961).
68. JORDAN, P., "Schwerkraft und Weltall", 2nd edition. Vieweg, Brunswick (1955).
69. COX, A., AND DOELL, R. R., *Nature, Lond.* **189**, 45 (1961).

Chapter 10

Ocean–Basin Evolution by Sea-Floor Spreading*

ROBERT S. DIETZ

I. Introduction 289
II. Spreading Sea-Floor Concept 292
III. Implications of the Concept 294
    A. Volumetric Changes of the Earth 294
    B. Continental Drift 294
    C. Persistent Freeboard of the Continents 295
    D. Youth of the Ocean Floor 295
    E. Spreading and Magnetic Anomalies 297
    References 297

I. INTRODUCTION

Any concept of ocean-basin evolution must be based on an earth model involving assumptions not fully established regarding the nature of the earth's outer shells and mantle processes. The view expressed here, which can be termed the sea-floor spreading concept, is largely intuitive, having been derived through an attempt to understand the meaning of bathymetry. Although no new proposals regarding crustal processes are postulated, the concept requires the acceptance of a specific crustal model, in some ways at variance with the present consensus of opinion. Since the model follows from the concept, no attempt is made to defend it. The assumed model is as follows:

1. Large-scale thermal convection cells, fuelled by the decay of radioactive minerals do operate in the mantle. They do provide the primary diastrophic forces affecting the lithosphere.

2. The sequence of crustal layers within the oceans is markedly different from that beneath the continents and is quite simple (Fig. 1). On an average 4·5 km of water overlies 0·3 km of unconsolidated sediments (layer 1). Underlying this is layer 2, consisting of about 2·0 km of mixed volcanics and lithified sediments. Beneath this is the layer 3 (5 km thick), commonly considered as forming a world-encircling

---

* This paper is a modified version of one appearing in *Nature, Lond.* **190**, 854-857 (1961) printed here by permission.

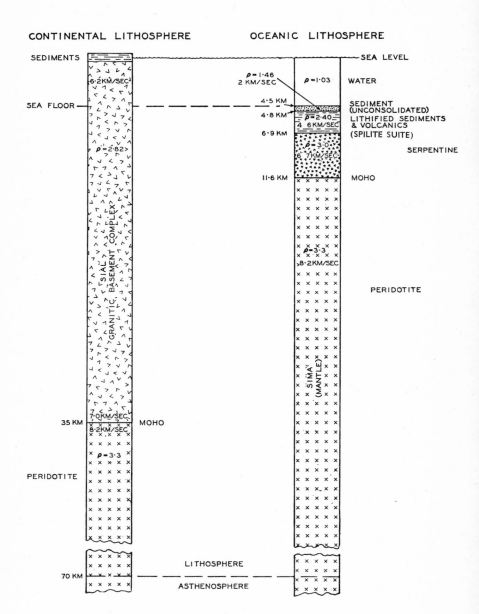

Fig. 1.

cap of effusive basic volcanics over the earth's mantle from which it is separated by the Mohorovičić seismic discontinuity. Since the term *basalt layer* implies the petrologic nature of this principal layer beneath the oceans, the composition of which is completely unknown, the term *oceanic layer* is much to be preferred. Here we accept the opinion of Hess and others that the oceanic layer is serpentine, i.e. peridotite altered largely by hydration. The mantle itself is most likely peridotite which, by partial fusion, produces basalt and leaves dunite as the residuum. Basalt in turn is the mother substance from which other rocks, gabbro to granite, are derived by gravitative and fractional differentiation. The Moho beneath the continents cannot be a peridotite to serpentine transition as the high temperature at this depth precludes the existence of serpentine. Presumably the continents become more basic with depth so that the transition may be from gabbro to peridotite or, if a phase change occurs, a transition from gabbro to eclogite with peridotite occurring at some greater depth. Since eclogite and peridotite have similar seismic velocities this transition would not be seismically apparent.

3. It is relevant to speak of the strength and rigidity of the earth's outer shell. The term 'crust' has been effectively pre-empted from its classical meaning by seismological usage applying it to the layer above the Moho, that is the sial in the continental regions and the oceanic or basaltic layer under the oceans so that the continents have a thick crust and the ocean basins a thin crust. Used in this now widely accepted sense, any implications equating the crust with rigidity must be dismissed. For considerations of convective creep and tectonic yielding, we must refer to a lithosphere and an asthenosphere. Deviations from isostasy prove that approximately the outer 70 km of the earth (under the continents and ocean basins alike) is moderately strong and rigid even over time-spans of 100,000 years or more; this outer rind is the lithosphere. Beneath lies the asthenosphere separated from the lithosphere by the level of no strain or isopiestic level; it is a domain of rock plasticity and flowage where any stresses are quickly removed. No seismic discontinuity marks the isopiestic level and very likely it is actually a zone of uniform composition showing a gradual transition in strength as pressure and temperature rise; and in spite of the lithosphere's rigidity, to speak of it as a crust or shell greatly exaggerates its strength. Because of its grand dimensions, for model similitude we must think of it as weak [1]. If convection currents are operating 'subcrustally', as is commonly written, they would be expected to shear below the lithosphere and not beneath the 'crust' as this term is now used.

4. As gravity data have shown, the continents are low-density tabular masses of sial—a 'basement complex' of granitic rocks about 35 km thick with a thin sedimentary veneer. Since they are buoyant and float high hydrostatically in the sima, they are analogous to icebergs in the ocean. This analogy has additional merit in that we assume that the convection of the sima cannot enter the sial. But the analogy gives the wrong impression of relative strength of sial and sima; the continental lithosphere is no stronger than the oceanic lithosphere, so it is mechanically impossible for the sial to 'sail through the sima' as Wegnerian continental drift proposes. In summary the model proposed here is that the mantle is ultramafic or peridotitic. The continents are buoyant rafts of sialic scum, the term sial is extended to include rocks even as basic as gabbro which would be buoyant relative to ultramafic rock. The sea floor is essentially the exposed mantle of the earth covered only by an oceanic rind. Since the sea floor is fully invaded by the convection circulation the term oceanic crust is a misnomer.

II. Spreading Sea-Floor Concept

Owing to the small strength of the lithosphere and the gradual transition in rigidity between it and the asthenosphere, the lithosphere is not a boundary to convection circulation, and neither is the Moho beneath the oceans because this is not a density boundary but simply a hydration of the mantle substance itself. Thus the oceanic 'rind' is almost wholly coupled with the convective overturn of the mantle creeping at a rate of a fraction of a cm per yr to perhaps as much as 1 or 2 cm per yr. Since the sea floor is covered by only a thin veneer of sediments with some mixed-in effusives, it is essentially the out-cropping mantle. So the sea floor marks the tops of large convection cells and slowly spreads from zones of divergence to those of convergence. These cells have dimensions of several thousands of kilometres; some cells are quite active now while others are dead or dormant. They have changed position with geological time causing new tectonic patterns.

The gross structures of the sea floor are direct expressions of this convection. The median rises [2, 3] mark the up-welling sites or divergences; the trenches are associated with the convergences or down-welling sites; and the fracture zones [4] mark shears between regions of slow and fast creep. The high heat-flow under the rises [5] is indicative of the ascending convection currents as also are the groups of volcanic seamounts which dot the backs of these rises.

Much of the minor sea-floor topography may be even directly ascribable to spreading of the sea floor. Great expanses of rough topography skirt both sides of the Mid-Atlantic Rift; similarly there are extensive regions of abyssal hills in the Pacific. The roughness is suggestive of youth, so it has commonly been assumed to be simply volcanic topography because the larger seamounts are volcanic. But this interpretation is not at all convincing, and no one has given this view formality by publishing a definitive study. Actually, the topography resembles neither volcanic flows nor incipient volcanoes. Can it not be that these expanses of abyssal hills are a 'chaos topography' developed as strips of juvenile sea floor (by a process which can be visualized only as mixed intrusion and extrusion) and then placed under rupturing stresses as the sea floor moves outward?

The median position of the rises cannot be a matter of chance, so it might be supposed that the continents in some manner control the convection pattern. But the reverse is considered true: conditions deep within the mantle control the convective pattern without regard for continent positions. Runcorn [6] for example has suggested that the mantle convective pattern has been controlled throughout geological time by the growth of the earth's core so that this pattern of overturning has changed its mode. By viscous drag, the continents initially are moved along with the sima until they attain a position of dynamic balance overlying a convergence. There the continents come to rest, but the sima continues to shear under and descend beneath them; so the continents generally cover the down-welling sites. If new up-wells do happen to rise under a continental mass, it tends to be rifted. Thus, the entire North and South Atlantic Ocean marks an ancient rift which separated North and South America from Europe and Africa. The axis of the East Pacific Rise now seems to be invading the North American continent, underlying the Gulf of California and California [7]. Similarly, the Indian Ocean Rise may extend into the African Rift Valleys, tending to fragment that continent.

The sialic continents, floating on the sima, provide a density barrier to convection circulation—unlike the oceanic Moho, which involves merely a hydration of the mantle. The convection circulation thus shears beneath the continents so that the sial is only partially coupled through drag forces. Since the continents are normally resting over convergences, so that convective spreading is moving toward them from opposite sides, the continents are placed consequently under compression. They tend to buckle, which accounts for alpine folding, thrust faulting and similar compressional effects so characteristic of the continents. In contrast, the ocean basins are simultaneously domains of tension. If the continental block is drifted along with the sima, the margin is tectonically stable (Atlantic type). But if the sima is slipping beneath the sialic block, marginal mountains tend to form (Pacific type) owing to drag forces.

III. IMPLICATIONS OF THE CONCEPT

Ad hoc hypotheses are likely to be wrong. On the other hand, one which is consonant with our broader understanding of the history of the earth may have merit. For example, invoking enormous changes of sea level to explain submarine canyons proved quite useful for that purpose alone; otherwise it raised havoc with geologic history generally and was abandoned when a simple and more conformable explanation was found in turbidity currents. While the thought of a highly mobile sea floor may seem alarming at first, it does little violence to geological history.

A. VOLUMETRIC CHANGES OF THE EARTH

Geologists have traditionally recognized that compression of the continents (and they assumed of the ocean floors as well) was the principal tectonic problem. It was supposed that the earth was cooling and shrinking. But recently, geologists have been impressed by tensional structures, especially on the ocean floor. To account for sea-floor rifting, Heezen [8], for example, has advocated an expanding earth, a doubling of the diameter. Carey's [9] tectonic analysis has resulted in the need for a twenty-fold increase in volume of the earth. Spreading of the sea floor offers the less radical answer that the earth's volume has remained constant. By creep from median upwellings, the ocean basins are mostly under tension, while the continents, normally balanced against sima creepage from opposite sides, are under compression.

The geological record is replete with transgressions and regressions of the sea, but these have been shallow and not catastrophic; fluctuations in sea-level as severe as those of the Pleistocene are abnormal. The spreading concept does no violence to this order of things, unlike dilation or contraction of the earth. The volumetric capacity of the oceans is fully conserved.

B. CONTINENTAL DRIFT

The spreading concept envisages limited continental drifting, with the sial blocks initially being rafted to down-welling sites and then being stabilized in a balanced field of opposing drag forces. The sea floor is held to be more mobile and to migrate freely even after the continents come to rest. The sial moves largely *en bloc*, but the sea floor spreads more differentially.

Former scepticism about continental drift is rapidly vanishing, especially as a result of palæomagnetic findings and new tectonic analyses. A principal objection to Wegener's continental drift hypothesis was that it was physically impossible for a continent to 'sail like a ship' through the sima; and nowhere is there any sea floor deformation ascribable to an on-coming continent. Sea-floor spreading obviates this difficulty: continents never move through the sima—they either move along with it or stand still while the sima shears beneath them. The buoyancy of the continents, rather than their being stronger than the sima, accounts for this. Drag associated with the shearing could account for alpine folding and related compressional tectonic structures on the continents.

C. PERSISTENT FREEBOARD OF THE CONTINENTS

A satisfactory theory of crustal evolution must explain why the continents have stood high throughout geological time in spite of constant erosional de-levelling. Many geologists believe that new buoyancy is added to continents through the gravitative differentiation from the mantle. Spreading of the sea floor provides a mechanism whereby the continents are placed over the down-wells where new sial would tend to collect, even though the convection is entirely a mantle process and the role of the continents is passive. It also follows that the clastic detritus swept into the deep sea from the continents is not permanently lost. Rather, it is carried slowly towards, and then beneath, the continents, where it is granitized and added anew to the sialic blocks. Thus some thickening of the continents would result by the injection of plutons of batholithic proportions in some cases, in others a generalized epeirogenic uplift would result such as that which has affected the Colorado Plateau of Arizona and New Mexico and the eastern zone of the Rocky Mountains and including the Great Plains.

D. YOUTH OF THE OCEAN FLOOR

It follows paradoxically from the spreading concept that, although the ocean basins are old, the sea floor is young—much younger than the rocks of the continents. Marine sediments, seamounts, and other structures slowly impinge against the sialic blocks and are destroyed by either under-riding them or accreting laterally. Probably along the axis of the Pacific trenches material is being actively thrust beneath the continental raft. Around the Atlantic great thicknesses of sediments are being accumulated to form the continental rises laid down by turbidity current action. If the spreading of the Atlantic were to become decoupled from the continents these prisms would be pressed against the

continents and added to them by sea floor spreading. This assumes that
the modern continental rises are the equivalent of eugeosynclinal prisms
of the past, of which the Magog series is an example along the Atlantic
margin of the U.S. while the Franciscan and the earlier greywackes into
which the Sierra Nevada batholith is intruded are west coast examples.
Thus sea floor spreading may account for the apparent accretionary
development of continents throughout geologic history.

Pre-Cambrian and perhaps even most Palæozoic rocks should prove
absent from the ocean floors; and Mohole drilling should not reveal the
great missing sequence of the Lipalian interval (Pre-Cambrian to
Cambrian) as hoped for by some. All this may seem surprising, but
marine geological evidence supports the concept.

On his discovery of the guyots of the Pacific, Hess [10] supposed these
were Pre-Cambrian features protected from erosion by the cover of the
sea. But Hamilton [11] proved the guyots of the Mid-Pacific Mountains
were Cretaceous, and these seem to be among the oldest of the seamount groups. In an analysis of the various seamount groups of the
western Pacific, I was forced to conclude that none of them was older
than mid-Mesozoic. The young age of the seamounts has been puzzling;
certainly they can neither erode away nor subside completely. Also,
there seem to be too few volcanic seamounts, if the present population
represents the entire number built over the past hundred million years
or more. The puzzle dissolves if sea-floor spreading has operated.
Modern examples of impinging groups of seamounts may be the western
end of the Caroline Islands, the Wake-Marcus Seamounts, and the
Magellan Seamounts [12]. All may be moving into the western Pacific
trenches. Seamount GA-1 south of Alaska may be moving into the
Aleutian Trench [13].

The sedimentary layers under the sea also appear to be young. No
fossiliferous rocks older than Cretaceous have yet been dredged from
any ocean basin. Radioactive dating of a basalt from the Mid-Atlantic
Ridge gave a Tertiary age [14]. Kuenen [15] estimated that the ocean
basins should contain on an average about 3·0 km of sedimentary rocks
assuming the basins are 200 million years old. But seismic reflections
indicate an average of only 0·3 km of the unconsolidated sediments.
Hamilton [16], however, believes that much of layer 2 may be lithified
sediments. If *all* layer 2 is lithified sediments, Hamilton finds that the
ocean basins may be Palæozoic or late Pre-Cambrian in age—but not
Archæan. But very likely layer 2 includes much effusive material and
sedimentary products of sea floor weathering. In summing up, the
evidence from the sediments, although still fragmentary, suggests that
the sea floors may be not older than Palæozoic or even early Mesozoic.

E. SPREADING AND MAGNETIC ANOMALIES

Vacquier *et al.* [17] recently have completed excellent sea-floor magnetic surveys off the west coast of North America. A striking north–south lineation shows up which seems to reveal a stress pattern (Mason, R. G., and Raff, A. D., [18]). Such interpretation would fit into the spreading concept with the lineations being developed normal to the direction of convection creep. The lineation is interrupted by Menard's [6] three fracture-zones, and anomalies indicate shearing offsets of as much as 640 nautical miles in the case of the remarkable Mendocino Escarpment [19]. Great mobility of the sea floor is thus suggested. The offsets have no significant expression after they strike the continental block; so apparently they may slip under the continent without any strong coupling. Another aspect is that the anomalies smooth out and virtually disappear under the continental shelf; so the sea floor may dive under the sial and lose magnetism by being heated above the Curie point.

By considering an earth crustal model only slightly at variance with that commonly accepted, a novel concept of the evolution of continents and ocean basins has been suggested which seems to fit the 'facts' of marine geology. If this concept were correct, it would be most useful to apply the term 'crust', which now has a confusion of meanings, only to any layer which overlies and caps the convective circulation of the mantle. The sialic continental blocks do this, so they form the true crust. The ocean floor seemingly does not, so the ocean basin is 'crustless'.

I wish to express my appreciation to E. L. Hamilton, F. P. Shepard, H. W. Menard, V. Vacquier, R. Von Herzen and A. D. Raff for critical discussions.

References

1. GRIGGS, D. T., *Amer. J. Sci.* **237**, 611 (1939).
2. EWING, M., AND HEEZEN, B. C., *Amer. geophys. Un. geophys. Mon. No.* 1, 75 (1956).
3. MENARD, H. W., *Bull. geol. Soc. Amer.* **69**, 9, 1179 (1958).
4. MENARD, H. W., *Bull. geol. Soc. Amer.* **66**, 1149 (1955).
5. VON HERZEN, R., *Nature, Lond.* **183**, 882 (1959).
6. RUNCORN, S. K., *Nature, Lond.* **193**, 4813, 311 (1962).
7. MENARD, H. W., *Science*, **132**, 1737 (1960).
8. HEEZEN, B. C., *in* "International Oceanographic Congress Preprints", p. 26. (M. Sears, ed.) American Association for the Advancement of Science, Washington (1959).
9. CAREY, W. S., "The Tectonic Approach to Continental Drift: in Continental Drift—A Symposium", 177. University of Tasmania (1958).
10. HESS, H. H., *Amer. J. Sci.* **244**, 772 (1946).
11. HAMILTON, E. L., *Mem. geol. Soc. Amer.* **64**, 97 (1956).

12. DIETZ, R. S., *Bull. geol. Soc. Amer.* **65**, 1199 (1954).

13. MENARD, H. W., AND DIETZ, R. S., *Bull. geol. Soc. Amer.* **62**, 1263 (1951).

14. CARR, D., AND KULP, J., *Bull. geol. Soc. Amer.* **64**, 2, 263 (1953).

15. KUENEN, PH., "Marine Geology". John Wiley and Sons, New York (1950).

16. HAMILTON, E. L., *Bull. geol. Soc. Amer.* **70**, 1399 (1959); *J. sediment. Petrol.* **30**, 3, 370 (1960).

17. VACQUIER, V., RAFF, A., AND WARREN, R., *Bull. geol. Soc. Amer.* **72**, 1251 (1961).

18. MASON, G., AND RAFF, A., *Bull. geol. Soc. Amer.* **72**, 1259 (1961).

19. MENARD, H. W., AND DIETZ, R. S., *J. Geol.* **60**, 3 (1952).

Chapter 11

Comparisons of Pacific and Atlantic Ocean Floors in Relation to Ideas of Continental Displacement

T. F. GASKELL

Professor Mohorovičić's notable measurements on the thickness of the earth's crust beneath the continents have been thoroughly confirmed by repeated observations on near earthquakes, and also by many controlled experiments using underground explosions as a source of seismic waves. In the last few decades physical oceanographers have made similar studies of the crustal thickness below the oceans.

The most striking result of all the seismic observations in the oceans is the demonstration of the universal existence of a rock layer a few kilometres below the sea-bed in which the compressional wave velocity is 6·7 km/sec. Hill has tabulated seventy-six observations and finds a standard deviation of 0·28; the small value of this standard deviation suggests that the rock layer is similar for all the areas investigated; the velocity is such as might be expected for a massive basic igneous rock, and is in excess of values found for any acidic rocks or sedimentary rocks except for hard dense limestone. Apart from the geological argument against the world-wide existence of a thick limestone layer, there are physical reasons why basic rock is more likely. The excellent propagation of seismic waves that is observed in all deep ocean experiments suggests that the 6·7 km/sec material is some crystalline rock rather than a limestone. Limestones usually show a tendency to lose seismic energy due to bedding, shale-breaks and faults, and in any case have an inherently greater attenuation for seismic waves than do crystalline rocks. Moreover, on land, limestones show enormous variations in velocity, contrary to the close grouping shown for the measurements in deep oceans.

Some evidence has been put forward [1, 2] to show that there is a significant separation of the 6·7 km/sec velocity into a lower value of about 6·3 km/sec for those deep water stations remote from topographical features in the sea-bed, and a higher value around 6·9 km/sec for stations near the roots of islands and seamounts. While the evidence is not conclusive, the existence of two different rock velocities cannot be completely ruled out; however, Raitt [3] whose experiments contain a great concentration of observations, does not find any subdivision of the 6·7 km/sec group.

There seems little doubt that the main continental blocks, delineated by the comparatively rapid transition from shallow (100–200 fm) to deep (2,500–3,000 fm) water rather than by the present-day coastline, have been in existence for a large part of geological history. The oceans, on the other hand, are constructed quite differently from the land; they lack the fifteen mile thick layer of sedimentary and granitic rocks that form the body of the continents. It is known that the continents move up and down in the course of geological time, because sedimentary rocks are mainly formed by deposition of clay, sand and shell-fish in shallow water. However, the structure that has been found for the oceans is definitely not that to be expected from a sunken continent.

The question of interest now is whether the various oceans are similar in all particulars, or whether, while differing essentially from continents, they also show some individual characteristics which distinguish them from each other.

Most interpretations of the seismic results agree that there are two rock layers above the 6·7 km/sec material, and that the upper one of these layers is unconsolidated sediment. Core sampling suggests that this sediment could be red clay or globigerina ooze or a mixture of the two, and its thickness has been measured in the Pacific from 0·1–1·5 km. with a mean value of 0·3–0·4 km. This mean value, and also the slightly higher mean values found for the Atlantic ocean, have been obtained without regard to the distribution of the observations, and therefore tend to be weighted to the areas where there are most measurements. Until sea-bed structure can be correlated with the topography of the sea-bed, or until sufficient observations are available to delineate areas of equal sediment thickness, it is difficult to calculate anything of greater significance than the unweighted mean; however, the method of derivation of the mean sediment thickness at present quoted should not be forgotten.

There is evidence that a "Layer 2" [4] exists between the soft sediment and the 6·7 km/sec Layer. This "Layer 2" has been recorded with velocities ranging from 4·3–6·3 km/sec and its normal thickness averages about 1 km. The seismic results do not indicate whether the "Layer 2" extends down to the 6·7 km/sec layer or whether it is a band of hard rock separating an upper and a lower layer of soft sediment. In some parts of the ocean basin refracted waves from a second layer are not observed because they are masked by the waves from the 6·7 km/sec layer, but evidence of a second layer is provided by a study of shear waves and of reflections [5].

When measurements are made near volcanic islands the 6·7 km/sec layer is deeper than normal and clear indications of "Layer 2" are provided by first arrival refracted waves. For example, near the Hawaiian islands more than 2 km of 4·5 km/sec material has been observed, and laboratory measurements made on samples from Hawaiian lava flows suggest that in this case the "Layer 2" is part of the root of the volcano. This view is supported by the fact that the "Layer 2" decreases in thickness away from the volcanic island. Raitt [3] does not make any distinction between observations taken near islands or seamounts and those where the topography is flatter, but if his results on "Layer 2" are divided into two groups, those with velocity above 4·9 km/sec have an average thickness of 1·05 km while those in the lower velocity group have an average thickness of 2·06 km. It is possible that the two groups may correspond to flat sea-bed and sea-bed near islands or seamounts and that there is a significant difference in the composition of "Layer 2" in the two groups. The whole of "Layer 2" may be volcanic material, but although there are many seamounts which could have been the sources of supply it seems unlikely that volcanic material covers the whole ocean floor. It is much more likely that the "Layer 2", remote from features such as seamounts and islands, is some form of cemented sediment, or clay that has been baked during a period of excessive crustal warmth. The velocities observed for "Layer 2" are certainly not incompatible with this. "Layer 2" might be a band of hard rock about 0·1 km in thickness underlain by 3·0 km/sec soft sediment. If this is so there will be a reduction in the depth of the 6·7 km/sec layer below the sea-bed from an average 1·3 km to one of 0·8 km (for places remote from obvious features); the two extreme profiles are:

Soft sediment (2·0 km/sec)	0·3	0·3 km
"Layer 2" (5·5 km/sec)	1·0	0·1 km
Soft sediment (3·0 km/sec)	0·0	0·4 km
	1·3	0·8 km

Hamilton [6] has suggested that the sediment in deep oceans could consist of unconsolidated material which is for the most part made up of red clay, together with a hard band of cemented limestone derived from a period of excessive animal life due to favourable climatic conditions. This would not be incompatible with the seismic evidence.

Hill gives a higher value (1·61–1·99 km) for the combined thickness of Layers 1 and 2 in the Pacific, but this is not unreasonable since all results have been used, with no attempt to separate the different velocity groupings for Layer 2. What may be significant, when differences in character between the Pacific and the Atlantic are sought, is the greater thickness of the combined Layers 1 and 2 for the Atlantic than for the Pacific. For the 4–5 km depths, Hill's values are:

	Layer 1	Layer 2	Layers 1 + 2
Western Atlantic	0·49 km	2·39 km	2·89 km
Eastern Atlantic	0·63 km	2·08 km	2·82 km
Pacific Ocean	0·42 km	1·59 km	1·99 km

If there is any significance in the subdivision of Raitt's values for Layer 2, which has been given above, then the Atlantic figures for Layer 2 are closer to the high thickness (average 2·06 km) group for the Pacific. This is the group which is the exception to the deep Pacific Ocean structure, being that which is affected by being in the vicinity of islands or similar eruptions of volcanic material. Therefore the average Atlantic geological structure would seem to be different from that in the Pacific in respect to Layer 2. This does not necessarily imply that the Layer 2 in the Atlantic is similar to that near Pacific islands. There may be a third form of Layer 2 which causes the increased thickness in the Atlantic. It may well be argued that the Atlantic Ocean observations have been affected by nearness to volcanic outpourings, but there does appear to be some doubt that the details of the geological structure of the sea floor are the same in the two oceans. There is at least enough evidence in the published results to call for a more careful subdivision of the Layer 2 information.

One explanation of the extra thickness of the Atlantic Ocean sediment is that the area of the Atlantic is much smaller than the Pacific, while the sources of sediment (estimated from the size of land masses which supply most of the sediment) are much the same for the two oceans. However, if the Atlantic was formed in Cretaceous times as Wegener suggested, while the Pacific is a relic of the earth's original ocean, then it is surprising, even with an extra source of supply of sediment, that the Atlantic has accumulated a greater thickness than the Pacific. There is no doubt that the thorough sampling of the sediment carpets which cover the ocean floors will go a long way to settle these uncertainties. It is to be hoped that the preliminary tests for the Mohole project will yield many complete sediment plus Layer 2 profiles in both the Atlantic and the Pacific oceans. This is the real way to find out whether there is the difference in respect of sea-bed structure that is hinted at by the seismic results.

The seismic measurements near islands and seamounts indicate that there is a depression of the 6·7 km/sec layer, to give a root of lighter, lower velocity material. Further evidence relating to the structure of oceanic islands in the Pacific is provided by the detailed seismic work at the atolls of Funafuti and Nukufetau [7] and by the seismic experiments and the drilling at Bikini and Eniwetok. All these observations show thicknesses of the order of a kilometre of coral rock resting on volcanic material, and they therefore provide a further argument for the strong case set out by Kuenen [8, p. 414 *et seq.*] in support of Darwin's theory of coral atoll formation. It is important, of course, to distinguish between those coral atolls that appear in deep water and the ones that lie on the fringes of continental areas. The arguments against Darwin are based on observations on atolls that have been raised out of the sea and show coral rock resting on marine sediments. In such cases it is quite probable that coral grew upwards from a submerged platform, but the great thickness of coral rock in the centre of their lagoons makes this process impossible for the atolls of the deep oceans.

Although Darwin did not possess the knowledge of the topography of the deep sea-bed that is available today, he did connect the subsidence of islands in deep oceans with volcanic activity, and he did visualize a regime in which volcanoes grew up from the sea-bed and subsequently sank slowly, to disappear beneath the surface except when coral animals created a monument over an island now lost. The existence of flat-topped seamounts (guyots) is difficult to explain without relative change of level between the sea and the flat top.

There are two ways in which seamounts and the foundation of atolls may sink. The sea may rise, for example, by displacement of water by sediment (Hess) or by accumulation of water from inside the crust of the earth (Revelle), or the volcanic island may sink relative to the sea-bed. The seismic experiments show that the thickness of sediments on the flat bed of the deep oceans is at the most a kilometre. The sediment has accumulated over a much longer period than the time taken for downward movement of seamounts (for example bottom samples from Sylvania seamount suggest that it was planed flat in late Cretaceous times) so change of sea-level by displaced sediments can only account for a fraction of a kilometre in the life-time of many seamounts.

All the observed facts point to a simple island regime in the Pacific Ocean. Volcanoes erupt from the sea-bed and the material that is given out solidifies to form a volcanic cone. The volcano dies after a certain period of intermittent activity, and its subsequent history depends on whether it attained a height sufficient to lift its peak above sea-level. If the peak never reached sea-level the volcano becomes a normal seamount. At the other end of the scale the volcano may be so massive that it towers above the sea-surface and remains an island for ever. The intermediate cases are those of the flat-topped seamounts and the coral atolls. The flat-topped seamounts could have been formed by planing off the top of a volcanic island by wave action, while atolls exist in those places where the coral growth was sufficient to keep pace with the slowly sinking volcanic mass.

Two reasons have been given for the universal sinking of volcanoes as separate units. The weight of the rock pile on the sea-bed could cause a deformation of the underlying rock layer, or there could be subsidence because of a void left in the rock layers from which the volcanic lava originated. There is evidence that the first of the processes is at least partly responsible for the sinking, because the majority of older islands and seamounts are in isostatic equilibrium.

There does not appear to be the same evidence of sinking in the Atlantic either on islands along the Mid-Atlantic Ridge or around Bermuda, or in the Indian Ocean at the Seychelles; there are no coral atolls with great thicknesses of coral rock and flat-topped seamounts are rare. This might possibly indicate that there are areas in the Atlantic and Indian Oceans where the crust has greater rigidity than in the Pacific, but the evidence is inconclusive. However, the distribution of atolls and guyots does not appear to be uniform over all the oceans and one reason for this might be a difference in past geological history as proposed by those who support continental drift.

Apart from the evidence supplied by the uneven distribution of those atolls and seamounts which follow the volcanic regime of building and subsequent sinking, there has been a long-standing doubt in the minds of volcanologists about the universal similarity of structure all over the Pacific. Although many geologists now prefer to think of gradation of properties rather than a positive difference between two species, there is a wealth of evidence to support the andesite line which was drawn to distinguish between the different chemical compositions of volcanic rocks, for example in the Philippine Sea as opposed to the central Pacific Ocean. Seismological evidence, both from earthquakes and from sea-seismic experiments indicates a difference in crustal thickness on the two sides of the andesite line, and it seems reasonable that some differences in erupted lava should follow this structural change. In "The Floor of the Oceans" Daly quotes figures for earthquake wave travel times across the oceans which suggest that the Atlantic is not exactly the same as the Pacific, while the Pacific itself is divided into the central area and the Philippine Sea [9]. Recent measurements by Press of the dispersion of long period earthquake waves show that, while the oceans differ markedly in crustal structure from the continents, there are areas of the ocean which are neither typically continental nor are they like the main body of the Pacific Ocean. Officer and Eiby found that the crustal thickness in the area of Melanesia to the north-east of New Zealand was about 15 km and there was an excessively large thickness of Layer 2 even at places far removed from any obvious island roots.

There seems to be no geological keenness to draw an andesite line for the Atlantic, but a boring in Bermuda entered andesitic rock after penetrating a mere three hundred feet of coral. The Azores, which grow out of the Mid-Atlantic Ridge, are also andesitic, and there is no doubt that both Bermuda and the Azores would be placed to landward of the andesite line if they were in the Pacific. The fact that volcanic rock is only a few hundred feet deep in Bermuda indicates that this island has not sunk, as have islands like Bikini in the Pacific. There is only a thin layer of coral at the Seychelles in the western part of the Indian Ocean, and the granite which forms the Seychelles shows no sign of marine conditions, so that it has not moved up or down by thousands of feet. On the other hand, there is a large flat-topped seamount in the eastern part of the Indian Ocean which appears to be similar, from a seismic point of view, to the Hawaiian Islands. The Cocos–Keeling group of islands were one of Darwin's typical atolls. There are thus several lines of superficial evidence for a sort of andesite line in the Indian Ocean— the line now being based not only on type of igneous rock, but also on the existence of atolls and on crustal thickness.

The western part of the Indian Ocean and the Atlantic are just those parts of the earth's surface over which Wegener and others have supposed the continents to have moved. One explanation of the two types of ocean structure might be the mixing of acidic and basic rock during movement. The mixture could have long-term strength adequate to support the weight of islands, while the basic rock of the primaeval ocean floor allows the sinking volcano regime of the Pacific.

The intermediate areas of the Philippine Sea and Melanesia are also places where continents may have wandered. A detailed examination of coral rocks by Ting Ying Ma [10] has made it possible to estimate the latitude in which coral polyps flourished in the past. In order to explain the various corals found in the countries which border the Pacific, considerable movement of the present land must have taken place. The movement may have taken the form of a rotation of the land relative to the Pacific Ocean basin. All the fault movements in the border countries, Japan, Kamchatka, the Aleutian Islands, Canada, California, Chile and New Zealand, are in the same direction, which confirms the idea of rotation of the land round the Pacific, and, incidentally, gives a present-day demonstration that horizontal movement of continents is actually feasible.

The rift valleys of Africa could be further examples of sideways continental movement, as a modern continuation of the general splitting up of the African Continent postulated by Wegener. The movement of India away from Africa could have left the islands of the Seychelles and Madagascar as relics, and in doing so produced a West Indian Ocean crustal structure, different from that in the eastern half of the ocean. These present-day movements agree with the ideas about continental masses that have been proposed recently by Dietz [11]. Here the moving force is provided by convection currents in the mantle, and a constant renewal of the sea-bed by altered upwelling mantle rock is postulated. The moving sea-bed slides under the continents, and so any accumulated sediment is pushed away beneath the continents. This would account for the thin sediment cover in the Pacific, and would also explain why no fossil earlier than Cretaceous has been found in the samples dredged from the Pacific. Whether Dietz's theory is capable of explaining the whole Layer 2 problem, will probably not be known until several holes have been drilled to the original floors of the oceans. It certainly seems that the Cretaceous period, which Wegener proposed for one of his major earth movements, was a time of great geological activity. But it is not necessary to look for one mechanism to account for all the oceans. One primary cause, such as overheating the earth, may have been sufficient to allow the Americas to drift apart from Europe and Africa and at the same time produce an unprecedented burst of volcanic activity in the Pacific Ocean.

Although there are not sufficient results from seismic and borehole probings into the oceans to say that differences in sea-floor structure do exist, there are very definite reasons for being hesitant in accepting a universal type of sea floor for the whole of the deep ocean province of the earth. Oceans and continents are certainly different in their vertical rock profiles. The Pacific andesite line is of seismic, as well as petrological significance, and it could well mark the limit of the permanent ocean basins as opposed to those which, like the Atlantic, may have been formed by movement in a comparatively recent phase of the earth's crustal activity. There is good reason to believe in extensive areas of sea floor which have a structure intermediate between that of true ocean and of continent. In these intermediate areas the Moho is 15–18 km below sea surface. However, the Atlantic, where one of the most definite movements of continents is required on any theory of continental drift, has a crust about as thin as that of the Pacific, although the results are confused to some extent by the interpretation of Layer 2.

On the other hand, the Atlantic does appear to possess the strength to resist the gradual sinking of islands that occurs in the Pacific. The present state of knowledge is not adequate, then, to do more than hint at the possibility of perhaps several types of ocean basin, which could be the result of continental wandering.

References

1. EWING, M., SUTTON, G. H., AND OFFICER, C. B., *Bull. seismol. Soc. Amer.*, **44**, 21 (1954).
2. GASKELL, T. F., AND SWALLOW, J. C., *Nature, Lond.* **170**, 1010 (1952).
3. RAITT, R. W., *Bull. geol. Soc. Amer.*, **67**, 1623–1639 (1956).
4. HILL, M. N., *in* "Physics and Chemistry of the Earth", Vol. 2, Chapter 7. Pergamon Press, London (1957).
5. GASKELL, T. F., HILL, M. N., AND SWALLOW, J. C., *Phil. Trans.* 251 (1958).
6. HAMILTON, E. L., Paper given at Ninth Pacific Science Congress in Bangkok (1957).
7. GASKELL, T. F., AND SWALLOW, J. C., Occ. Pap. Challenger Soc. **3** (1953).
8. KUENEN, PH. H., "Marine Geology". J. Wiley, New York (1950).
9. DALY, R. A., "The Floor of the Oceans". University of North Carolina Press, Chapell Hill (1942).
10. TING YING MA, Publication of the Overseas Branch of the National Academy of Peiping, Vol. III (1956).
11. DIETZ, R. S., *Nature, Lond.* **190**, 854 (1961).
12. BULLARD, E. C., AND GASKELL, T. F., *Proc. roy. Soc. A.*, **177**, 476 (1941).
13. EIBY, G. A., New Zealand Department of Scientific and Industrial Research Geophysical Memoirs (1957).
14. GASKELL, T. F., AND SWALLOW, J. C., *Nature, Lond.* **167**, 723 (1951).
15. OFFICER, C. B., *Trans. Amer. geophys. Un.* **36**, 449–59 (1955).
16. RAITT, R. W., AND PERKINS, B., *Prof. Pap. U.S. geol. Surv.* 260–K (1954).

M

Chapter 12

Memories of Alfred Wegener*

J. GEORGI

Memories of an important man will always contain a subjective element, the overall picture of him emerging only from the sum of many individual glimpses from different angles. Since my meetings with Wegener were mainly in the fields of meteorology and Greenland exploration it is advisable to turn not only to my personal memories of the years 1910–30 but also to other personal sources, above all to his biographer, Professor H. Benndorf [1], who was his friend and colleague at the Physical Institute of the University of Graz (Austria) from 1924–30. I am also grateful to Professor W. Wundt of the University of Freiburg i.B., a fellow student of Wegener's in Berlin from 1903–5, for letters relating to that period. The two became acquainted during Professor von Bezold's meteorology seminars and practicals and, having many interests in common, became close friends. Wundt informs me that even at that time (1903) Wegener showed him the route by which he wished to cross the Greenland ice-cap at a more northerly latitude than that taken by Fridtjof Nansen in 1888; and at the same time Wegener pointed out to his friend the apparent congruence of the western and eastern Atlantic coasts – an idea which, according to S. K. Runcorn [2], has continuously fired the imagination of eminent explorers such as Alexander von Humboldt [3] since the time of Francis Bacon (1561–1626).

We know that Wegener re-examined this problem in 1910, that early in 1912 he gave his first public lecture about it to the Geological Association, and in the same year brought out his first great publication on the origin of the continents [4]. We also know how strangely and unexpectedly this field of work came into contact with Wegener's Greenland explorations in that measurements of longitude on Sabine Island (the larger of the Pendulum Islands, East Greenland 74·5°N) since the time of Edward Sabine in 1823 seemed to point to a continuous westward drift of Greenland and thus to give a proof of the theory of the

* By courtesy of the publishers, these reminiscences are taken from "Alfred Wegener✠ zum 80. Geburtstag" [176].

horizontal displacement of continental landmasses (a supposition that happened to prove untrue [5]).

The "Grand Old Man of Meteorology", Professor W. Köppen of Hamburg, with whom Wegener had close contact from 1910 onwards and whose daughter became his wife, adds [6] a not unimportant detail to the story of the development of the displacement theory: Wegener was led to a serious analysis of the problem by a compendium which "fell into his hands" one day in 1911, from which he learned of the great similarity in the older faunae of South America and West Africa: this led him to study all the available literature on the subject. Köppen, who incidentally [7] had warned Wegener against spending too much time in allied fields in order to be able to devote all his energy to his meteorological research, remarks that probably many a scientist when looking at the map of the world had already wondered at the similarity of the Atlantic coasts. "But now this similarity had been noticed by an expert geophysicist, a brilliant man of unbounding energy, who would spare no pains in following up the matter and gaining any facts from other fields of science that might seem to have a bearing on the question."

Köppen also foresaw the drawback from which Wegener was later to suffer so much: "To work at subjects which fall outside the traditionally defined bounds of a science naturally exposes one to being regarded with mistrust by some, if not all, of those concerned, and being considered an 'outsider'. The question of the displacement of continents involves geodesists, geophysicists, geologists, palaeontologists, animal- and plant-geographers, palaeoclimatologists and geographers, and only by consideration of all these various branches of science, as far as is humanly possible, can the question be resolved."

Let us consider for a moment how strongly these two interests had gripped Wegener even during his student days. His friend, Wundt, recalls that he was already testing his powers of endurance by long, exhausting walks, and by days of skating through the winter-bound Spreewald, getting himself in training for the Arctic. In 1901 at Innsbruck during the summer holidays he undertook with his brother, Kurt, very ambitious alpine climbs that were not entirely without danger; and in the winter of 1903–4, when visiting a friend, who was a meteorological observer on the Brocken, the highest mountain in the Harz, he turned seriously and enthusiastically to skiing. From all of which there emerges a sense of purpose and determination that is encountered all too rarely and which always heralds great achievements.

There was the same aim in his practical study of the new technique of aerology, using kites and captive balloons, which had just been developed by Rotch, Teisserenc de Bort, Köppen and Assmann at the Royal

Prussian Aeronautical Observatory, Lindenberg (SE of Berlin), to master the then most modern and most difficult meteorological methods in order to make use of them later in his own field-work. In the service of the Observatory he and his brother took part in 1906 in the Gordon Bennett Contest for Free Balloons. With an unbroken flight of 52 hours they easily broke the world record of 35 hours.

Alfred Wegener, aged 27.

Such careful preparations have probably never been more handsomely rewarded, for in 1906 Wegener was allowed to accompany, as official meteorologist, the Danish "Danmark" Expedition led by Mylius-Erichsen to north-east Greenland, where he spent two winters at more than 77°N. From there he made long and difficult journeys with dog-sledges south to 74·5°, and north to almost 81°; and with man-hauled sledges he went up to the edge of the ice-cap. During that time he was able to put into practice all his physical and intellectual abilities, his scientific knowledge and his practical skill for the exploration of the upper layers of the atmosphere in the Arctic, for meteorological investigations of all kinds, for astronomy, meteorological optics and glaciology, as is shown by publications which have not, even today, been superseded [8]. Equally he was able to stand his ground in fitness and endurance with the experienced polar explorers in the expedition; this is shown by an impressive drawing of him, completely self-possessed, by the painter Achton Friis [9], who was also a member of the expedition.

After a safe return, Wegener settled down in Marburg a.d. Lahn, working on his abundant Greenland material and giving lectures and demonstrations in astronomy and meteorology. When I arrived there at Easter 1910 for the finals of my studies in physics I found a notice on the board of the Physical Institute, in a clear and attractive hand-writing, announcing that Privatdozent Dr. Wegener was to give some meteorological lectures and demonstrations. In the small observatory of this famous old Institute the three or four students who were in-terested met the hearty, fresh-faced young man of medium height who was to be their tutor and who quickly won their hearts by the firm yet at the same time modest and reserved manner in which he immediately introduced them to the fundamentals of the subject. Only here and there could we catch a glimpse of the lion behind the lamb-like manner, as when he criticized certain precautionary measures necessary for work-ing under extreme climatic conditions, which were not then practised.

His lecture on "The Thermodynamics of the Atmosphere" was re-markable for the ease of his delivery, which was in complete contrast to the difficulty of the subject. Numerous examples were taken from his recent observations in Greenland; and here for the first time the attempt was made to relate the bulk of measurements from the free atmosphere during the last dozen years to general physical rules for the explanation of the manifold phenomena, such as the different atmospheric layers (only eight years had passed since the discovery of the stratosphere!) and the various types of cloud formation. Whoever in those days had the opportunity of following the lectures and practical work of famous scholars would have had to admit that Dr. Wegener's lecture bore no professorial stamp at all. On the contrary, the tutor came down to the level of his audience and developed with them the theme which he had just set down in an epoch-making book [10]. It is true that the final result still had to be formulated mathematically, but neither before nor since have I had the experience of hearing a tutor state quite simply: "This deduction is not mine; you will find it in the physics textbook by . . . on page . . .' This little anecdote points to the fact that Wegener had no special gift for mathematics. He had already remarked to Wundt, to whom we are indebted for many illuminating stories of Wegener's early life, that, although he had made considerable advances in astronomy, he had no great inclination for it, and considered that for any great achievements in this direction a special mathematical gift was necessary, which he himself lacked. Frau Else Wegener quotes from a letter [7] from her former fiancé to her father, in which, after first calling his attention to a similar concept of G. H. Darwin's in his standard work on tides,* he continues: "I myself hold the crass and probably exaggerated point of view that such mathematical treatises as I cannot understand (i.e. in which I can no longer follow the gist of the thing— for one can often follow the gist without working through the formulae) are wrong or do not make sense. When one cannot follow the printed or written word one should not always put the blame on oneself. When logic is lacking, one can still usually fill out a few lines with formulae." If his talents here show a gap, he always compensated in two ways: firstly he always took the greatest pains even in his most specialized work to be as intelligible as possible and not to write only for his fellow experts, and secondly an outstanding trait of his character was his frankness even towards his students. He had an unusually high degree of integrity in such a natural and unpretentious way that one had the impression that he was exempt from the common human temptation of occasionally making oneself appear a little more important than one actually is.

I am sure that young people in particular feel this immediately; and the simplicity in his lectures and demonstrations, obviously based on experience and achievement, always won him the hearts of his audience. At the end of the lectures in Marburg he used to bring out a number of photographs to illustrate the subject he had been discussing, usually cloud formations, the refraction of light in the layers near the ground, air-optical phenomena produced by the reflection and refraction of light in ice crystals, or photographs of the formation, movement and transformation of sea mists; mainly photos that we were the first to be shown. These pictures were discussed as examples of the subject just dealt with in the lecture. It was also an innovation for us students to see that senior academics, such as the assistants at the Physical Institute, and in particular Prof. K. Stuchtey, who carried out several free-balloon measuring flights together with Wegener and later remained his loyal helper, did not consider it beneath their dignity to come and listen to these lectures by a young private tutor. How highly Wegener valued photography as a method of research he himself mentioned in a letter (an understatement of course): "On Koch's expedition (i.e. on Koch-Wegener's Greenland Expedition 1912–13) I did practically nothing but take photos: clouds, ice, micro-photos, aurora, mirages, colour photos

---

* "Tides and Kindred Phenomena in the Solar System", London and Boston (1898); German edition: "Ebbe und Flut usw," Leipzig (1902).

(using the Lumière system), neutral spots, always using different cameras and plates. Even on the "Danmark" Expedition, as well as the normal photography, I used the Miethe Three-Colour Method of photography which, of course, because of technical difficulties, could only rarely be shown in lectures."

The winning simplicity of his nature, which was seen for the first time in Marburg remained with Wegener all his life, even long after he had become famous. This we see from a reminiscence of the late twenties from his friend and colleague Prof. Benndorf-Graz [1]: "In the afternoons he was always a guest to tea in the Institute. He would regale us then with stories of his travels, and the students who did not know much about his experiences listened eagerly and with the greatest attention. That our young academics who are so sports-minded and, in Graz, especially keen on skiing were highly impressed by his feats goes without saying. Most of them also knew that he was already a famous scholar. But one would never have guessed it by looking at him, and it was the simple and unpretentious manner that he had of talking on an equal footing to even the youngest student that took the hearts of the young people by storm. I think that they would have gone through fire for Wegener; and if anyone had dared to doubt the theory of continental drift, they would not have hesitated to use their fists as arguments."

It was a hard blow to his students and assistants when in early 1912 Wegener once more gave up his academic work in Marburg to make another trip to Greenland—and Greenland was heartily cursed, especially by me, as I had become fired with enthusiasm and wanted to stay with this teacher and devote myself entirely to meteorology, which was then possible at only a few universities. But, for Wegener himself, the new expedition with his friend of 1906–8, the Danish Captain J. P. Koch, spending the winter for the first time ever on a high Arctic glacier and the subsequent crossing of the ice-cap for a distance of 1,200 km was the completion of his work on Greenland's climatology and glaciology, begun on the "Danmark" expedition. At the same time this undertaking made the highest of claims on his physical capabilities so that all in all it was probably his greatest achievement as a man—the account of this journey is and will remain a classic of the exploration of Greenland [11].

Scarcely had Wegener, now newly married, set foot again in Marburg than he was caught up into the maelstrom of the First World War and was twice wounded. In 1919 he took over as W. Köppen's successor the Meteorological Research Department of the Deutsche Seewarte (German Marine Observatory) in Hamburg which was to be completed by the building of a modern meteorological experimental station in the grounds of Köppen's historic Balloon Station at Grossborstel, north of Hamburg.

As I too was to work there, my personal relationship of many years standing with Wegener was once again renewed. If the new building, planned to the last detail and unique of its kind, fell a victim to inflation, nevertheless a period of highly interesting and inspired collaboration began. During the preliminary discussions for the new experimental work that was planned I observed how cautiously Wegener made use of his intellectual superiority. We were walking along the corridors of the Seewarte one day when Wegener talked about various experimental equipment and also wanted to hear my suggestions. Although a meteorologist, I happened to have read about some hydrodynamic experiments with pulsating balls in water, which had been described in 1876 by the father of the famous meteorologist Wilhelm Bjerknes. Wegener listened with interest, and I was flattering myself that I had told him about something new when, without any unkind intent on his part, he showed in the course of conversation that I had not mentioned all the facts of the matter—in short, that he knew far more about those old and rather off-track experiments than I did. That was not the only occasion during the course of the next ten years that I came away red in the face after conversations with him, shamed by his more extensive knowledge and at the same time by his kindheartedness.

With the technical facilities now at his disposal in Grossborstel he was able to investigate various instrumental problems such as the stopping of the clockwork meteorological and aerological recording instruments when used in a polar climate or in the upper atmosphere. He also designed a new and efficient balloon theodolite for following pilot or other balloons from ships up to great heights, an instrument useful for decades afterwards. This problem he solved in a way characteristic of him, by combining a normal pilot-balloon theodolite with an ordinary ship's sextant. I also recall a big rotating iron drum used for experiments to show the effect of the rotation of the earth on fluid motion.

But while, several times a week, he had to cope with official correspondence in the Seewarte, which was to his great distaste and which he rightly regarded as a waste of his time and energy, he could also, in his primitive workroom in the Met. Experimental Station, at last devote himself to the theory of continental drift.* The working out of this was

---

* Imbued as we are with Wegener's ideas, we can no longer appreciate the revolutionary effect they had on scientists. As an example of his influence, let us look at the famous lecture delivered by Alfred Penck in 1885. Still only a young man, this leading glacial geologist who had at his command a vast collection of geological and paleontological data, came to the conclusion that both poles of the earth, then regarded as invariable, had been the centres of organic development (Verhandlung 5.deutsch. Geographentag, Hamburg 1885, pp. 5–50, 174–196.) At that time this conclusion must have been regarded as both theoretical and abstruse, but thirty years later Wegener's theory supplied the key to the solution of Penck's astonishing enigma.

now progressing well. After the end of the war, with the renewal of contacts with the rest of the world, there came not only news from colleagues in various faculties about new findings for or against Wegener's theory, but also these experts from all over the world came in person to visit the modest wooden huts in Grossborstel or the nearby Köppen-Wegener house. At that time one could regard Grossborstel as the Mecca of geophysicists and ecologists interested in this problem just as, twenty years earlier, because of Köppen, it had been the Mecca for the new science of aerology. The most important result of the continental drift theory was its application to palaeoclimatology by Köppen and Wegener working in collaboration [12, 13].

For those of us who were Wegener's scientific colleagues in Grossborstel and who, of course, were also on a very friendly footing with our chief, there were exciting days when new support for his theory presented itself, and depressing ones when he had to argue with his opponents or even defend himself against apparent misunderstandings. We had the good fortune during this time to meet many famous scholars; in particular I remember a visit from Wegener's former Greenland colleague J. P. Koch, then a colonel on the Danish General Staff, a man who in appearance and manner was just as we had always imagined the Vikings of the Icelandic sagas. Their discussions about the meteorological and glaciological problems in Greenland then being tackled and about those that still remained increased my appetite for scientific work in the polar regions, which had already been whetted in Marburg.

A source of great pleasure were the informal invitations to the Köppen-Wegener home. Our houses were only a few yards apart, and our children used to play in each other's gardens. Köppen himself was a man of uncommonly wide interests and a most stimulating companion, especially on the social-ethical side. His neighbour, a highly respected schoolmaster, and a convinced and active pacificist, was very close to him and to his household. Both families were also friendly with a well-known Hamburg lawyer, who represented in word and print the philosophical preachings of W. Ostwald. There is no doubt that Wegener also was sympathetically inclined towards these views as we, his later colleagues on the 1929–30 expedition, were often able to observe. I was very impressed, however, on our occasional visits by Wegener's taking his leave of the little company, to attend to urgent work in his study, usually correcting proofs. Without such economy of his time his astonishing productivity would not have been possible. We were later to witness, on the journey out to start the preparatory expedition to Greenland in 1929, the iron devotion to duty which he showed by correcting proofs on board ship, even during heavy seas which claimed the rest of us as victims. The voluminous proofs for the great two-volume work on the expedition to Greenland by himself and Koch in 1912–13 [14], were dealt with as carefully as at his desk at home.

It may be mentioned in these personal reminiscences how very much Wegener's colleagues regretted the fact that this great scholar, pre-destined for research and teaching, could not get a regular professorship at one of the many universities and technical high schools in Germany. One heard time and again that he had been turned down for a certain chair because he was interested also, and perhaps to a greater degree, in matters that lay outside its terms of reference—as if such a man would not have been worthy of any chair in the wide realm of world science. So our universities had to look on while in 1924 a regular professorship in meteorology and geophysics was created especially for him at the University of Graz in Austria. This post met his approval, partly because of the number of colleagues there with like interests and partly because it freed him from the burden of administrative duties, to the advantage of the whole world of geophysics.

For myself a new period of even closer association with Wegener began in 1928. In 1926 and 1927 I had been doing aerological work for the first time in the far north-western point of Iceland and had discovered there the high storms known today as the 'jet stream'. I was planning an aerological winter base on the Greenland ice-cap for further research and it was only natural that I should inform my teacher and former chief of this plan as he was the greatest expert on Greenland and ask him for his opinion and support. As his reply shows, this request seems to have caused an inner revolution in him: ". . . You mention also the question of a station on the inner ice-cap. That is an old plan of Freuchen's, Koch's and mine! If only the (First World) War had not happened, it would have been carried out long ago. But meanwhile Freuchen has lost a leg, Koch is in hospital, and I too have had my own trouble and am no longer a young man. I intend to write an article in the first number of *Arktis* about the conditions of work and the scientific problems of such a station. Here only a few hints . . ." There follows in the letter* an outline programme which enlarged my own limited con-ception of measuring high winds into a complete geophysical programme, with a winter base in the middle of Greenland, such as I had envisaged, and in addition a similar scientific station in West Greenland. He added almost prophetically, with double underlining which was rare for him: "Both stations must remain there for *two* winters, otherwise they cannot fulfil their purpose." However, this could not be carried out because of

* For a full quotation of this letter dated 15th January 1928 see [16].

M*

his tragic death on his great 1930–1 expedition. The letter ends: "You will see from this how much your plan interests me. I should like it very much if you would keep me informed about its further development."

I was soon able to give him positive news because of the favourable attitude of the German Science Emergency Committee in Berlin and especially of its president, Minister of State Dr. F. Schmidt-Ott. I was entirely in agreement when the organization of the project was put in the experienced hands of Wegener and when, later, at the instigation of the Göttingen geographer Prof. W. Meinardus, the task of measuring ice thicknesses by means of a seismic method newly developed in Göttingen by Prof. Wiechert was also incorporated. This three-fold origin of the last and greatest of Wegener's Greenland Expeditions is described in his expedition plan [17] on which the preparation and execution of the expedition were still based even after his death in November 1930. It is an important document in the history of polar exploration, especially as it combines the 'classical' methods of travel by hand- or dog-sledges with modern methods of transport. It is to be regretted that this work, which was so important as an intermediate stage in geophysical polar exploration between the two world wars and also so characteristic of Wegener's thought and work, has remained almost unknown, for it was not published in the big scientific report [17a].

The personal relationship resumed by our correspondence in 1927–8 continued with Wegener's visit to Hamburg in July 1928, followed by further visits there and also meetings in Berlin until the time came for the departure of the expedition. It was characteristic of him that he came to Hamburg in July not only to arrange my release from the Seewarte but also to get my wife's approval. He himself was engaged when in 1912 he went to Greenland for the second time and knew how much those who stayed at home suffered from the separation, especially if the expedition could not continue according to the programme. I shall never forget his long and friendly conversation with my wife; how Wegener explained, when naturally she asked what risk was entailed for me, how he hoped to minimize the risk by careful planning keeping in mind his own experiences there; how what one usually calls bad luck is very often only a result of errors or inadequacies in preparation. This assertion of Wegener's in 1928 is almost word for word the same as that of the eminent later Greenland explorer, R. A. Hamilton who, as second in command and scientific leader of the British North Greenland Expedition of 1952–54, twice wintered north of 77° [18]. Here may be cited another example of how tireless Wegener was in trying to avoid causing suffering or even misunderstandings. He travelled to see a former colleague for the sole purpose of explaining to him why he judged it better *not* to invite him to take part in his Greenland Expedition.

This is not the place to tell of the hectic rush that accompanied the preparations for the 1929 expedition, when sometimes there were three letters or telegrams a day from Graz to Hamburg and often as many back; it has been described in many books dealing with the expedition, also in that of R. A. Hamilton [18]. The preliminary expedition itself, whose most important responsibility was to search for and prepare an ascent for heavy equipment from the west coast of Greenland up to the ice-cap, has been described by the leader himself in a most delightful book [19], and one can read between the lines more about the man and his personality than from the best descriptions of his character by others.

One might ask why Wegener made no provision in his planning of the expedition for investigating the supposed westward drift of Greenland even though an experienced geodesist had joined the main expedition of 1930–31 for the purpose of carrying out latitude and longitude determinations and geodetic levelling into the interior. Technically it would have been possible to have made really accurate measurements of longitude using wireless time comparisons but this scheme was rejected with some regret as the Danes had recently begun making precision longitude measurements in Greenland with a fixed meridian circle at Qôrnoq near Godthaab [5], and our expedition, with the means at its disposal, would never have been able to reach the same degree of accuracy. How preoccupied he was, however, with the western drift of Greenland his colleagues know from conversations during the long reconnaissance marches the party made on glaciers and the ice-cap; they knew just how content the actual renaissance of this idea of his would have made him.

The preparation of the great Main Expedition of 1930–31 in the few months between our return from Greenland in late autumn 1929 and the departure of the first ship for Greenland in April 1930 must have been a nightmare for Wegener; negotiations with the Danish government who valued and supported Wegener's person and project—and supported it in spite of doubts which had arisen about the gravimeter measurements; negotiations with the Emergency Committee for German Science which, because of difficulties in the Reichstag, was not at the critical moment able to supply the funds which had long ago been granted in principle; the search for suitable members for the expedition's three stations and time-wasting negotiations about this with institutes and authorities; the making of lists of requisites for the hundred and one daily needs of the expedition for two years; and the delegation to individual members of the responsibility for certain things such as clothes, provisions and instruments, wherever Wegener had not taken this over himself. He made many journeys to Berlin, Copenhagen, even to Helsinki where Finnish propellor-driven sledges were inspected and ordered. In addition to all this he had his lecturing in Graz and also, after Koch's illness, the sole task of completing the great work about the 1912–13 expedition.

The thick folder of letters that I received from him during these months shows Wegener to have been astonishingly unremitting not only where the continual appearance of new problems was concerned but also in the sphere of human relationships where his equanimity and kindliness were often put to bitter tests. Often during these months of hard and unenjoyable work (out in Greenland, one assumed, physically harder work would be waiting for him but it would at least be more congenial to him) he may have thought of his experiences as a young and lively member of the earlier expeditions and of his sometimes quite sharp criticism of the leader and his fellow-members on the "Danmark" Expedition. This can be seen from his diaries, recently edited by Frau Else Wegener [7]. Often he stood between the incomprehensible stipulations of the authorities and our own claims which had been based on Wegener's own expedition plan. This is the chief source of friction in expeditions, since every member of the expedition wants to carry out as perfectly as possible the task he has been allotted, even when the overall situation calls rather for a more limited performance. We had all, thanks to Wegener's tireless help, got ourselves so inside the parts we were to play on the ice-cap that we found it very hard to brook any economies which would make very little difference to the total cost of the expedition but which would considerably affect and lessen the final usefulness of our carefully planned work. The same argument was also raised by the English Greenland explorer R. A. Hamilton [18]. Wegener had the bitter lot of keeping the peace so that there was no breakdown before the journey commenced. Once out there, he knew, the logic of events would make its own imperative demands; or, as he said consolingly to me when a difference of opinion had arisen with the patron of the expedition about a point in the expedition's programme: "We may sometimes have to give way despite our convictions, but when we come home triumphant, laden with new scientific knowledge, then such legal quibbles will be of as little importance as a scrap of paper!" I can remember no occasion during all these difficult situations when Wegener became angry and lost his self-control. We attributed this to his long years of collaboration with the deliberate Danish explorers; and he had learnt to use his diary instead as a kind of personal lightning-conductor.

Thus he was able to write to me in a wonderfully human letter about the conflict mentioned above: "You will certainly not, because of a passing ill mood, make a decision which for many years, perhaps for your whole life, would cloud the memory of our expedition. I believe rather— at least, I hope—that when you reach such a point you will bury the hatchet and grab a camera instead and re-affirm the principle which I too have used to smooth away many a difficulty during my expeditions: Whatever happens, the cause must not suffer in any way. It is our sacred trust, it binds us together, it must go on under all circumstances, even with the greatest sacrifices. That is, if you like, my expedition religion, and it has been proved. It alone guarantees an expedition without recriminations."

Contrary to his expectations, in Greenland too there were more than enough causes for such entries in his diary, mainly because impenetrable winter ice blocked the coast delaying us by six weeks. Wegener himself was continuously skirting the ice margin in his motor-boat *Krabbe* or standing in the crow's nest on the look-out for some place to slip through. He sat for days on end in the base camp, planning with the Greenlanders who were to help with the dog sledges, the boat, or the ascent of the glacier. He negotiated with the leaders of the settlements at Umanq, Uvkusigsat, Ikerasaq, Nugaitsiaq, etc. over the catching and drying of shark for dogfood, the hiring of dog teams, the collecting of hay for our horses and about taking some strapping Greenlanders with us on our main journeys into the interior. He repeatedly made the long journey from the fjord to the edge of the ice-cap at a height of almost 1,000 metres above sea level to test and improve the first man-made road in Greenland along a moraine and, most of all, to help and to encourage everywhere when unexpected hold-ups occurred. He checked time and again the flow of huge quantities of expedition material from an intermediate depot to the next and later on to the ice-cap; he took part in the trial trips of the new propellor-driven sledges which he had been the first to bring into the Arctic—but the only thing that would have compensated him for the burden of his many duties as leader of the expedition would have been a journey with dog sledges to the "Mid-Ice" station in the best season of the year, and this, just because of his duties, he had to renounce. When, in late autumn, he finally thought that he would have to take additional provisions to this station himself by dog-sledge, enormous quantities of snow fell but, instead of a sudden storm, which would have packed the snow hard and made a wonderful sledge-track, the weather did not break. So this trip became an awful ordeal but also an achievement of which he and his two colleagues could be proud. Yet, amidst all this hectic activity, he retained the inner calm to talk to his fellow-workers about their own personal problems at opportune moments, to discuss their future after their return home and also to talk about not only scientific or technical matters, but also general literary, cultural and human problems in the widest sense.

I shall not forget the last meeting I had with him, when his success-ful journey eventually ended on 30th October 1930 at "Mid-Ice" with the temperature −50 to −54°C. He greeted with beaming en-thusiasm our dirty, low dug-out as a comfortable living room after the icy air in the tents during the preceding days, with joy shining in his face because Dr. Ernst Sorge and I, despite the lack of many provisions, were going to try to keep the station going until the following summer. He began enquiring at once about meteorological and glaciological observations and, with his thoughts already working on an enthusiastic report home, began to copy down in his notebook the most important temperature information. Now after he had, in his capacity as expedition leader, taken a look to see that things were all right there, he pushed back to his own glaciological problems in the western border region. On his 50th birthday, fully fit and with rested dogs, he set off, certain of making a quick march back in comparison with the tedious journey out. Even with this difficult journey ahead of him he did not forget our state of mind, our downheartedness because, due to the absence of necessary scientific equipment, our work must remain patchy. "The fact that you have spent the winter here in the middle of Green-land, even without any particular results in research, doing only the simplest and most routine measuring, is something which is worth all that has gone into the expedition," he said; and who knows if it was not this encouraging word that helped us psychologically to get through that winter?

Wegener himself would have opposed very strongly any attempts to make a hero out of him or to say that he never made mistakes. The best part of our memories of him is that in every respect he was close enough to us for true mutual understanding and yet at the same time he towered so far above us that we, in spite of his ever friendly attitude, always looked up to him with respect.

Professor W. Wundt, a friend of his from student days, has summed up his memories of him thus: "Alfred Wegener started out to tackle his scientific problems with only quite normal gifts in mathematics, physics and the other natural sciences. He was never, throughout his life, in any way reluctant to admit this fact. He had, however, the ability to apply these gifts with great purpose and conscious aim. He had an extraordinary talent for observation and knowing what is at the same time simple and important, and what can be expected to give a result. Added to this was a rigorous logic, which enabled him to assemble rightly everything relevant to his ideas. One can call this ambition, but it was a justified and legitimate ambition, which never led him to hurt or detract from anyone else. A noble mind and great loyalty were amongst his basic character traits. If he was somewhat authoritarian and obstinate in great matters, he shared this charac-teristic with all men who have achieved something significant in their lives. A compensating factor was his dry sense of humour that spared himself least of all."

To this reminiscence of Wegener's early days let there here be added as conclusion one from a friend of his later years, Professor Benndorf [1]: "I believe that Wegener took his military service (as an officer in World War I) very hard. Not because of dangers and hardships, because that would have appealed rather to a nature like his, but because of the difficult conflict it must have caused in him between his duty to his fatherland and his inmost conviction of the futility of war. Wegener was one of those rare men who do not willingly stop at duty for the good of self, family or native land but who rather see in the promotion of the well-being of mankind as a whole the true purpose of life."

References

1. BENNDORF, H., *Beitr. Geophys.* **31**, 337 (1931).
2. RUNCORN, S. K., *Science*, **129**, 1002 (1959).
3. ROSSMANN, F., *Z. angew. Met.* **48**, 257 (1931).
4. WEGENER, A., *Petermanns Mitt.* **58**, 185, 253, 305, (1912); *in book form:* "Die Entstehung der Kontinente und Ozeane" (Sommlung Vieweg, H.23), Vieweg & Sohn, Brunswick (1915); 2nd edn. (1920); 3rd edn. (1922); 4th edn. (1924) revised by A. Wegener (1929); 5th edn. revised by Kurt Wegener (1936). 3rd edn. translated into English, French, Spanish, Swedish and Russian. 4th edn. reprinted 1961 (Sammlung Die Wissen-schaft).
5. SAXOW, S., *Medd. dansk geol. Foren.* **13**, 522 (1958).
6. KÖPPEN, W., *Petermanns. Mitt.* **77**, 169 (1931)
7. WEGENER, ELSE, "Alfred Wegener". F. A. Brockhaus, Wiesbaden (1960).
8. Various authors. In *Medd. Grønland*, **42** and **46** (1909 and 1911).
9. FRIIS, ACHTON, "Im Grönlandeis mit Mylius Erichsen; die Danmark-Expedition 1906–08". German edition, Leipzig (1910). Pencil sketch, p. 237; photograph, p. 351.
10. WEGENER, A., "Thermodynamik der Atmosphäre", J. A. Barth, Leipzig (1911).
11. KOCH, J. P., and WEGENER, A., "Durch die weisse Wüste, die dänische Forschungsreise quer durch Nordgrönland 1912–13", German edition, J. Springer, Berlin (1919). Pictures of A. Wegener, pp. 80, 125, 173, 174, 177 and 244. For the scientific report see ref. 14. This edition, which is based

mainly on Koch's diary, shows, as stated by Wegener in the German edition, that the experiences of both men were identical. This is proved by Wegener's own diary, which has been published recently by Frau Wegener[7].

12. KÖPPEN, W., and WEGENER, A., "Die Klimate der geologischen Vorzeit". Borntraeger, Berlin (1924).

13. WEGENER, E., and KUHLBRODT, E., "Wladimir Köppen, ein Gelehrtenleben" Bd. 18: Grosse Naturforscher. Stuttgart 1955. Includes a list of Köppen's publications.

14. KOCH, J. P., AND WEGENER, A., Medd. Grønland, 75, Bd. I, II, Copenhagen (1930).

15. GEORGI, J., Arktis, 1, 83, Fig, 7 and Table 24 (1928).

16. GEORGI, J., "Im Eis vergraben. Erlebnisse auf Station Eismitte der letzten Grönland-Expedition Prof. A. Wegener's 1930–31", p. 303. F. A. Brockhaus, Leipzig (1955). Material on the early history of the Mid-Ice Station.

17. WEGENER, A., "Denkschrift über Inlandeis-Expedition nach Grönland" Deutsche Forschung (Aus der Arbeit der Notg.d.D.Wiss.) H.2, 181. Berlin (1928); reprinted in [17b]. This plan was to form the basis of Wegener's preparations for and execution of the 1929 and 1930–31 expeditions. The plan as published in 17a was not authorized.

17a. "Wiss. Erg. d.D.Gørnland-Exp. A. Wegener" Vol. 1, 3, Leipzig (1933).

17b. GEORGI, J., "A. Wegener✠ zum 80. Geburtstag (1.11.60)". Polarforschung 2, Beiheft 1960, 45. Holzminden (Weser).

18. HAMILTON, R. A., Polarforschung, 28, 103 (1958).

19. WEGENER, A., "Mit Motorboot und Schlitten in Grönland". Velhagen & Klasing, Leipzig (1930). Pictures of Wegener, pp. 40, 57, 120, 128, 184, 185. Further recollections of A. Wegener in:

20. DRYGALSKI, E.v., "Alfred Wegener; Nachruf a.d.D.Geographentag Danzig 1931". Verhdl. & Wiss. Abh. d.24.D.Geographentages, Breslau (1931).

21. GEORGI, J., Ann. Hydrogr. Berl. 68, 341 (1940);
    Georgi, J., Polarforschung, 26, 1 (1956).

22. LOEWE, F., Polarforschung, 26, 1 (1956).

23. WEGENER, E., and LOEWE, F., "A. Wegener's letzte Grönlandfahrt". F. A. Brockhaus, Leipzig (1933).

24. SCHMAUSS, A., Ann. Met., Hamburg, 4, 1 (1951).

25. FICKER, H.v., Met. Z. 48, 241 (1931), esp. p. 244.

26. Poggendorff, Handwörterbuch "Biographisches-literarisches", V, 1342 (1926); VI, 2826 (1940). Includes an obituary of A. Wegener.

27. SIMON, W., "Das Festland hat keinen Anker". Alfred Wegener, dem Geophysiker und Polarforscher zum Gedenken, Vol. 13 (1961), pp. 204–214. Ruperto-Carola, in collaboration with the Freunde der Studenten der Universität Heidelberg. With five figures on Continental Drift.

Author Index

Numbers in parentheses are reference numbers, and those in italics are pages on which the references are listed.

A

Adams, F. D., 195 (1), *232*
Adams, L. H., 218 (57), *233*
Aki, Keiiti, 122, 129 (31, 32), *134*, 263 (51), *287*
Allen, Clarence, 118 (16), 134
Almond, M., 61 (48), *65*
Anderson, E. M., 95 (23), *102*, 225 (78), *234*
Askelsson, J., 259 (41), *287*

B

Balakina, L. M., 75 (5), *102*
Banks, M. R., (61 (34), *65*
Bateman, P. C., 116 (15), *134*
Beck, A. E., 221 (68), *234*, 285 (66), *288*
Bellizzia, A., 47 (13), *64*
Benioff, H., 99 (25), *102*, 105 (3), 112 (11), 113 (12), 115 (3, 13), 118 (17, 18), 119 (17), 120 (17, 21), 123 (13, 17), 124 (18), 126 (18, 28), 127 (18), 130, 132 (13, 18), *133*, *134*, 200 (13), 215 (54), *232*, *233*
Ben-Menahem, Ari, 119 (20), *134*
Benndorf, H., 309, 314, 323 (1), *323*
Bernal, J. D., 146 (1), *176*, 282, 283 (58), *287*
Bessonova, 74 (4), *102*
Bidgood, E. D. T., 61 (40), *65*
Bijlaard, P. P., 101 (28), *102*
Billings, M. P., 209, 210, 224 (31), *233*
Birch, F., 31, *40*, 146 (2), 149 (3), *176*, 180 (13), *194*, 213 (44, 45), 220 (44), *233*
Bisshopp, F. E., 186, 188 (19), *194*
Blackett, P. M. S., 137 (5), *144*
Bödvarssom, G., 259 (41), *287*
Bowen, R., 42 (3), *64*
Bramlette, M. N., 251 (29), 252 (32), *286*
Broecker, W. S., 271 (55), *287*
Brooks, H., 219 (58), *233*
Brune, James N., 125 (27), *134*
Bucher, W. H., 196, 209 (30), *232*, *233*
Buchsbaum, R., 42 (2), *64*

Bullard, E. C., 4 (7), 30 (30), *39*, *40*, 210 (35, 36), *233*, 259 (40), *287*, *307*
Byerly, P., 76 (9, 11), *102*, 110, 112, 113 (10), *134*

C

Carr, D., 296 (14), *298*
Carey, W. S., 135 (1), *144*, 283 (60), *287*, 294 (9), *297*
Cattala, L., 61 (50), *65*
Chamberlin, R. T., 221 (66), *234*
Chandrasekhar, S., 31 (35, 36), *40*, 178, 181, 185 (6, 18), 187 (6, 20), 190, 192, *193*, *194*
Chaney, R. W., 48 (16), *64*
Christie, J. M., 85 (19), 87 (19, 20), *102*
Clegg, J. A., 30 (28), *40*, 61 (48), 62 (54), *65*, 137 (5), *144*, 177 (3), 180 (3), *193*
Collinson, D. W., 20 (14, 16), 23, 33 (14), *40*, 61 (32), *65*, 177 (1), *193*
Cook, A. H., 209 (33), *233*
Cook, M. A., 285 (67), *288*
Coulomb, J., 225 (77), *234*
Cox, A., 61 (35), *65*, 137 (6), *144*, 212 (42), *233*, 285 (69), *288*
Crampin, S., 214 (51), *233*
Creer, K. M., 20 (13, 14), 21 (13), 23 (14), 24, 33 (14), *40*, 61 (43, 45, 53), *65*
Crowell, John C., 109 (7), *133*

D

Daly, R. A., 304 (9), *307*
David, T. W. E., 54 (20), *64*
Davis, G. L., 36 (43), *40*
De Noyer, John, 110, 112, 113 (10), *134*
Deutsch, E. R., 30 (28), *40*, 177, 180 (3), *193*
Dibblee, T. W., 30 (26), *40*, 109, 110, 114 (6), *133*, 143 (9), *144*, 177 (5), *193*, 210 (37), *233*
Dicke, R. H., 221 (70), *234*, 283, 285 (61), *287*
Dietz, R. S., 242 (22), 279, 281 (57), *286*, *287*, 296 (12, 13), 297 (19), *297*, *298*, 306 (11), *307*

Dirac, P. A. M., 221 (69), *234*
Doell, R. R. 61 (35), *65*, 137 (6), *144*, 212 (42), *233*, 285 (69), *288*
Dorman, J., 213 (46), *233*, *287*
Drake, C. L., 239, 240 (11), *286*
Drygalski, E. v., *324*
Du Bois, P. M., 61 (37), *65*
Dunbar, C. D., 54 (18), *64*
Durham, J. W., 48 (17), *64*
Du Toit, A. L., 56, 57 (23), *64*

E

Eardley, A. J., 197, 224 (8), *232*, 285 (67), *288*
Egyed, L., 283 (59), *287*
Eiby, G. A., *307*
Einarsson, T., 259 (41), *287*
Elbert, D., 190 (20), *194*
Ellison, A. G., 47 (12), *64*
Elsasser, W. M., 4 (5, 6), *39*
Epstein, S., 42 (2), *64*
Ericson, D. B., 246 (23), 255 (37), 269 (23), *286*, *287*
Evison, F. F., 222, 223 (71), *234*
Ewing, J. I., 207 (21), *232*, 235, 261 (3), *286*
Ewing, W. M., 198 (10), 205 (15), 206 (16), 207 (21), 210, 213 (46), *232*, *233*, 235 (1, 3, 9), 239 (11), 240, 242, 244 (1), 246 (23), 251 (27), 255 (1, 37, 38), 259 (38), 261 (3, 45), 269 (23), 277 (1), *286*, *287*, 292 (2), *297*, 299 (1), *307*

F

Fallot, 156 (5), *176*
Faure-Muret, 156 (5), *176*
Ficker, H. v., *324*
Fischer, A. G., 61 (42), *65*
Fisher, R. L., 261 (43), *287*
Flint, R. F., 44, 56 (7), *64*
Fortier, Y. O., 59 (27), *65*
Friis, Achton, 312 (9), *323*
Frost, D. V., 61 (36), *65*
Furon, R., 252 (33), *287*

G

Garland, G. D., 207 (20), *232*
Gaskell, T. F., 223 (73), *234*, 299 (2), 300 (5), 303 (7), *307*
Gastil, G., 36 (42), *40*

Gee, E. R., 55 (22), *64*
Gellman, H., 4 (7), *39*
Georgi, J., 309 (176), 317 (16), *324*
Gerard, R. D., 249 (26), *286*
Gianella, Vincent, 116 (14), *134*
Gilbert, F., 77 (14, 15), *102*
Gilluly, J., 208 (27), *233*
Graham, J. W., 15 (11), *40*, 61 (39), *65*
Graham, K. W. T., 61 (51), *65*
Green, R., 25, 30 (29), *40*, 43 (5), 61 (47, 49), *64*, *65*, 177 (2), *193*
Griffiths, D. H., 30 (28), *40*, 177 (3), 180 (3), *193*
Griggs, D. T., 30 (31), *40*, 174 (14), *176*, 223, 228 (74), *234*, 291 (1), *297*
Gutenberg, B., 100 (27), *102*, 104 (2), *133*, 180 (11), *194*, 200, 207 (22), 214, 216 (47), 224 (47, 75), 225 (12), *232*, *233*, *234*, 235 (10), 263, 268 (48), *286*, *287*

H

Hales, A. L., 61 (51), *65*, 215 (53), 224 (76), *233*, *234*
Hamilton, E. L., 251, 252 (35), *286*, *287*, 296 (11, 16), *297*, *298*, 301 (6), *307*
Hamilton, R. A., 318, 319, 320 (18), *324*
Hamilton, Warren, 109 (9), *134*
Hapgood, C. H., 223, 230 (72), *234*
Harder, E., 43 (6), *64*
Hargraves, R. B., 61 (42), *65*
Harland, W. B., 55 (22), 61 (40), *64*, *65*
Harrington, H. J., 55 (21), *64*
Hassan, E. S. M., 214 (49), *233*
Hawkes, L., 208 (29), *233*
Healy, J. H., 76 (13), *102*
Heezen, B. C., 143 (11), *144*, 205 (15), 206, 210 (16), *232*, 235, 238, 240, 242 (1), 244 (1, 20), 246 (23, 25), 249 (26), 255 (1, 37, 38), 259 (38), 261 (45), 263 (46), 269 (23, 46), 271 (55), 277 (1), 283 (63, 64, 65), *286*, *287*, *288*, 292 (2), 294 (8), *297*
Heiskanen, W. A., 154, 156, 161, 167 (12), *176*, 228, 229 (80), *234*
Henson, F. R. S., 47 (15), *64*
Hess, H. H., 144 (14), *144*, 221, 225 (65), *234*, 240, 279, 280, 281 (56), *286*, *287*, 296, *297*

Higgins, Charles G., 109 (8), *134*
Hill, M. J., 210 (40), *233*
Hill, M. L., 30 (26), *40*, 109, 110, 114 (6), *133*, 143 (9), *144*, 177 (5), *193*, 210 (37), *233*
Hill, M. N., 235, 251(5), *286*, 287, 300 (4, 5), *307*
Hills, G. F. S., 31 (37), *40*
Hirshman, J., 261 (45), *287*
Hodgson, J. H., 73 (2), 75 (2, 8), 78 (16, 17), 88, 92 (22), *102*, 103, 125 (24), 128 (29), *133*, *134*, 203 (14), *232*
Holmes, A., 198, 210, 211, 223, 224 (9), *232*
Honda, H., 74, 78 (3), *102*, 105 (4), *133*
Howell, B. F., 206, 224 (17), *232*
Howell, L. G., 61, 62 (38), *65*
Hughes, D. S., 214 (48), *233*

I

Irving, E., 10, 12 (10), 20 (13, 14), 21 (13), 23, 25, 30 (29), 33 (14), *40*, 60, 61 (34, 43, 46, 47), 63 (55), *65*, 177 (2), *193*

J

Jacobs, J., 29 (25), *40*
Jacobs, J. A., 196, 210, 220, 224, 225, 227, 230 (6), *232*
Jaeger, J. C., 61 (48), *65*
Jeffreys, H., 27 (21), 33 (23), *40*, 179, 180 (10), 183 (16), *194*, 206, 208, 209, 212, 213 (18), 214 (18, 51), 216 (18), 219 (59), 222, 224, 225, 230 (18), *232*, *233*
Johnson, F. W., 47 (13), *64*
Joly, J., 220 (61), *234*
Jordan, P., 285 (68), *288*

K

Katz, S., 251 (27), *286*
Kay, M., 239, 242 (15), *286*
Kennedy, George C., *134*
Keylis-Borok, 74 (4), 102
King, L. C., 58 (26), *64*
King, P. B., 211 (41), *233*
Kjartansson, G., 259 (41), *287*
Knopoff, L., 77 (14, 15), *102*
Koch, J. P., 314 (11), 317 (14), *323*, *324*

Köppen, W., 310 (6), 316 (12), *323*, *324*
Komarov, A. G., 61 (44), *65*
Kordes, E., 148 (4), *176*
Krumbein, W. C., 46 (25), *64*
Kuenen, Ph. H., 156 (5), *176*, 251 (28), *286*, 296 (15), *298*, 303 (8), *307*
Kuhlbrodt, E., 316 (13), *324*
Kulp, K., 296 (14), *298*

L

Ladd, H. S., 47 (11), *64*, 252 (32), *286*
Lamb, H. H., 44 (10), *64*
Landisman, M., 235 (9), *286*
Lange, I., 4 (4), *39*
Lanteaume, 156 (5), *176*
Laporte, L., 4 (4), *39*
Lensen, G. J., 95 (24), *102*
Light, B. G., 61 (36), *65*
Loewe, F., *324*
Lomnitz, C., 28 (24), *40*, 214 (52), *233*
Lowenstam, H. A., 42 (2), 57 (24), *64*

M

Macdonald, G. J. F., 35 (40), *40*, *176*, 180 (14), *194*, 214 (50), 218 (55), 222 (50), 223, 231 (55), *233*, 268 (52), *287*
McIntyre, D. B., 85 (19), 87 (19, 20), *102*
McWhae, J. R. H., 55 (22), *64*
Martines, J. D., 61, 62 (38), *65*
Mason, R. G., 136, 137 (2), 143 (10), *144*, 210 (38), *233*, 297, 298 (19), *298*
Matthews, W. D., 268 (54), *287*
Maxwell, A. E., 210 (36), *233*
Menard, H. W., 136 (3), 139 (3, 7), *144*, 210 (39), *233*, 244 (19, 21, 22), 246 (24), 249, 252 (34), 254 (36), 255, 259 (24), 261 (44), 270, 271, 279, 280, 281 (44), *286*, *287*, 292 (3, 4), 293 (7), 296 (13), *297*, *298*
Milne, W. G., 125 (24), *134*
Moody, J. D., 210 (40), *233*
Munk, W. H., 35 (40), *40*, 180 (14), *194*, 214 (49, 50), 222, 223 (50), *233*

N

Nairn, A. E. M., 1, 3 (1), *39*, 60 (29, 31), 61 (36, 52), 63 (52), *65*
Nalivkin, D. V., 54, 56, 57, 58 (19), *64*

O

Officer, C. B., 299 (1), *307*
Oliver, J., 213 (46), *233*, 263 (49), *287*
Opdyke, N. D., 1, 3, 8, 33 (2), *39*, 42 (4), 60 (29, 30), 61 (33), *65*

P

Paterson, C., 35 (41), *40*
Perkins, B., *307*
Pettijohn, R. J., 242 (16), *286*
Poggendorff, *324*
Press, F., 76 (12, 13), *102*, 120 (21), *134*, 198 (10), 207 (23), *232*, 263 (50, 51), *287*
Prey, A., 32 (38), *40*, 178, 193 (7), *194*

R

Radakrishnamurty, C., 62 (54), *65*
Raff, A. D., 139 (8), 143 (8, 10), *144*, 235, 246, 250 (7), *286*, 297 (17), *298*
Raitt, R. W., 235, 251, 261 (4), *286*, 299, 301 (3), *307*
Rankama, K., 44 (8), *64*
Rayleigh, Lord, 183 (15), *194*
Renz, H. H., 47 (13), *64*
Revelle, R., 210 (36), *233*
Rich, J. L., 221 (64), *234*
Richter, C. F., 100 (27), *102*, 104, 131 (34), *133*, *134*, 200, 225 (12), *232*, 235 (10), *286*
Riedel, W. R., 252 (32), *286*
Ringwood, A. E., 148 (7), *176*
Ritsema, A. R., 75, 80 (6, 18), *102*
Roberts, P. H., 184 (17), *194*
Robertson, W. A., 63 (55), *65*
Robie, R. H., 47 (13), *64*
Roche, A., 61 (50), *65*
Rossmann, F., 309 (3), *323*
Rubey, W. W., 220, 221 (62), *234*
Runcorn, S. K., 1 (2, 3), 3 (2), 8 (2, 8, 9), 9 (8), 16 (12), 20 (13, 15, 16), 21 (13, 15), 23, 25 (15, 18), 26 (18, 19), 29 (27), 33 (2, 14), *39*, *40*, 42 (4), 61 (32, 43), *64*, *65*, 177 (1, 4), 178 (4, 8), *193*, *194*, 196 (7), 212 (43), *232*, *233*, 293 (6), *297*, 309 (2), *323*.
Russell, R. D., 196, 210, 220, 224, 225, 227, 230 (6), *232*
Rutten, L. M. R., 208 (28), *233*

S

Sahama, Th. G., 44 (8), *64*
Sahasrabudhe, P. W., 62 (54), 65
St. Amand, P., 99 (26), *102*, 118 (16), 119 (19), 125, 127 (23), 130 (33), *134*.
Saxow, S., 310 (5), 319 (5), *323*
Scheidegger, A. E., 73 (1), 88 (21), *102*, 196, 203, 211, 214, 219 221, 222, 224, 225, 227, 229, 230, 231 (2), *232*
Schmauss, A., *324*
Schove, D. J., 60 (29), *65*
Scott, W. E., 4 (4), *39*
Shand, S. J., 235, 252, 268 (2), *286*
Shirokova, H. I., 75 (5), *102*
Shurbet, G. L., 199, 207 (11), *232*
Simon, W., *324*
Smith, Stewart, 120 (21), *134*
Spiegel, E. A., 183 (16), *194*
Stauder, W., 76 (9, 10, 11), *102*, 125 (25, 26), *134*
Stille, H., 206 (19), *232*
Stott, P. M., 63 (55), *65*
Stubbs, P. H. S., 137 (5), *144*
Sutton, G. H., 235 (6), 239 (11), 240 (6, 11), 241 (6), *286*, 299 (1), *307*
Swallow, J. C., 299 (2), 300 (5), 303 (7), *307*

T

Talwani, M., 235, 240, 241 (6), 263, 269 (46), *286*, *287*
Tarling, D. H., 63 (55), *65*
Tatel, H. E., 207 (24), *232*
Taylor, F. B., 242 (17), *286*
Teichert, G., 44 (9), *64*
Tharp, M., 143 (11), *144*, 206, 210 (16), *232*, 235, 240, 242, 244 (1), 246 (25), 249 (26), 255, 277 (1), *286*
Thellier, E., 137 (4), *144*
Thellier, O., 137 (4), *144*
Thorarinsson, S., 259 (41), *287*
Tilton, G. R., 36 (43), *40*
Ting Ying Ma, 305 (10), *307*
Tocher, Don, 125 (37), 132 (35, 37), *134*
Tracey, J. I., Jr., 252 (32), *286*
Turekian, K. K., 271 (55), *287*
Turner, F. J., *268* (53), *287*
Tuve, M. A., 207 (24), *232*
Twenhofel, W. H., 47 (14), *64*

U

Umbgrove, J. H. F., 209 (34), *233*
Urey, H. C., 34, 35 (39), *40*, 42 (2), *64*, 178 (9), *194*, 221 (67), *234*

V

Vacquier, V., 139 (7, 8), 143 (8), *144*, 235, 246, 250 (7), *286*, 297 (17), *298*
Vall, J. M., 47 (13), *64*
van Bemmelen, R. W., 220 (63), *234*
Veldkamp, J., 75 (7), *102*
Vening Meinesz, F. A., 30 (32), 31, 32 (34), *40*, 150 (10, 11), 153 (10), 154 (8, 9, 12), 156, 161, 167 (12), 170 (13), *176*, 193 (21), *194*, 207 (25, 26), 209 (25), 228, 229 (80), 230 (26), *233*, *234*, 240, 281 (12), *286*
Verhoogen, J., 180 (12), *194*, 218 (56), 220 (60), *233*, 268 (53), *287*
Veronis, G., 183 (16), *194*
Vestine, E. H., 4 (4), *39*
Von Herzen, R., 235, 263 (8), *286*, 292 (5), *297*
Von Humboldt, Alexander, *see* Rossmann, F.
Vvedenskaya, A. V., 75 (5), *102*

W

Ward, M. A., 63 (55), *65*
Warren, R. E., 139 (8), *144*, 235, 246, 250 (7), *286*, 297 (17), *298*
Wayland, E. J., 259 (39), *287*
Wegener, A., 27 (22), *40*, 242, 252 (18), *286*, 309 (4), 312 (10), 314 (11), 316, 317, 318 (17), 319 (19), *323*, *324*
Wegener, Else, 310, 313 (7), 316 (13), 320 (7), *323*, *324*
Wellman, H. W., 129 (30), *134*
White, D., 27 (20), *40*
Whitten, C. A., 109 (5), *133*
Wilson, J. T., 196, 210, (4, 5, 6), 220, 224 (6), 225 (4, 5, 6), 227 (6, 79), 230 (6), *232*, *234*, 283 (62), *287*
Wilson, R. L., 61 (41), *65*
Wollin, G., 246, 269 (23), *286*
Worzel, J. L., 199, 207 (11), *232*, 235, 240, 241 (6), 263, 269 (46), *286*, *287*

Y

Young, G. A., 47 (13), *64*

Subject Index

A

Abyssal (see Oceans)
Accretion theory (see Core), 218
Africa, E., rift valley, 210, 259, 293
Aftershock
  epicentre, 113
  mechanism, 111
  strain, 112
Age
  of earth, 35
  of oceans, 269, 295
  radioactive determinations of, 36
Alaska–British Columbia tectonic segment, 124
Alaska, Lynn Canal of, 259
Aleutian
  island arc, 126
  Islands, 91
  tectonic segment, 126
Alpine, 200
  arc, 155
  folding, 295
  roots, 207
Andes, 118, 227
Andesite (see Lavas)
  line, 304, 305, 306
Antarctic ice-cap, 223
Appalachians, 207
  geosyncline, 242
Arctic basin, 175, 259
Argentine rise, 274
Asthenosphere, 291
Atlantic, 30, 236, 240
  median ridge, 37, 167, 210, 275, 277
    305
    displacement, 246
    gravity anomalies of, 240
    heat flow of, 240
    rift valley of, 206, 261
    slip faults of, 240
    structure of, 269
  seismic reflection profiles of, 273
Atmosphere
  circulation of, 1
Australia
  movements of, 26
Axial dipole, 2, 212
Azores, 305

B

Banda basin, 156, 170
Basalts (see Lavas)
Batholiths, 209, 295
  Sierra Nevada, 296
Bauxites, 43
  Cainozoic distribution of, 46
  Palaeozoic range of, 59
Belemnoidea, 42
Bénard convection, 178
Ben-Menahem's method, 120
Bermuda
  boring, 305
  plain, 255
  rise, 244, 274
Bicausal theory, 220
Bikini Atoll, 303
Bioherms, 44
  Cainozoic distribution of, 47
  Palaeozoic range of, 59
Black Sea, 169
Block faulting of crust, 139
British Columbia–Alaska tectonic segment, 124
Byerly's method, 72, 103

C

Cainozoic
  bauxite distribution, 46
  bioherm distribution, 47
  climatic indicators of, 45, 48
California, 72, 82
  earthquake, q.v.
  Gulf of, 259, 293
Canary Islands, 200
Caribbean
  island arc, 154
Caspian Sea, 84
Caucasus, 200
Celebes basin, 156
Chandler wobble, 214
Chile
  canals of southern, 261
  1960 Earthquake, 118, 122
  tectonic segment, 118
Climate
  fluctuation curve, 44
  indicators of, 43 et seq., 53

Climate (*contd*)
  Permian, 156, 175
  Pleistocene variations of, 44
Coccolithophoradae, 251
Cocos–Keeling islands, 305
Collapse model, 74 *et seq.*, 78, 80
  mechanism, 75
Colorado plateau, 207, 211, 295
Conrad discontinuity, 198, 207
Continents
  associated earthquakes, 224
  composition of, 229
  crust of, 198, 300
  development of, 210
  distribution of, 31, 161
  margin of, 236 *et seq.*
  origin of, 169
  radioactivity of, 154
  regression of, 154
  transgression of, 154
Continental shelf
  deposition of, 242
  erosion of, 242
Continental slope
  location of, 242
Continental drift, 132, 135, 156, 169,
    175, 211, 222, 228 *et seq.*, 242, 294
    et seq.
  and ocean floor, 277 *et seq.*
  and palaeoclimatology, 41 *et seq.*
  palaeomagnetic evidence for, 1 *et seq.*
  velocity of, 30, 230
  Wegener's hypothesis, 177, 242, 252
Convection cell, 228
Convection currents, 144, 219, 229, 306
  cell dimensions of, 163, 173
  driving force of, 151
  energy of, 5
  half-turn, 158
  harmonic analysis of, 178
  in the mantle, 29, 145 *et seq.*, 279 *et*
    seq., 288
  magnitude of, 177
  period of, 155
  temperature gradient for, 152
Corals
  Cretaceous reefs, 252
  Seychelles, 305
Core of earth, 4, 181, 229
  formation of, 36, 169

heat flow from, 220
Coriolis force, 164, 180, 182, 188, 222
Coupling
  core mantle, 8, 39
  transverse, 115
  viscous, 111
Creep, 212
  in rocks, 28
  in the mantle, 28
  Lomnitz relation, 215
Crust
  sequence of, 288
  thickness of, 251, 299
  viscosity of, 216
Currents
  turbidity, q.v.
Curie temperatures, 137, 297

D

Day
  variations in length of, 8
Declination
  angle of, 1
Demagnetization
  A.C. and thermal methods, 17
Deviatoric stresses, 74
Diastrophic forces, 212
  causes of, 197
Dipole
  axial, 2, 212
Discontinuity
  Conrad, 198
  Mohorovičić or M, 112, 198, 220, 291,
    292, 306
  Mohorovičić curvature of, 199
  relaxation of, 111, 112
Dynamo
  self-exciting, 5

E

Earth
  age of, 35
  contraction theory of, 217, 218, 224,
    225, 227
  deceleration of, 35
  ellipticity of, 27
  evolution of, 32, 34, 35, 221
  expansion theory of, 227, 283, 294
  heat flow from, 178
  nutation of, 27

Earth (*contd*)
  planetesimal theory of, 221
  radiation of, 150
  shape of, 32
  shrinking of, 294
  tides, 214
Earthquakes
  accumulated slip of, 109
  Chilean, 118, 122
  deep focus, 74, 79
  East Indies, 75, 80, 92
  focus (hypocentre), 104
  generation of, 105
  intermediate, 79
  locations of, 104
  mathematical model of, 69
  mechanism of, 68
  Mediterranean, 93
  normal focus, 79
  of San Francisco, 69, 73, 105, 107, 113, 119, 122
  on continental belts, 224
  Pacific, 79, 88, 91, 92, 129
  Queen Charlotte, 125
  repetition rate, 109
  submarine, 282
  zones of, 82
Easter Island Ridge, 259
  heat flow of, 263
East Indies
  earthquakes in, 75, 80, 92
  gravity anomalies off, 29
Echogram, 139
Ecuador–Peru tectonic segment, 123
Elastic constants
  distribution of, 213
Elsinore fault, 115
Eniwetok, 303
Enstatite, 148
Eötvös force, 222
Epicentre, 67, 72, 104
  regions, 75
Epeirogenesis, 211
Equatorial bulge, 223
Eurasian–Melanesian
  volcanic belt, 205
Europe
  ancient position of, 34
Evaporites, 43
  Palaeozoic range of, 59

F

Faults
  dihedral, 111
  dip-slip, 105
  Elsinore, 115
  Fairview–Dixie, 116
  fling, 77
  Garlock, 114
  land, 128 *et seq.*
  marginal, 203
  mechanism of, 75
  Mendocino, q.v.
  models of, 74 *et seq.*, 81
  Nevada, 118
  oceanic, 203
  plane, 73, 85, 88
  plane solution of, first motion, 105
  regional system of, 225
  reverse planes of, 201
  San Andreas, q.v.
  San Jacinto, 108, 115
  secondary, 105
  stress pattern of, 105
  strike of, 73
  strike-slip, 103
  surface grooves and marks of, 117
  transcurrent, 96, 103 *et seq.*
  vertical, 69
Faulting
  dip-slip, 84, 105, 203
  depth of, 110
  extent of, 119
  Mid-Atlantic Ridge, 269
  speed of, 119
  transcurrent, 82, 84, 103 *et seq.*, 203, 210
  transcurrent radial, 105
  transcurrent tangential dextral, 105
  strike-slip, 82, 84, 105, 115, 255
Fennoscandian ice sheet, 27
  gravity anomalies of, 206
  uplift of, 180, 216
Foraminifera, 251
Fracture
  brittle, in rocks, 213
  conjugate, 114
  zone, Murray, 136
Funafuti Atoll, 303

G

Gabbro, 291
Garlock fault, 114
Geodetic measurements, 109
Geomagnetic field, 1
    analysis of, 4
    generation of, 30
    westward drift of, 4, 6, 8
Geomagnetic mean field, 3
Geomagnetic measurements, 155
Geosyncline, 154, 175
    oceanic, 175
    sedimentation in, 223
    theory of, 209
Geothermal gradient, 137, 152
Glacial deposits, 43
Glaciations
    Permian, 156, 175
    Permo-Carboniferous, 25
    Pleistocene, 47
Graben, 155, 259, 264
Granite, 291
Gravity anomalies, 207
    Atlantic Ridge, 270
    Fennoscandian, 206
    off East Indies, 29
Gravity traverses of continental mountains, 207
Graywacke, 242
Great Lakes, Hudson Bay area, 216
Guadalupe Island, 252
Gutenberg's low velocity layer, 215, 263
Guyots, 254, 271, 296, 303

H

Hawaiian Islands, 301, 305
Heat flow
    from Atlantic Ridge, 271
    from earth, 178
    from Easter Island Ridge, 263
    from oceans, 268, 279
    from Pacific Ridge, 271
Hindu-Kush Mountains, 79, 84
Himalayas, 200
Hudson Bay, 216
Hooke's law, 213

I

Ice-caps, 223

Iceland
    central graben of, 259, 264
    vulcanism of, 259
Inclination, angle of, 1
Indonesia
    island arcs of, 154, 156, 170
Indian Ocean, 236, 240
    crustal structure of, 306
    median ridge of, 167, 293
Island arcs, 82, 85, 98, 154, 170, 225
    Aleutian, 126
    Caribbean, 154
    Indonesian, 154, 156, 170
    Japanese, 80, 154
    Kurile, 80, 227
    New Zealand–Tonga, 81
    Pacific, 278
Islands
    Aleutian, 91
    Cocos–Keeling, 305
    Hawaiian, 301, 305
    Pacific, structure of, 303
Isopiestic level, 291
Isostasy
    equilibrium of, 27
    principles of, 206

J

Japan, 72
    island arc, 154
    ocean trench, 129

K

Kamchatka shock, 128
Kara Kum Desert, 43
Kinematic axes, 87
Kurile–Kamchatka
    tectonic segment, 127
    trench, 127, 129
Kurile
    island arc, 80, 227
    trench, 129

L

Lava
    andesitic, 203
    basaltic, 203
    flows, 137

Layer 2, 300 *et seq.*, 305, 306 (see also
    Low velocity layer)
    profiles of, 301
Limestones, 299
Lithosphere, 291
Low velocity layer, 251, 263 (see also
    Layer 2)
Lunar tidal friction, 27, 35

M

Magma
    differentiation of, 221
Magnetic
    anomalies, 37, 135, 143, 246, 261,
        297
    intensity profiles, 137, 139
    intensity vectors, 136
Magnetite, 136
Magnetization
    remanent, 137
    thermoremanent, 137
Magnetostriction, 15
Mantle
    composition of, 31
    convection in, 29, 145 *et seq.*, 154,
        162, 178 *et seq.*
    core coupling, 8, 39
    density of, 146
    electrical conductivity of, 8
    flow of, 29
    horizontal density variations of, 207
    mean thermal diffusivity of, 180
    radioactivity in, 177, 268, 288
    specific heat of, 150
    temperature gradient of, 152, 177
    viscoelasticity in, 214
    viscosity of, 216
    viscous and buoyancy forces of, 29
    upper, composition of, 199
    yield point of, 157
M-discontinuity (see Discontinuity)
Mediterranean
    basin, 156
    earthquakes, 93
Melanesia, 305
Melanesian trench, 225
Mendocino Fault, 139, 143
    Cape, 259
    escarpment, 246, 297
    rise, 244

Mesozoic
    climatic indicators of, 52
    continental distribution of, 33
Meteorites
    non-ferrous, 146
Mississippi delta, 206
Mittelgebirge, 155
Mohole
    drilling, 296
    drilling apparatus, 252
    project, 302
Mohorovičić (Moho), Professor, 299
    (see also Discontinuity)
Mountains, formation of, 208 *et seq.*
Murray
    fracture zone, 136

N

Navier-Stokes equation, 182
Nevada faults, 118
New England trench, 240
New Zealand, 82, 169, 305
    Kermadec–Tonga trench, 85
    Kermadec–Tonga area, 87
    Tectonic segment, 129
    Tonga island arc, 81
Nodal lines, determination of, 72
Nodal plane, 75, 78, 80, 87
    solutions, 73
North America, seismic solutions, 92
Nukufetau Atoll, 303

O

Oceans
    age of, 269, 295
    Atlantic, q.v.
    basalts of, 137
    crust regeneration of, 143
    crustal thickness of, 299
    distribution of, 31
    earthquakes of, 282
    floor of, 236 *et seq.*
    floor displacements of, 139
    geosynclines of, 175
    heat flow from, 263, 268, 279
    Indian, q.v.
    Pacific, q.v.
    petrography of, 268
    ridges of, 154, 167, 205, 210, 236
        et seq., 255 *et seq.*, 263, 278, 280

Oceans (*contd*)
  structure of, 300, 302, 303
  tensile stresses of, 224
  topography of, 242, 244, 272
  trenches, q.v.
  turbidity currents, q.v.
Olivine, 146, 148 *et seq.*, 152, 153, 173, 220
Ooze, globigerina, 300
Orogeny
  periods of, 153, 159
  time distribution of, 208 *et seq.*
Owens Valley Fault, 115

P

Pacific Ocean, 236, 302
  andesite line, 306
  arcs of, 104, 105, 118, 124, 278
  basin, 99
  circum belt, 242
  earthquakes, 79, 88, 91, 92, 129
  heat flow from, 271
  islands of, 303
  N.E. fracture zones of, 210, 278
  floor of, 135 *et seq.*
  ring, 200
  rotation of basin of, 130, 305
  topography of, 278
  trenches of, 127, 225, 295
Palaeoclimates of
  Cambrian, 58
  Carboniferous, 54
  Cretaceous, 50
  Devonian, 55
  Jurassic, 51
  Ordovician, 57
  Permian, 53
  Silurian, 56
  Triassic, 52
Palaeoclimatology, 1, 41 *et seq.*, 211
Palaeomagnetic poles, 60, 61
  African, 20
  Antarctic, 21
  Asian, 17
  Australian, 18
  European, 9–12
  Indian, 19
  N. American, 13–16
  S. American, 22

Palaeomagnetism, 177, 211
  evidence for continental drift, 1 *et seq.*
Palaeontology, 143
  record of, 27
Palaeotemperatures, 42
Palaeowinds, 177
  directions of, 1, 33
Palaeozoic
  climatic indicators of, 53 *et seq.*, 59
  eugeosyncline, 242
  miogeosyncline, 242
  mountain systems, 206
Pamirs, 84
Permian glaciation, 156, 175
Peru–Chile trench, 240
Peru–Ecuador tectonic segment, 123
Phase change, equilibrium temperature of, 150
Philippine–New Guinea area, 87, 200
Philippine sea, 304
Planetesimal theory of the origin of the earth, 221
Pleistocene
  climatic variations of, 44
  glaciation of, 47
Polar wandering, 156, 177, 211, 222
  causes of, 164
  curves, 20, 24
    for Europe and N. America, 23
  path, 3
  velocity of, 30
Pole positions (magnetic)
  Africa, 20
  Antarctica, 21
  Asia, 17
  Australia, 18
  Europe, 10 *et seq.*
  India, 19
  N. America, 13 *et seq.*
  S. America, 22
Potassium Argon dates, 272
Prandtl number, 183
Puerto Rico Trench, 207, 240
P waves, 70 *et seq.*
Pyroxene, 146, 149 *et seq.*

Q

Queen Charlotte earthquake, 125

R

Radiation, cooling of earth by, 150
Radioactive decay in mantle, 288
Radioactive heat sources in mantle, 177, 268
Rayleigh waves, 119
    approximation, 180
Rayleigh numbers, 32, 39, 180, 183, 191, 219
    theory, 32
Rift valley
    East African, 210, 259, 293
    N. and S. Atlantic, 206, 261
Rocky Mountains, 295
Rutile, 149

S

San Andreas Fault, 30, 69, 81, 106, 177, 259
    bend in, 114
    epicentres of, 110
    shear-stress system of, 118
    strain zone width of, 122
San Francisco earthquake, 69, 73, 107, 113, 119, 122
San Jacinto Fault, 108, 115
Satellites, rotation of, 27
Scripps Institution of Oceanography, 135, 139
Seamounts, 244, 252, 253
    movement of, 296
    volcanic, 252, 292
Secondary magnetization, 25
Secular variations of magnetic field, 3, 8
Sedimentation, rate of, 272, 273, 274
Seismic
    profiles, 139
    ray, curvature of, 72
    refraction, 138
    solutions for S. and N. America, 92
    sub-bottom reflections, 272
    velocities, 146, 251, 299
Seismograph
    Japanese network, 76
    network, 74
    Rayleigh wave, 122
    Soviet Union network, 76
    strain, 120
Seismologists
    De Bilt, 75
    Japanese, 74

Ottawa, 75
Soviet, 74
Seychelles, 305
Serpentine, 291
Shield areas, 210
Sial, 283, 291, 292
Siberia, continental shelf of, 259
Sierra Nevada, 259
    batholith of, 296
    rocks of, 207
Silicates, Ternary system of, 147
Sima, 135, 249, 268, 283, 289, 292
Solenhofen limestone, 174
South America
    seismic solutions for, 92
    tectonic fabric of, 86
Southern hemisphere
    Mesozoic continental position, 33
Spherical harmonics, 6 *et seq.*, 159 *et seq.*
    analysis of convection pattern, 178
    analysis of topography, 32, 164, 167, 169, 229
Spherical polar co-ordinates, 4
Spinel, 148 *et seq.*, 152, 153, 173, 220
Stereographic projection, 73, 85
Strain
    accumulated, along fault plane, 77
    horizontal displacement pattern of, 112
    rate of accumulation of, 109
    rebound characteristics of, 215
    secular, 111
    seismograph, 120
    short period, 111
    zone, earthquake-generating, 113, 123
    zone width, 126, 128
Stresses
    deviatoric, 174
    hydrostatic, 73
    intermediate duration, 214
    long duration, 216
    principal horizontal, 96, 97
    short duration, 213
Stress–strain, statical field, 78
S waves, 70 *et seq.*

T

Taylor number, 180, 183
Tectogene, 207, 209

Tertiary
  extent of tropics in, 49
  floral distribution in, 48
Tillites, 44
Tides
  earth, 214
  effects of, 222
  lunar, 27, 35
Titanium, 137
Topography
  of ocean floor, 167
  preferred dimensions of, 172
  spherical harmonic analysis of, 32,
    164, 167, 169, 229
Transition layer, olivine–spinel, 153,
  173, 220
  instability of, 153
Transition zone, continent to ocean,
  168
Trenches
  continental margin, 240
  East Indies, 29
  Japan, 129
  Kurile–Kamchatka, 127, 129
  Melanesian, 225
  New England, 240
  New Zealand–Kermadec–Tonga, 85
  ocean, 124
  offshore, 200
  Pacific, 127, 225, 295
  Peru–Chile, 240
  Puerto Rico, 240, 207
  Verkhoyansk, 259
Turbidity current, 244, 295
  sedimentation by, 240, 246
  smoothing by, 255

U

Uniformitarianism, 44
Ural mountains, 208
Urcontinent, 169, 229
U.S. Coast and Geodetic survey, 135,
  244
  ship Pioneer, 135, 139
U.S. S.E. coastal plain, 211

V

Varvites, 44
Vema, research vessel, 244
Verkhoyansk
  mountains, 259
  trough, 259
Vibration magnetometer, 4
Viscosities of mantle and crust, 216
Volcanoes, 220
  Eurasian–Melanesian belt, 205
  of Iceland, 259
  on island arcs, 225
  on sea bed, 252, 303, 304
  situations of, 203

W

Wegener, 309 *et seq.*
  continental drift hypothesis, 177,
    242, 252
White Wolf Fault, 105, 115

Y

Yakutat shock, 125
Yield point of mantle, 157